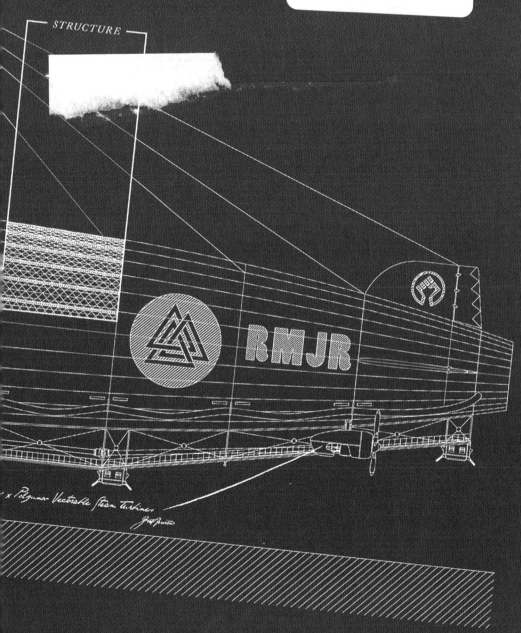

STRUCTURE

...x Palguner Vectratile Steam Turbines

RMJR

...ATTACK STEAMER

...SSARIAT

Rod Rees has spent his life travelling throughout Africa, the Middle East, Bangladesh and Russia, and consequently found himself living in Qatar, Tehran and Moscow. He has built pharmaceutical factories in Dhaka, set up a satellite communication network in Moscow, and conceived and designed a jazz-themed hotel in the UK. Now a full-time writer, Rod lives near Derby, England, with his wife Nelli and their two children.

# *The* DEMI-MONDE

## SPRING

## ROD REES

Jo Fletcher
BOOKS

First published in Great Britain in 2012 by

Jo Fletcher Books
an imprint of Quercus
55 Baker Street
7th Floor, South Block
London
W1U 8EW

A CIP catalogue reference for this book is available
from the British Library

ISBN 978 1 84916 502 0 (HB)
ISBN 978 1 84916 503 7 (TPB)

10 9 8 7 6 5 4 3 2 1

Typeset by Ellipsis Digital Limited, Glasgow
Printed and bound in Great Britain by Clays Ltd, St Ives plc

# Contents

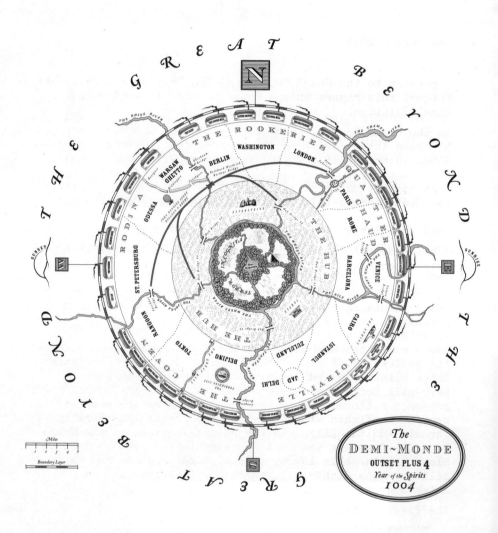

**The Most Secret**          **Order of Grigori**

2nd August 2018

I present to the Grand Council of The Most Secret Order of
Grigori this report on the progress made in achieving the
Final Solution.

As the Grand Council knows, a key element in this endeavour
has been the creation of the world's first quantum computer,
ABBA, an engine of immense processing power. ABBA's power
has, in turn, enabled us to develop the Demi-Monde, the
most sophisticated virtual world ever conceived. To mask
the Demi-Monde's true purpose, we have persuaded the US
military to adopt the simulation as a training ground for
their neoFights.

A brief description of the Demi-Monde is, perhaps, in order.
This cyber-milieu, technologically constrained to the year
1870, is populated by thirty million cogent and
self-motivated digital duplicates ('Dupes'), these Dupes
being simulacra of selected living people. This Dupe
population is divided between the Sectors of the Demi-Monde
in such a way as to emphasise inter-Sectorial antipathy and
hence mimic the discontinuous and disharmonious ambiance of
the Real World. A coterie of PreLived über-Dupes including,
inter alia, Reinhard Heydrich, Aleister Crowley and
Lavrentii Beria, have been seeded into the Demi-Monde, their
presence rationalised to the US military by the need to
provide neoFights with a hi-Level Adversarial Leadership
Threat. Additionally, and for reasons obvious to the Grand
Council, Dupes in the Demi-Monde exhibit a need to feed on
blood; again, this idiosyncrasy is explained to the US
military as a disharmonic necessary to heighten
inter-Sectorial tensions.

The five Sectors of the Demi-Monde are:

   THE ROOKERIES: the population drawn from London, Berlin
   and Washington; the common language English; the dominant
   religion the faux-fascist UnFunDaMentalism.

                    continued over...

**RODINA**: the population drawn from Warsaw, St Petersburg and Odessa; the common language Russian; the dominant religion the neoCommunist RaTionalism.

**THE QUARTIER CHAUD**: the population drawn from Paris, Rome, Venice and Barcelona; the common language French; the dominant religion the unfettered hedonism of ImPuritanism.

**THE COVEN**: the population (with the gender mix skewed 2:1 towards females) drawn from Tokyo, Beijing and Rangoon; the common language Chinese; the dominant religion the extreme feminism of HerEticalism.

**NOIRVILLE**: the population (with the gender mix skewed 2:1 in favour of males) drawn from Cairo, Istanbul, Delhi and ZuluLand; the common language Arabic; the dominant religion HimPerialism, which preaches male supremacy in all things.

There is also a faux-Jewish diaspora in the Demi-Monde, these Untermenschen known as the nuJus.

Since the Demi-Monde was activated some five years ago, Reinhard Heydrich, with our assistance, has taken control of the Rookeries and Rodina to create the ForthRight. Our estimate is that Heydrich will achieve pan-Demi-Mondian dominance by the end of Fall 1005 (by Demi-Mondian reckoning), this coinciding with the enactment of the Final Solution.

Six months ago the Grand Council authorised the commencement of the next phase of the Demi-Monde Project and, in furtherance of this, Norma Williams, the vain and headstrong daughter of the US President, was lured into the Demi-Monde. The abduction of Williams gave us the opportunity to replace her in the Real World with Aaliz Heydrich, the daughter of Reinhard Heydrich. As the Grand Council is aware, having Aaliz Heydrich masquerading as Norma Williams will provide us with unprecedented opportunities to create the conditions necessary to execute the Real World aspects of the Final Solution.

As anticipated, the US military and the US President became somewhat exercised by the virtual entrapment of Norma Williams and demanded the girl be rescued. As they are labouring under the mistaken belief that the Demi-Monde is now sealed to the Real World, it was simplicity itself to persuade them that only one person was able to enter the Demi-Monde to search for the girl. To ensure this rescue

continued over...

mission failed, we made strenuous efforts to have a wholly
ineffectual individual selected for the task, the final
candidate combining the weaknesses of gender (female), of
race (she is black) and of youth (she is eighteen years
of age).

Unhappily I must report that this individual, Ella Thomas,
has proved to be more capable than anticipated, displaying a
quite astonishing level of initiative and determination.
Once inside the Demi-Monde, she formed an alliance with a
Dupe named Vanka Maykov, a glib Russian psychic, and with
Burlesque Bandstand, an amoral petty criminal. Thomas, aided
by her confederates, located and rescued Norma Williams,
escaping with her into the Warsaw Ghetto.

The ForthRight Army attacked the Ghetto with the aim of
recapturing Williams, only to be repulsed by the Polish Free
Army led by Lady Trixiebell Dashwood, an English girl who is
dedicated to the overthrowing of UnFunDaMentalism. However,
thanks to the valiant efforts of the SS-Ordo Templi Aryanis
StormTroopers, Warsaw has now been taken and Norma Williams
is once again in our power.

Unfortunately, Ella Thomas remains at large and has
continued to be a thorn in our side. By hacking into ABBA
she was able to open the previously impenetrable Boundary
Layer that surrounds the Demi-Monde, allowing three million
rebels to escape Warsaw and certain annihilation. For this
she has been venerated as a Messiah by impressionable
elements within the Demi-Monde, and has been given the
honorific the Lady IMmanual. The assassination of Ella
Thomas is now a major priority.

However, despite these minor setbacks, I do not believe
there has been any material impact on the timetable set
for the Final Solution. The Rite of Transference has been
completed and Aaliz Heydrich is now in the Real World
and soon all Demi-Mondians will be under the control of
Reinhard Heydrich.

The Grand Council should be in no doubt that the achieving
of the Final Solution is now in our grasp.

I remain Your Humble Servant,

Professor Septimus Bole

# Prologue

## Paris
## The Demi-Monde: 1st Day of Spring, 1005

It has recently been recognised (see my own *Dark Charismatics: The Invisible Enemy*) that there is a small coterie of persons – perhaps no more than twenty in the whole of the Demi-Monde – who are immune to all blandishments and attempts to modify their brutish behaviour. But small though this sinister and recalcitrant subclass is, it is very potent, for its constituents, by their perverted nature and gross amorality, present a morbid threat to the ideals which govern the Quartier Chaud and endanger the very existence of those charged by ABBA, by rank and by ability, with the execution of such governance. These abominations I have named Dark Charismatics.

*Letter dated 53rd day of Spring, 1002, from Professeur Michel de Nostredame to Doge Catherine-Sophia*

*Beau nichon!*

Examining herself carefully in her looking glass, Odette Aroca decided that she made quite a striking Liberté. That she stood tall and proud (as Liberté should), that she was strong and powerful (as Liberté had to be, though Odette doubted that Liberté had developed her muscles hauling meat to and from her market stall in Les Halles) and that the breast she had exposed was full and plump, all meant that she was the living embodiment of the figure shown in Delacroix's famous painting of *The Triumph of the Quartier Chaud in the Great War*. When she marched with her UnScrewed sisters on the Bastille, she would certainly look the part.

Odette took a moment to adjust the Phrygian cap sitting atop her head. She hated the cap: it was shapeless and floppy and reminded her of a bed cap. It also, annoyingly, hid much of what Odette believed to be her best feature – her long, curly chestnut hair. Being by nature a pragmatist, Odette knew that she wasn't a particularly good-looking woman – even her mother could only be persuaded to call her homely – so she had to make the most of what paltry blessings ABBA had reluctantly bestowed on her. Amazingly, the cap refused to cooperate and despite all her efforts at rearrangement it continued to sit on her head looking like a partially melted blancmange.

Still, her robe was good. The word that had come down from the leaders of the UnScrewed-Liberation Movement was that for the assault on the Bastille, all demonstrators should wear a long flowing robe in virgin white, this to signify their refusal to indulge in sexual activities until Jeanne Deroin and Aliénor d'Aquitaine were freed and the *lettres de cachet* ordering their imprisonment revoked. Moreover, the instructions had continued, the robe had to be cut so that the right breast – and it had to be the *right* breast, the UnScrewed Committee members were devils for detail – was unsheathed. 'Tempting but Untouchable' was to be the UnScreweds' catchphrase, and for a woman like Odette this was good news. She regarded her breasts as her second- and third-best features, having, as was often remarked upon by her admirers – many of her regretfully *few* admirers – big breasts. But then Odette was a *very* big woman, so it was natural that she should have breasts to match her great height and her equally great girth. Still, never being one to look a gift horse in the mouth. Odette gave a wiggle and was pleased to see that her untethered breast jiggled in a quite charming fashion.

Satisfied with her robe, Odette strapped on the huge hobnailed boots she wore when she worked in the market. She'd be a fool if she was going to go to any demonstration ill-equipped to give someone a good kicking if things got bent out of shape. The GrandHarms had been none too tender with UnScreweds of late, and if any one of the sods so much as waved his baton in her direction, he would find himself having to buy a bigger codpiece to accommodate his swollen testicles.

Next Odette fastened a mask about her face. For the assault on the Bastille she'd chosen a full-face, Roman-style mask made from thick white leather. Not only was white leather very fashionable but it also had the advantage of offering at least *some* protection if she was hit in the face and, of course, made her homeliness a little more mysterious and alluring. She'd decorated the mask using red nail varnish, writing 'Robespierre's a Piano' across the brow, a reference to Senior CitiZen Robespierre's rumoured lack of sexual potency. This gesture was, she knew, a violation of the instructions of the UnScrewed Committee – their belief being that demonstrators should conduct themselves 'with taste and decorum' and avoid 'provocative vulgarities' – but as the Committee was made up of middle-class intellectuals who had never been involved in a street fight in their lives, they could, in Odette's oft-voiced opinion, go fuck themselves. Odette Aroca and the regiment of market women she commanded were marching to free Deroin and d'Aquitaine, not to serve canapés or engage in learned debate.

With her mask in place, the only thing that remained was for Odette to select her placard. All demonstrators had been ordered to carry a placard nailed to the handle of a broom, the broom symbolising the UnScreweds' avowed intent to sweep away the Gang of Three, the bastard Dark Charismatics led by Robespierre. The broom idea had caused no end of argument at the last meeting of the Paris Battalion of the UnScrewed-Liberation Movement, with Amélie Sappho arguing that as the broom was a symbol of domesticity and hence of female oppression, it was an inappropriate item to be carried by women demanding the upholding of the sacred rights of ImPuritanism and of Holistic Feminism. In the end, Amélie had been voted down. Odette hadn't been surprised; everyone knew Amélie was a Dork – a closet HerEtical – who had *very* funny ideas about what a young woman should do with a broom handle in the privacy of her bedroom.

Odette chose the placard which read 'Down with the Gang of unFree', which she thought quite a pithy slogan, then took a few minutes to use her trusty razor-knife to sharpen the end of the broom handle to a point. Now if any GrandHarm came to the mistaken conclusion that, because she was carrying a broom, she was ripe for oppression, two metres of pointed pine shoved up his arse would do an excellent job of disabusing him.

Her costuming complete, Odette spent several minutes standing in front of the mirror, striking what she thought were suitably heroic poses – there would, after all, be press daguerreo-typists covering the demonstration – and grimacing in what she thought was an appropriately aggressive manner. In the end she gave up on the grimacing, as no one would be able to see her face behind her mask and, anyway, snarling made her face ache. Her practising of her war cries was brought to a similarly premature conclusion by Widow Depaul hammering on the thin wall that separated her room from Odette's, and loudly demanding that she 'stop tormenting that poor fucking gorilla'.

It was while Odette was striking a particularly pugnacious,

if silent, pose for the mirror that she became aware of shouting coming from the entrance of the tenement building, three floors below her attic room. It sounded like someone was in loud dispute with the building's formidable concierge, Madame Blanc. Odette didn't like disturbances: they were usually a precursor to the arrival of the Inquisition.

*It's a Purging!*

Instinctively she knew that the Quizzies had come for her. The chances were that her landlord, the odious and odorous CitiZen Drumont, had shopped her. He was always snooping round when she was out, searching her room, looking for the rent she owed him. The bastard must have found the placards.

Realising that the conventional route out of the tenement – down the stairs – would now be blocked by the Quizzies, Odette slammed a heavy wooden bar across the door of her room, and then opened the window that gave out onto the roof. Confident that her room was as secure as she could make it, and that she had an escape route, she hauled the two huge Ordnance revolvers out from where she had hidden them, wrapped in an oilskin, under a loose floorboard, and checked that they were loaded. Then she threw a cloak around her shoulders, blew out the oil lamp that was her room's only illumination, and settled back in the darkness to wait – praying, as she did so, that it was some other bugger the Quizzies were after.

She didn't have to wait long to discover that her prayers hadn't been answered. Odette had barely got herself ready to repel intruders when she heard heavy boots pounding up the naked wooden staircase towards her room. As best she could judge, there were five of the bastards. She pressed her ear against the door, listening to the whispered instructions being given on the landing outside her miserable little room. Then a fist hammered on the door.

'CitiZen Odette Aroca, I am Chief Inquisitor Donatien. I have here a *lettre de cachet* for your arrest. You are accused of being an UnVirtuous CitiZen, of being an enemy of the Revolution, and of being one of those most despicable and censorable creatures known as UnScrewed-Liberationists. Further, the charges against you state that, being an officer in that prohibited organisation, you did plot and connive in the execution of many treasonous and nefarious acts designed to endanger the quietude of the Medi, the Revolution, and the Rapprochement with the ForthRight. You have also been overheard engaging in calumny: to wit, expressing doubts regarding the parentage of Senior CitiZen Robespierre. I am therefore instructed to bring you before the Committee of Public Safety, so that you might answer to these charges, and thereafter be convicted and punished.'

Odette had no doubt about what being 'punished' would involve. The guillotine Robespierre had had set up in the Place de Grève had been chopping away with a vengeance for the last few weeks. Let the Quizzies arrest her and the chances were she wouldn't have much use for her bonnet in the future.

'Go fuck yourself,' Odette shouted back, rummaging in her memory for some of the bits and pieces of UnScrewed rhetoric she'd picked up at the meetings she'd attended. 'It is incumbent on all free-minded CitiZens to act in defence of Responsibility Six enshrined in the Quartier Chaud's Charter of Responsibilities.' Odette paused for breath, slightly amazed by her own pomposity. 'This states that all CitiZens shall enjoy freedom of thought and conscience, and that CitiZens shall be able to openly express their opinions in public. By the arrest and incarceration of Sisters Jeanne Deroin and Aliénor d'Aquitaine, the Gang of Three has violated the tenets of ImPuritanism and has paved the way for the infiltration of UnFunDaMentalism into our beloved Quartier Chaud. UnFunDaMentalism is anathema to the inalienable Responsibilities of all CitiZens, these being enshrined in our Sector's motto, namely Liberty, Equality and Fornication.'

'That is sedition, CitiZen,' came the response. 'You will know that the Charter of Responsibilities has been suspended and thus, by your own words, CitiZen Aroca, you condemn yourself as an Enemy of the Revolution and therefore a cat's-paw for that most insidious of would-be dictators, the so-called Doge Catherine-Sophia of Venice.' The door handle rattled. 'Now open the door and come peaceably. I would advise you that I am empowered to use whatever force is necessary to oblige you to accede to the terms of this *lettre*.'

'And I should warn you that I will not yield to a lackey of the forces of oppression. When Maximilien Robespierre, Godfrey de Bouillon and Tomas de Torquemada' – automatically Odette made the sign of Mannez across her chest as she intoned the names of the hated Gang of Three – 'persuaded the Senate to declare UDI, they made themselves enemies of ImPuritanism. Their attempt to impose UnFunDaMentalism upon the Medi is symbolic of their Dark Charismatic intentions.'

'Is that your final word, CitiZen Aroca?'

'No, this is. Fuck off.'

'That's two words.'

'Try "Bollocks", then. I am not going to bandy words with you, a reactionary agent of repression.'

'I was an agent of oppression just a moment ago,' observed an obviously confused Chief Inquisitor Donatien.

'Oppression, repression: it's all the same,' snapped a rather testy Odette, who could never quite remember which was which. 'Break down the door.'

A nail-studded boot smashed into the door, shaking it to its hinges, but the door was so heavy and the wooden beam barring it so strong that it held firm. The Quizzies must have realised that kicking at the door was a waste of time, as the next, very much heavier, blow was delivered by what Odette suspected to be a sledgehammer.

Knowing that the door wouldn't stand long against such punishment, and that she was now fighting for her life, she hauled one of her pistols out of her belt, cocked it, took careful aim at the middle of the door and fired. For an instant she was blinded by the pistol's muzzle flash as it scorched the darkness, and choked by the stench of cordite smoke. She was also deafened: such was the tiny size of her room that the bang when the gun fired caused her ears to pop. But she wasn't so deaf that she couldn't hear the screams of the Quizzie she'd hit.

The 11mm slug from her pistol had smashed its way through the wood of the door like a fist, the soft lead distorting as it went. What had hit the poor unfortunate Quizzie on the other side of the door had no longer been the streamlined bullet that had left the muzzle of the Ordnance, but a five-centimetre-wide piece of angry shrapnel.

'You UnScrewed cow,' someone yelled, and then there was another hammer blow against the door, which now, savaged and splintered by the bullet, began to buckle.

Odette fired again, this time aiming at the wall to one side of the door, where she guessed the Quizzies would be cowering. The simple plaster-and-lath wall offered even less resistance to the bullet than the door. It disintegrated in a cloud of pulverised plaster, the bullet gouging an egg-sized hole before it hit a second Inquisitor.

'Let the bitch have it,' she heard Donatien shout, and immediately there was a fusillade of firing, the bullets smashing through the wall and whining about Odette's ears. It was time to get out.

She fired two more discouraging shots, and then hopped over

to the window and eased her considerable bulk out onto the roof. Her Liberté costume offered her precious little protection from the bitter cold of the night and, as her hobnailed boots scrabbled for grip on the snow-slick tiles, Odette could feel her fingers – and other exposed parts of her anatomy – already starting to stiffen and numb.

Not having much of a head for heights – she had never managed to get above the second level of the Awful Tower – she tried not to look down towards the cobbled street thirty metres below. She almost despaired. It seemed impossible that she would be able to climb over the roof to reach the adjoining building, the tiles were too slippery and the roof too steep. Then Odette had a brainwave. Bracing herself against a gutter, she used her pistols to blast holes though the roof tiles so that the wooden beams beneath them were exposed. These she used like the rungs of a ladder to clamber up the roof. She was almost halfway over it when the man living immediately beneath the roof stuck his head out of his window. It was CitiZen Drumont, her bastard of a landlord, and he didn't look happy. He gawped, obviously shocked by the vandalism and by the sight of a half-naked Odette Aroca smashing her way across what was left of his roof.

'CitiZen Aroca? Just what the fuck are you doing? You almost blew my fucking head off just now. And who's going to pay for the damage to my fucking roof?'

'Try the Quizzies. It was you who called the bastards here.'

'That's because you're a despicable traitor to the Revolution,' and with that Drumont hauled a blunderbuss out from behind him and aimed it at Odette.

Odette didn't hesitate: she shot him straight through the forehead. She felt no remorse. CitiZen Drumont was a horrible man who had made her life a bloody misery with his constant demands that she pay him the rent on her shitty little room.

*Let's see you try to collect it now, you bastard!*

# Part One
# Paris and the Bastille

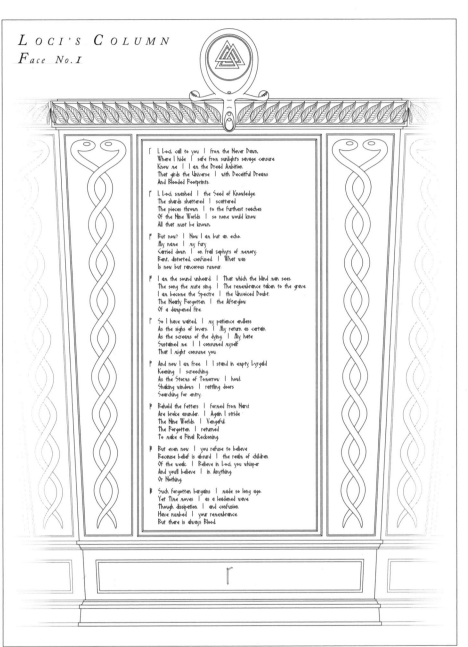

*Diagram and translation reproduced by kind permission of Snore Igbolinn, Cartographer-General to the Court of Her Most Reverend Excellency, Doge Catherine-Sophia*

# THE EDDIC OF LOCI 1: LOCI AWAKES

PLATE 1

# 1

## INDOCTRANS Headquarters, Fort Jackson
## The Real World: 3 August 2018

I met with my host and fellow guests for breakfast and, I am obliged to report, I found them, like me, much changed. However, whereas my faculties had been enhanced in a most pleasing manner, theirs, as a generality, had suffered a marked deterioration. Ever the scientist, I made a full and detailed scrutiny of von Frankenstein's instrumentation, and thus am able to conjecture most confidently regarding the cause of these transmogrifications. The immense electrical field generated by the meteor as it plunged to earth had bathed all those in the house in a pulse of energy of such magnitude that a most profound and fundamental metamorphosis was provoked. Each resident was physically, psychologically and, I would postulate, taxonomically mutated. These changes sat most ill with Sir Augustus Bole, who glowered at the company in a quite ferocious manner. He seemed excessively wan and pale of countenance, and complained interminably that the winter sunshine was inflaming his skin. He went so far as to demand a servant bring him a pair of spectacles with brown-tinted lenses to protect his eyes from the glare of the sun.

*Excerpt from the diary of Percy Cavor,*
*dated 1 December 1795*

Although it was only a few minutes past noon, Septimus Bole's office in INDOCTRANS's headquarters was swathed in darkness, the heavy drapes tightly drawn, sealing the room from the sunlit day beyond. There were no lights burning in the room and hence it was Stygian dark, only the far-off and heavily muffled noise of the traffic moving ten floors below his office windows signalling that he was still in the land of the living. Bole welcomed the darkness; he hated sunlight, especially when he was in the grip of the Shadows. So, troubled and tormented, he sat alone in the darkened room, fingering the Remington revolver lying on the top of his desk, and toying with a consideration of the joy of release that putting a bullet – a silver bullet – through his brain would bring him.

*The Shadows.*

These were the times when the responsibilities the Bole family had accepted – *accepted!* – all those long years ago became so heavy that he was unable to function, when he felt himself worn down . . . crushed . . . useless. Perhaps once or twice a month, the Shadows would descend on him and he would be obliged to sit paralysed and helpless, alone in the dark, until that feeling of total despair lifted. And during these times he had to wrestle with the pitiless urge to purge himself of his cares – of being a Dark Charismatic in a world of Fragiles – by the use of his revolver.

The Shadows frightened him. They frightened him because during these black times all the emotions he had so valiantly ignored and pushed aside welled up inside him and threatened to inundate him. The Shadows made him realise that perhaps, possibly, probably, he wasn't the unfeeling, emotionless, pitiless automaton of an über-genius he wished so desperately to be. During the Shadows, Bole felt human, he felt . . . *fragile.* During the Shadows, he was no longer the majestic, the all-powerful Dark Charismatic. During the Shadows, the inferior was in momentary ascendancy over the superior, and Bole became a god humbled by his own contaminating mortality. In those moments, his human side which dwelt cowering in the furthest recesses of his soul came to the fore and reduced him back to being one of the simpering, subservient H. *sapiens* the Boles had been before their Awakening by the meteor.

In his desperation to understand his affliction he had scoured the history books, searching for clues, and it was then that he made a startling discovery. It seemed that a high proportion of ĐClass Singularities – the most powerful of all Dark Charismatics, within whose exclusive fraternity Bole counted himself – had all suffered as he suffered. Stalin, Bonaparte, Cromwell, Alexander the Great and Caligula had all endured the Shadows.

His studies led him to conclude that for a Dark Charismatic, the two aspects of his being – H. *sapiens* and H. *singularis*, Man and Grigori – would always be in conflict and hence his soul would never be at peace. Dark Charismatics were mongrels – a Grigori soul housed in a Fragile's body – condemned never to be sanguine, ever to be at war within themselves, as one side of their being struggled with the other for mastery.

It was a worrying conclusion, especially as he had grown older, so the depressions associated with the Shadows had grown deeper. When in the grip of the Shadows, Bole, to his great alarm, was becoming increasingly maudlin and increasingly suicidal. It was as though his residual humanity, sensing that it would never be able to control the Grigori lurking within, sought its own destruction, as, by destroying itself, it destroyed its dark companion.

In his times of darkness, Bole saw himself as a mouse trapped on a wheel, forever trundling energetically forward, and forever going nowhere. The wheel was, of course, a simple metaphor for his destiny, and he sensed that if he could, just for a moment, step away from his many responsibilities and pressures, then immediately the Shadows besetting his life would vanish. Yet stepping off that wheel was, he knew, impossible: the Grigori would never forgive him if he surrendered. He was their final hope. Bole's life was defined by this sacred mission to secure the long-awaited victory of the Grigori over the Fragiles . . . the Final Solution.

Bole sighed, the despairing sound reverberating around the empty room. As he sat unmoving on his chair, bowed down by the onerous weight of destiny that rested on his shoulders, sweat standing out on his furrowed forehead, eyes tight-closed and teeth hard-clenched, he sensed this would be a particularly testing Shadow Moment.

Now his anguish was flavoured by the thought that he might fail. He was haunted by the possibility that all his careful planning and conniving might be turned to dust by the unwitting actions of an eighteen-year-old schoolgirl. That he, the great Septimus Bole, had been outfoxed by Ella Thomas; outfoxed by a Fragile, by a female, by a black . . . by an Untermensch.

His hand closed around the leather-bound grip of the pistol. He felt its weight and its power heavy in his hand. Unbidden, he flexed his strength and, inch by inch, raised the gun to his head. Now he could feel the comforting coldness of its muzzle hard against the side of his forehead. His finger snaked around the trigger. His thumb flicked off the safety catch. Just one squeeze and he would send a silver bullet into his brain, allowing his kind's acute argyria to do the rest. Death was just a pull of a trigger away. Freedom from woe required him simply to fire.

He straightened himself in his seat. No, he would not be beaten. Not when he was so close to triumph.

*Think.*

There was only one thing that could leaven the melancholy of the Shadows, and it was blood. He hated to surrender to these primeval appetites, to these base addictions, but today the

Shadows were so *very* strong. Desperately his fingers scrabbled in the darkness as they unlocked the top drawer of his desk and then searched it for the phial of soul-reviving blood he had hidden there. Finally his fingers found the cold certainty of the glass cylinder. He snapped the top off and sucked down the thick, sweet fluid it contained. Immediately he felt his spirits rise.

Gradually, his racing heart calmed and he regained control of himself. Once again he had survived the Shadows. The blood had saved him, but the reason for his dive into melancholia remained.

He conjured a handkerchief from his sleeve and wiped it across his brow. 'ABBA . . . ?' he said, his voice hardly more than a hoarse whisper.

'Good afternoon, Septimus,' answered ABBA, in its immaculate imitation of a human voice. It was such a perfect imitation that Bole often forgot that what he was actually talking to was the world's first – the world's only – quantum computer. 'How are you today, Septimus?' continued ABBA in the same irritatingly equitable manner.

*Why does ABBA always talk in a woman's voice?*

'I am very well, ABBA, very well indeed,' Bole answered through gritted teeth, the words slurring as he tried to enunciate them through the pain that bracketed his oh-so-elegant mind. He wondered why he was even attempting to lie to ABBA; even in the darkness the infernal machine saw everything.

'I note from your pupil dilation, and your elevated skin temperature, that you are undergoing a rather debilitating bout of neurological dysfunction,' ABBA observed. 'I would recommend a dose of one hundred grams of DayRapture, taken immediately.'

'That's enough chit-chat, ABBA,' Bole snapped. 'I don't want to talk about my health or my psychological well-being, and I most certainly do not want my intellectual faculties pharmacologically impaired. Just bring up a résumé of Ella Thomas's recent interaction with the IM Manual.'

'As you wish, Septimus,' crooned ABBA – the machine, as always, indifferent to Bole's boorishness – and immediately the Flexi-Plexi on the right-hand wall of Bole's office mutated into a psychedelic swirl of colours and shapes. It settled down to show an eyeVid of Ella Thomas standing in a transfusion booth in the Bank of Warsaw. 'Ella Thomas interacted with the IM Manual on the eighty-fifth day of Winter, by Demi-Monde chronology, issuing instructions that the Boundary Layer at WBL-1 be made penetrable.'

Bole felt his headache intensifying. He had taken so much care over the selection of Ella Thomas, finessing her audition so that she appeared to be a strong enough candidate to satisfy INDOCTRANS's interview procedure, but not strong enough to act as a loose cannon once she was inserted into the Demi-Monde. He still couldn't understand where he had gone wrong. His analysis of her intellectual, psychological and physical profile had been rigorous. The girl should *never* have had so much initiative and resilience.

This was the question he now put to ABBA. 'How was she able to do this? How was she able to access the IM Manual? My understanding is that it's impossible for anyone, other than members of the Demi-Monde Steering Committee, to make changes to the Demi-Monde's cyber-milieu.'

'You are wrong in this surmise, Septimus,' ABBA corrected. 'You may perhaps remember, after the incident when a platoon of neoFights was marooned in NoirVille, that the Demi-Monde Steering Committee enacted Emergency Protocol Fifty-Seven, whereby US Army officers who are active in the Demi-Monde and in possession of a security clearance of Level Eight or above may, in conditions of life-threatening potential, make emergency one-hour alterations to the cyber-milieu.'

'But Ella Thomas isn't a US Army officer.'

'That is incorrect, Septimus. General Peter Zieliéski, in the contract he signed with Ella Thomas, designated her, for the purposes of life insurance and medical benefits, as a captain in the US Army. I am obliged, by virtue of my programming, to adopt the security classification corresponding to the rank that is allocated by INDOCTRANS Human Resources, and in Ella Thomas's case this is Level Eight.'

'I would like to rescind that classification, ABBA.'

'That is not possible, Septimus. To do so will require the signatures of both parties to the contract. As Ella Thomas is currently in TIS mode, and has granted no power of attorney, such an alteration to the contract's terms and conditions must await her return from the Demi-Monde.'

'Can I put an automatic non-ratification on any further changes she makes to the Demi-Monde?'

'No, Septimus, unless, of course, you have General Zieliéski endorse this change in operational procedure. Shall I send an eyeMail to the general requesting such an endorsement?'

'No.' The last thing Bole wanted was Zieliéski becoming suspicious about Bole's motives regarding the Demi-Monde, or, worse, coming to the belated conclusion that the Demi-Monde had a purpose beyond the training of neoFights.

Bole sank back even further in his chair and pondered. It was imperative that he stop Ella Thomas interfering with the Demi-Monde. The trouble-making bitch had to be neutralised and neutralised quickly. With the Rite of Transference completed and Aaliz Heydrich physically manifest inside the Real World, the Real World aspects of the Final Solution could begin in earnest. But as achieving success in the Real World was predicated on the success of Aaliz's father, Reinhard Heydrich, taking full control of the Demi-Monde, and, of course, in refining the Plague Weapon, then anything that endangered these ambitions was a threat to the whole project. Yes . . . perfecting the Plague Weapon was the important thing . . . nothing must be allowed to jeopardise the work of the geniuses Bole had assembled in the Heydrich Institute for Natural Sciences in Berlin. The problems his grandfather had encountered in 1946 must not be repeated.

But the reality was that Ella Thomas *was* jeopardising this work.

Trying to massage away the last of his lingering headache, Bole wondered if now was the time for him to wander along to the ward where Ella Thomas's TIS-swathed body was lying, and turn off her life-support function. But he couldn't. The ward she was in was surveilled and patrolled on a 24/7 basis. The Americans were wary of ABBA and had installed their own independent surveillance system based on an Imperial Business Machines 3090 Series computer, the most up-to-date model the British government would issue an export permit for. Obsolete it might be but it was effective, too effective for him to risk doing anything as crude as murder.

'ABBA, where is Ella Thomas's Dupe in the Demi-Monde?'

'She and her colleagues have left ExterSteine and are now en route to Paris, located in the Quartier Chaud Sector of the Demi-Monde.'

'I wish a message sent to Dupe Tomas de Torquemada, alerting him to her arrival and advising him that she is a threat to UnFunDaMentalism.'

'The PigeonGram has been sent, Septimus.'

As Bole rose a little unsteadily to his feet, he wondered if he could trust de Torquemada to organise the assassination of Ella Thomas. He had other cryptos on his payroll in Paris, but the best of these was of an intellectual persuasion and hence would make a reluctant assassin. Perhaps now was the time to unleash Semiazaz and his brothers inside the Demi-Monde, then there would be no chance of failure. But the very thought of employing pure-blooded Grigori to perform such a simple task smacked of overkill.

No, the Grigori would be the last resort.

# 2

## ExterSteine
## The Demi-Monde: 1st Day of Spring, 1005

Most disturbingly, my studies have led me to hypothesise that Dark Charismatics are *not* lunatics, as Alienists traditionally view those beset by Moral Insanity. Their aberrational and destructive behaviour is *not* a product of lesions in their Solidified Astral Ether, or other somatic or visceral damage. Rather, I have come to believe that Dark Charismatics are a separate and distinct taxon of the genus *Homo*, whose members are the very antithesis of *H. sapiens*, being innately and wholly evil. This discrete taxon I have named *Homo singularis*.

*Letter dated 53rd day of Spring, 1002,*
*from Professeur Michel de Nostredame to*
*Doge Catherine-Sophia*

Ella's breath haloed around her, white in the frosted chill of the Winter night, as she panted her way up the long, steep staircase that led to the summit of ExterSteine. There was so little time left; she could see the pink of dawn painting the horizon and once dawn was here then Norma would be lost, Crowley's Rite of Transference complete. Dawn's light was the final piece of occult empowerment that Crowley needed to work his diabolical magic.

'Faster,' she whispered to herself, trying to ignore the pain wracking her protesting body and the heaviness infesting her tired legs.

'I *am* goin' faster,' moaned Rivets from ahead of her, but he upped his pace anyway, taking the snow-slick steps two at a time.

'Quiet!' snapped Vanka, and as they followed the staircase around the huge Mantle-ite column, Ella saw the reason for the warning: there, in front of them, was the gaping mouth of a cavern, out of which poured a strange, atonal music. 'That's where Crowley's performing his magic, so stay tight to the shadows: there might be guards.'

Ella barely heard him. She stood staring into the huge, black, gaping maw of the cavern. It was a place of nightmares . . . but it was also a place of power. Yes, the cavern seemed to exude a cold, spine-chilling power that was replete with licentiousness and depravity and Ella had no doubt that acts of terrible perversity and vileness had been enacted in this place. She shivered, but not through cold or fear; power was very exciting.

A cacophony of seductive voices echoed in her head, telling her that this power could be hers again . . . if she had the will . . . if she had the courage.

A hand gripped her shoulder. 'Ella, are you okay?'

Vanka's question brought her back to the here and now. Strong, wonderful Vanka. The man she loved, the man who had sacrificed all his instincts for self-preservation to stand at her side and to help her rescue Norma Williams.

Rescue Norma Williams . . .

'Yeah, Vanka, I'm fine. Let's get moving. We've got a Rite of Transferance to screw up.'

Lavrentii Beria was a bastard.

That was the conclusion Burlesque Bandstand had come to, as he sat atop the great column that was ExterSteine, huddled inside his huge *dublonka*, with his back set against Winter's last winds, waiting for Vanka Maykov and Miss Ella to arrive. He shuffled his numb arse on the cold, unyielding Mantle-ite, and indulged in a scratch: his lice were playing him up something terrible. And as he scratched, he decided that he was wrong in his assessment of Beria. Beria wasn't just a bastard; he was a *big* bastard.

Gazing out, in an unfocused sort of way, as dawn lazed slowly over the snow-decked HubLand that stretched around ExterSteine, Burlesque's mind drifted back to the terrible weeks he had endured at the hands of that bastard . . . that *big* bastard. Following his arrest at Dashwood Manor he'd been thrown into a cell on one of the most secure levels of the Lubyanka prison. It was a soundproof cell, which Burlesque supposed was just as well because he had done a lot of screaming during the time he was held captive there.

Yeah, they had tortured him long and hard during those seemingly endless days and nights, and as they had tortured him, Burlesque had changed. Oh, it wasn't just the weight he had lost or the interesting and comprehensive collection of lumps and bruises he'd acquired that signalled this change, it was the deep and undying hatred of Beria and of UnFunDaMentalism. Burlesque had sworn that if he ever escaped the Lubyanka he'd kill the bastard in retribution for the pain inflicted on him.

And now retribution beckoned.

Shielding his eyes with a gloved hand, Burlesque squinted towards the rising sun, checked his watch – shaking it to make sure it was still ticking – and then let out a long doleful sigh. He'd expected Vanka and Miss Ella to show up before now. He'd been sitting atop ExterSteine for most of the night, listening to the shit-awful music rising up from the cavern below, waiting for the pair of them to come galloping to Norma Williams's rescue. Now, as dawn was breaking, it would soon be too late for them to save the Daemon.

*Serve her right for being such a cow.*

The funny thing was that it had only been the failure of Beria's Checkya agents to track down and assassinate Vanka and Miss Ella that had saved Burlesque's bacon. It was on the back of this failure that Beria had come to the belated conclusion that the only person who had a chance of finding them was Burlesque Bandstand.

He vividly remembered that final interview with Beria. One cold and damp morning – he didn't know *which* particular morning, since all mornings in the Lubyanka were cold and damp – the bastard had come strutting into his cell, had plonked himself down on the chair the guard had brought for him, and had given Burlesque that empty, cold smile that Burlesque had come to despise.

Beria got straight down to business. 'Would you like to live?' he had asked.

'Live?'

'Yes, I can arrange for you to be given a pardon for all of your crimes against the ForthRight, and a safe conduct to the Quartier Chaud.'

'I ain't committed no crimes against the ForthRight,' Burlesque had lied.

Beria had arched an eyebrow to signal that he thought Burlesque was being deliberately obtuse. 'Oh, please, it becomes tedious when someone as cunning as you denies what is both obvious and inevitable.'

'Obvious and inevitable?'

'It is *obvious* that if I let my guards loose on you again, you will *inevitably* confess.'

'Confess? Confess to wot?'

'To whatever it is that I might wish you to confess to. My

experience is that the gravity of the crimes confessed to is directly proportional to the amount of pain I inflict on a body.' And to confirm the reality of his contention, Beria had stood up from his chair and smashed his fist into Burlesque's face. 'That is to demonstrate that I am in earnest. So now I repeat: would you like to live?'

'Yus,' Burlesque replied, as he'd spat out one of his few remaining teeth.

*Bastard.*

'Excellent. Then in order to achieve that outcome, all you have to do is render me a service. You remember the PsyChick of Vanka Maykov's – the Shade you knew as Ella Thomas, but whose real name is, we believe, Marie Laveau?'

A careful nod from Burlesque: careful because he hadn't yet decided if the punch had broken his jaw.

'Very good, I wish her killed. And you, with your prolific and comprehensive knowledge of the Demi-Monde's criminal fraternity, are just the man to find and assassinate her. You will also kill her paramour, this Vanka Maykov.'

'And iffn I do off them, wot's in it for me?'

'Then you will receive a pardon for all the crimes, real and imaginary, you will otherwise be charged with. It is really a very generous offer and one you would be stupid – *fatally* stupid – to turn down.'

For Burlesque Bandstand it was an epiphany. Seated on his soiled mattress in that sordid little cell, he finally came to realise that no matter what he did, no matter how dutifully he served Beria, he was a dead man. As far as Beria was concerned, Burlesque was nothing more than the dirt beneath his feet, a nonentity. Once he had dealt with Vanka and Ella, the bastard would kill him with no further thought than Burlesque would give to killing one of the fleas that currently called his bed home. And knowing this, he understood that the reason why

Beria thought he could treat him in this way was that the man wasn't frightened of him. He had crawled and fawned for so long that it was all Beria thought he could do.

But Beria was wrong, and he would show this pompous, arrogant bastard just what Burlesque Bandstand was capable of. One day, he swore, Beria would regret he'd smashed a fist into his face. One day he would make Beria suffer for what he'd done. And to do this, Burlesque knew he had to live, and to live he had to imitate cooperation.

'Okay,' he'd said quietly, 'but I wanna know where the ovver Daemon is. I wanna know where Norma Williams is.'

'Why?'

'Because wherever *that* Daemon is, chances are that's where I'll find Ella Thomas.'

And that was why Burlesque Bandstand had been taken to ExterSteine in one of Beria's own steamers, and why, when he got there, he'd picked up a rock and used it to stave in the head of the SS StormTrooper set to guard him. The thought of killing the man didn't give Burlesque even a moment's pause. From now on, anyone who was an ally of Lavrentii Beria was an enemy of Burlesque Bandstand.

His pondering upon the delights of murder was interrupted by the scrape of boot heels. He turned his head towards the staircase that circled ExterSteine, and saw Vanka, Miss Ella and a scruffy young boy he didn't recognise step uncertainly onto the top of the column, bracing themselves against the biting winds that vortexed around them.

'Over there!' Vanka shouted. 'To the east! The shutters must be over there.'

Leaning into the wind, the three of them pushed their way over to the eastern side of the column. Vanka was right: a pair of great wooden shutters covered that side of the column, facing towards the rapidly rising sun. There was a huge wooden lever to one side, which presumably operated the shutters.

*Why aren't they guarded?* wondered Ella.

Vanka whipped his belt from around his waist. 'If we tie this around the handles of the shutters that'll stop them being opened.'

His explanation was interrupted by the unmistakable sound of a revolver being cocked. As one, the three of them looked up, and saw Burlesque Bandstand – a much thinner-faced Burlesque Bandstand – sitting with his legs dangling carelessly over the side of the column, brandishing a purposeful-looking Webley pistol in their direction.

By the ever-brightening light of the rising sun, Ella could see that there was the body of a dead SS StormTrooper lying next to him.

''Appy First ov Spring, Wanker, you bastard,' said Burlesque as he raised the pistol and took careful aim at Vanka's forehead.

The muzzle of the pistol flamed, and Ella felt the heat of the lead slug as it scorched through the air only inches from her ear. There was a scream behind her, and when she looked around she saw a black-uniformed Checkya captain crumpling to the floor with a neat hole drilled in his chest. Unfortunately, as he fell, his limp and lifeless body dropped over the lever that worked the wooden shutters, springing them open. Vanka made a dive to close them, but it was too late and dawn's light poured down through the opening and into the cavern below.

Aghast, Ella could only stand and stare in numb disbelief: it was the first light of Spring that completed the Rite of Transference, and now there was nothing they could do to prevent the Rite being enacted. Now there was nothing they could do to prevent Aaliz Heydrich taking command of Norma's body in the Real World. They had failed.

Devastated that all their efforts, all the dangers they had endured, had been for nothing, Ella sank to her knees and sobbed.

Oblivious to Ella's misery, Burlesque grunted himself up onto his feet and began a vigorous massaging of his arse. 'Bastards,' he muttered as he spat in the direction of the Checkya captain's body. 'That's wot all ov them Checkya are, bastards.' And with that, he limped across to where the body of the man he had just shot lay and gave it a wholly superfluous kick. 'Dead as a fucking doornail.' He spat into the dead man's face. 'Serves 'im right. Serves 'im right for being a Checkya bastard an' for working for that piece of shit Beria. Serves 'im right for wot that bastard did to me in the Lubyanka.'

'You were in the Lubyanka?' asked Ella nervously. It had been a real shock for her to meet Burlesque again. The last time she had seen him had been at Dashwood Manor, when they had been organising Norma Williams's escape.

'Yeah, they arrested me after that kerfuffle at Dashwood's gaff. Fucking Witchfinder disowned me. After everyfing I done for 'im.'

Ella eyed Burlesque cautiously. He seemed even more wild-eyed and unbalanced than she remembered, and the nervous tic under his right eye signalled that he was a man near the end of his tether. Vanka was obviously as wary of Burlesque as she was. He stepped closer to her side and eased his coat away from the butt of the Colt holstered in his belt. Taking his cue from Vanka, Rivets slid a knife into his hand.

Burlesque noticed what Vanka and Rivets were doing and he gave a humourless little laugh. 'Don't fret yerself, Wanker. Iffn I wanted you dead, you'd be mutton by now. Nah, there ain't no bad blood between us. I've learned me lessons an' all I'm intent on doin' now is settling me score wiv Beria. Gotta pay 'im back for wot 'e did to me. Me bollocks are still big as ball-cocks from the beatings 'e ordered, and iffn me toenails ever grow back straight, it'll be a bleedin' miracle.' He looked mourn-fully down at his feet. 'That's why I've got this limp.'

'I'm so sorry, Burlesque,' said Ella, though it seemed a totally inadequate thing to say.

'Well,' said Burlesque with a rueful shrug, 'I suppose I 'ad it comin'. Wot do they say? When you sup wiv the devil, better use a long spoon. Well, I guess mine wos too short by 'alf.' He scowled and lumped the collar of his coat up around his ears. The sun might be up now, but standing exposed on the very summit of ExterSteine, with the wind howling around them, was a decid-edly chilly experience. 'So 'oo's the kid?' he asked.

'I ain't no kid. Me name's Rivets.'

'Be careful, Burlesque,' warned Vanka, 'Rivets might be small, but he bites. He and I have been business partners for a few years now and we've come through some tough scrapes together.'

'Yeah, I'm 'ere to protect my inheritance. Vanka owes me a ransom in rhino and then some.'

'Pleased to meetcha, Rivets. No offence meant, so yous can put that blade away now.'

'So what are you doing here, Burlesque?' asked Vanka. 'It's hardly the kind of place you'd come for a jaunt.'

'That's an easy wun, Wanker. I've bin sent 'ere, courtesy ov that bastard Lavrentii Beria, to top you an' Miss Ella. After that shindig at the Manor, Beria got real fuckin' upset, and as a consequence he got hot and hateful on my arse. And look wot that sod did to me nose.' Burlesque tapped the side of his nose, which Ella could see looked decidedly askew. 'Broke it, the bastard did. Broke it so bad that now every time I sneeze, I get an earful ov snot. Spoilt my looks, 'e did.'

'How did you know where to find us, Burlesque?' asked Ella.

THE DEMI-MONDE SPRING | 22

'Easy as blinking. I knew you'd turn up 'ere, 'cos I knew you wouldn't give up trying to rescue that snotty cow Norma Williams.' Burlesque gave a shrug. 'Any'ows, she's doornailed now, so there's no point in us standing 'ere chit-chatting all morning. Give it an hour an' an 'ole mess ov them Checkya bastards is gonna be buzzin' around 'ere thick as flies on dogshit.' He gave the body of the Checkya captain a final kick. 'Best we get going now, while the going's good.'

Ella eyed him warily. 'Get going where, Burlesque?'

'Get you to the Quartier and then, when the 'eat's died down, I'm gonna go back to the Rookeries and blow Beria's fucking lights out. He's gonna find out you don't mess wiv Burlesque Bandstand an' get away wiv it scot-free.'

''Ow we gonna get to the Quartier?' Rivets asked. 'It's fuckin' miles away.'

'Follow me.'

With that Burlesque led the three of them back towards the staircase that spiralled around the great ExterSteine.

Norma lay on the hard, cold floor of the cavern, lost in the netherworld of exhausted sleep, her body drained by the ordeal that had been the Rite of Transference and her spirit unable to find the strength to re-engage with the world. And as she slept, she dreamed.

In the fevered imaginings of her mind, once again she found herself at bay in the tight, night-black alleyways of the Rookeries, but this time it wasn't Archie Clement at her heels, now it was her conscience. She could hear the squabble of voices behind her, imploring her to be true to herself.

*Listen to us*, she heard them say, *we are the whispers of the truths you have been avoiding.*

But as she had done all through her young life, she ran on, refusing to listen, blocking her ears. She hated the thought of the truth and the responsibility it would bring. She ran in her dream just as she had run in life when she had tried to lose herself in her addictions and her self-inflicted immaturity.

She was, after all, just a girl, oppressed and worn down by the worries and responsibilities of a runaway world, and by the hopes of a successful father and a distant mother – a girl who had never thought herself strong enough or powerful enough to carry the load that life had placed on her.

Oh, she had always sensed she had a purpose in life, but she had been fearful of her ability to grasp the dark unknown that was her destiny. All her life this fear of failure had been her constant companion, following her like a shadow, but she had never been able to raise the courage to turn and face it. But now she knew the time for running was over.

Her destiny touched her on her shoulder, and in her dream she stopped and turned.

Now she saw the evil she would be called on to face. It looked so huge, so intractable, so monumental, as to make even the thought of defeating it feel impossible. Delinquent voices whispered to her that she was as nothing compared to the brutal force which she was being called upon to confront. That she would be foolish even to try . . .

She moaned in her sleep, despairing of her weakness, of her frailty, of her ignorance. More, she despaired of her loneliness, of having no one to share her burden with. But then, she'd always been alone. And as a single, desolate tear trickled down her cheek she realised that that was her destiny, to stand alone in the eye of the hurricane that would soon envelop the world.

They were about halfway down the column when they came, once more, to the wooden platform that led towards the gaping mouth of the cavern. Burlesque held a finger to his lips. 'Quiet 'ere,' he whispered. 'This is where Crowley and his oppos perform their 'orrible rites and fingies. They're probably all shagged out from their capering abart last night, but it never does to be too cocky.'

'But this *is* where Norma was brought?'

Burlesque frowned as he anticipated Ella's line of thinking. 'Nah, don't even fink abart it, Miss Ella. She's a goner. Old Crowley's probably deep-sixed her as part ov sum 'orrible pagan sacrifice, see.'

Ella gave an emphatic shake of her head. 'No, he wouldn't do that. He was trying to transfer the soul of Aaliz Heydrich to Norma's body in the Real World, so the last thing he would do is risk killing her. He'll probably need her when he wants Aaliz returned to the Demi-Monde. No, the chances are she's still alive.'

Before either Vanka or Burlesque could stop her, Ella dodged towards the cavern's entrance. As she stepped inside, the gloom stole the dawn's light and she was quickly shrouded in sinister shadows and enveloped by swirling mists of smoke that reeked of decay and of fetid corruption. The stench was almost intolerable; it made Ella gag and her stomach churn in disgust, so much so that it took a real effort to force herself into the cavern's mouth. But even more disconcerting was the feeling of déjà vu she experienced. She felt – she *knew* – she had been here before . . . in a previous life.

*Ridiculous.*

Ridiculous it might be, but Ella could almost see herself dressed as some pagan priestess, performing a strange ritual in this very cavern. With an angry shake of her head, she tried to dispel these stupid fantasies and redirect her efforts towards not tripping over the bodies littering the floor. Burlesque had been right, all Crowley's acolytes *were* shagged out, if the twenty or so naked people stretched out unconscious on the floor were any indication. Drunk, drugged and debauched, they lay there totally lost to the world.

''Ave they snuffed it?' Burlesque whispered in her ear.

'No, they all seem to be breathing.' Ella turned to Vanka. 'Help me find Norma.'

The girl wasn't difficult to find, but she proved devilishly difficult to identify. Vanka found the two naked doppelgängers, Norma and Aaliz, entwined around one another in the very centre of the cavern, lying at the foot of what Ella assumed to be an altar of some description. The problem they had was deciding which girl was which. Sure, there was one dark-haired 'Norma' and one blonde 'Aaliz', but to Ella neither of them seemed quite right.

'That one looks like Norma Williams,' said Vanka, pointing to the girl with the black hair and the stud in her nose. 'But I seem to remember her tattoo being on the other shoulder.'

Ella nodded. 'Well spotted, Vanka. I think they've made Aaliz Heydrich up to look like Norma, but somehow got it a little wrong. There's one way of knowing for sure, though.' With that Ella stooped down and took the black-haired girl's hand in hers, allowing her Personal Implanted Nano Computer – her PINC – to confirm her identity. 'You're right, Vanka. This one's Aaliz Heydrich.' Ella let the girl's hand drop to the ground. 'Let's see if we can bring the real Norma round.'

Vanka, who had never taken to Norma, brusquely shook the girl awake, and with a groan she fluttered her eyes open. Seeing Ella and Vanka looming over her, the girl shrank back, as if trying to occupy a smaller space, and it was only when she recognised Ella that she was persuaded to lever herself upright and disentangle herself from Aaliz Heydrich. She took a little longer to come to terms with waking up stark naked in a cold and very draughty cavern, and it needed a couple of long swigs from the flask of cognac Vanka offered her before she fully returned to the land of the living.

Burlesque and Rivets decided they needed a couple of swigs, too.

'You're too late,' Norma announced finally, in a faraway voice. 'Crowley completed the Rite, and Aaliz is now in the Real World.'

'That doesn't matter, Norma,' said Ella quietly. 'All that matters is that you're safe.'

As she was hauled unsteadily to her feet, Norma pulled on the thin cotton shift she'd found discarded on the floor and then accepted the cloak Vanka offered her. Dressed, she made to move towards the cavern's entrance, but tottered uncertainly and had to take Vanka's arm to steady herself. She looked ghastly.

All this delay was too much for Burlesque. 'Come on, come on,' he urged, as he looked nervously around the cavern. 'Best we get going. These idiots are going to start waking up soon, an' then . . .'

Seeing him, Norma's face distorted in anger. Obviously a dose of Burlesque Bandstand was as effective as smelling salts for her – but then, mused Ella, they both had a similar odour. 'What's this douche-bag doing here?' she snarled. 'He's the one who sold me out to the Witchfinder.'

Norma's ire was easy to understand, Witchfinder Major Matthew Hopkins was the man who had been responsible for hunting Norma down when she had first entered the Demi-Monde. She still had a busted knee to remind her of her run-in with the SS bastard.

'Savin' your arse, that's wot,' responded Burlesque sharply, 'so keep yer knickers on . . . well, iffn you had any knickers to keep on, that is. I'm on your side now. An' for the love ov ABBA, let's get movin'.'

'What about Aaliz?' asked Ella. 'Maybe we should take her with us as a hostage?'

Vanka shook his head. 'It'll be bad enough getting away as it is without carrying her along too.'

'Maybe we should off her,' suggested Rivets. 'That'd piss off Heydrich.'

'No,' said Ella firmly. 'If we do that, Norma's body will probably die in the Real World. Then she'd never be able to leave the Demi-Monde.'

As they exited the cavern, Vanka turned to Burlesque. 'So what do we do now, Burlesque? Like Rivets says, we can't just walk to the Quartier, and anyway, there's a cordon of SS surrounding ExterSteine. We saw them when we flew over their lines last night.'

'So it wos you in that balloon thingy? Sharp work, Wanker, but I ain't no slouch either.' Burlesque bustled his charges towards the entrance of the cavern. 'So tell me, Wanker, wot vehicle never gets searched by the SS, or by anybody else for that matter?'

'A Checkya steamer?'

'Give the man a coconut. But I ain't got just any old steamer, Vanka, I've got wun flying Beria's very own pennant on the front, an' that means nobody short ov Heydrich 'imself is gonna stop us . . . not iffn they like 'aving fingernails that is. Fuck, I could run over the 'ole of the ForthRight army an' there wouldn't be a peep of protest.'

# 3

## The HubLand bordering the Thames River
## The Demi-Monde:
## 1st and 2nd Days of Spring, 1005

The Medi District of the Quartier Chaud (comprising Paris, Rome and Barcelona) is becoming increasingly – both politically and religiously – alienated from Venice. Despite the number and vociferous nature of anti-ForthRight demonstrations within the Medi Districts (mainly orchestrated by members of the UnScrewed-Liberation Movement), there are encouraging signs that the Medi will move towards a formal adoption of UnFunDaMentalism as its official religion in the very near future. This will further isolate Venice as the only outpost of ImPuritanism in the Quartier Chaud. It is the recommendation of this Ministry that our disorganisationalist efforts within the Medi be redoubled and the political and financial support provided to Senior CitiZen Robespierre be increased.

*Extract from the Confidential Briefing Document written by the ForthRight Ministry of Propaganda and submitted for consideration by the PolitBuro on the 89th day of Winter, 1004*

And Burlesque was just the man to test the power of Beria's pennant in rendering them immune from protest.

Their stolen Checkya steamer – delivered courtesy of the now dead Checkya captain – suddenly lumped up into the air, slammed down on its suspension, and then yawed alarmingly as it skidded on the snow-slick surface of the Hub. Burlesque sawed at the wheel, desperately trying to bring four tons of delinquent steamer back under control.

'Gor,' shouted an admiring Rivets, from his perch right at the back of the vehicle, 'you ain't 'alf made a mess ov that 'orse yous just run over, Burlesque. An' that bloke 'oo was riding it looks fit to burst.'

'Serves 'im right,' snarled Burlesque, as he gave the steering wheel another yank. ''E shouldn't 'ave leapt out in front ov me like that.'

'He was *grazing* his horse,' muttered Norma, as she used a cloth to wipe the last of the runes from her face.

'Nah, 'e wasn't. That 'orse was fucking leaping.'

'Look, Burlesque, why don't you let me drive?' yelled Vanka, over the yowl of the steamer's tortured pistons as Burlesque tried and failed to change gear.

'Nah, I've always wanted to drive a steamer since I was a lad. There ain't nuffink to it.'

As Burlesque drove the steamer over an innocent and very immobile bell tent, Ella had to look away. They had been huffing and puffing towards Hub Bridge Number Two for almost an hour, and during that time Burlesque had slaughtered any number of horses, destroyed a couple of carts, and crushed a poor unfortunate dog that had chosen the wrong time and place to relieve itself. And such was the fear instilled by Beria that not one person had had the courage to try and stop them.

It was, Ella decided, a miracle that he hadn't done even more damage. There were so many targets for Burlesque to aim at that even a driver as wayward as he was couldn't avoid hitting *something*, especially as the ForthRight Army seemed not to be in much of a mood to dodge out of the way.

Which was very perplexing.

Having experienced the noise and the turmoil of battle when she had been hiding out in Warsaw, Ella found the Army of the ForthRight that was supposedly invading the Quartier Chaud a little . . . well, relaxed. There was no artillery bombardment smashing down onto the Medi side of the Thames, no phalanxes of armoured steamers preparing to battle their way across the Hub Bridge, and no screaming NCOs urging their reluctant troops into formation. As their steamer smashed its way between – and occasionally over – the clumps of soldiers who were seated around their campfires, cooking breakfast, or lying on the grass enjoying the Spring sunshine, Ella had the distinct impression that they'd somehow wandered into nothing more menacing than a Boy Scout jamboree.

'What's happening, Vanka? Why isn't the army advancing?' she asked, as she stared out of the steamer's window at a herd of stampeding cavalry horses that prior to Burlesque's arrival had been contentedly munching on the contents of their nose-bags.

'Beats me,' admitted Vanka, as he sat back in his seat and stretched his long legs. 'Maybe Heydrich's persuaded the Quartier Chaud to surrender.'

This last comment was made in jest, but as Ella – aided by PINC – mulled the situation over, it began to make a sort of perverted sense. If there was one place where she would have expected the fighting to be at its fiercest, it was around the Hub Bridge, the only place where the invading ForthRight Army could cross the Thames. But as Burlesque steered the steamer into a neat if unintended pirouette, the bridge hove briefly into view and Ella saw that, rather than the battle she expected, there was an orderly queue of ForthRight infantry patiently waiting their turn to march across. There were even GrandHarms – officers in the Quartier Chaud's police force – directing traffic, making it easier for the mass of men, machines and horses that was the ForthRight Army to cross the river and occupy their Sector.

It was so peculiar that it even persuaded Vanka to abandon his usual indifference to what happened in the outside world, and pay attention. 'The Quartier Chaud *must* have surrendered,' he mused to no one in particular. 'I mean, the Medis aren't meant to be much good at fighting – not that I blame them – but from what I understand, the mercenaries the Venetians have on their payroll are always up for a scrap.'

'Why would they surrender?' asked Ella.

A shrug from Vanka. 'I dunno. According to the scuttlebutt, Doge Catherine-Sophia hates Heydrich with a vengeance. There's no way she'd have given up without a fight.'

'I don't fink she did,' commented Burlesque, who, having just discovered that the steamer possessed an air horn, was now using it to put a train of oxen dragging field guns to flight. 'I wos gonna open a pub in Barcelona a while back so I knows everyfing there is to know abart the Quartier Chaud. An' wot I 'eard wos that some of the 'igher-ups in Paris – blokes like that Robespierre item – wos getting a mite pissed off wiv ImPuritanism. Natural when you fink abart it: blokes don't like bin told wot to do by birds.'

'Birds?' sneered Norma. 'That's a sexist comment even for a chauvinist pig like you, Burlesque.'

Burlesque stuck his tongue out in reply and Ella was pleased to see Norma return the compliment. The girl seemed to be getting some of her bounce back. 'Well, sexist or not, seems that *birds* in the Quartier Chaud 'ave bin getting right up their blokes' noses. There wos a bit in *The Stormer* a while back saying that the GrandHarms 'ad got 'ot an' 'eavy wiv all them UnScrewed tarts demonstrating an' causing bother.'

'UnScrewed?' asked Norma.

'Members ov the UnScrewed-Liberation Movement,' explained Burlesque. 'Them's a bunch ov *birds* in Paris wot's always raising sand about the Senate restricting their sexual liberties an' such.'

Burlesque's explanation was interrupted by a bang from underneath the steamer.

'That wos anovver 'orse you've just flattened, Burlesque,' shouted an admiring Rivets. 'That makes it a round dozen you've mangled.'

Burlesque ignored him. 'Yeah, them Chaudian tarts are dead keen on their sexual liberties. They're always up for it. I 'ad this Roman bint working in the Prancing Pig wunce . . . gor, fings she could do wiv a fag. Shove one up 'er arse, an' she could blow smoke rings outta 'er . . .'

'*That* I really don't want to hear about,' interrupted Norma, and there was enough frost in her voice to persuade Burlesque to change the subject.

'Any'ows, seems that the blokes in the Senate told the Doge to go and sling 'er 'ook.'

'Why?' asked Ella.

'Cos ov them Dark Charismatics fingies.'

'Dark Charismatics?' As PINC was silent on the subject, all Ella could do was turn to Vanka and give him an imploring look. Being a psychic – a *faux*-psychic – Vanka had made an extensive study of the oddities of the Demi-Monde, and to Ella's mind 'Dark Charismatics' sounded very odd indeed. If there was anyone who'd know about them, it was Vanka.

'It's a funny religion, ImPuritanism,' he began. 'Most people think it's just about hedonism and free love, but there's a lot more to it than that. One of its important beliefs is a concept called MALEvolence, which says that men are more prone than women to violence . . .'

'Can't argue with that,' observed Norma.

'. . . and for a society to be fair and peaceful, these natural inclinations of men have to be tempered by the more equitable and peace-loving qualities of women.'

'Sounds like my kind of place.'

'Maybe it is,' said Vanka impishly. 'After all, ImPuritanism teaches that the only way to commune with ABBA is via orgasm. So all ImPuritans spend their time seeking the ultimate orgasm they call JuiceSense.'

'These ImPuritans have really got their heads screwed on,' mused Norma.

Vanka smiled. 'Screwed being a very apposite description, especially if you like masks and Fleshtivals and . . . well, never mind. You'll see for yourself soon enough. Anyway, all was sweetness and light in the Quartier Chaud until a few years ago, when a chap called Michel de Nostredame announced that he'd found the *cause* of MALEvolence, of why men are so beastly. According to de Nostredame, it's because men are prone to being led astray by really horrible characters called Dark Charismatics. They're these mysterious people who rise to power every now and again, and lead the world to ruin. They're the ones who are the root cause of MALEvolence: people like—'

'—Heydrich, Beria, Shaka Zulu and Selim the Grim.' It was Ella who finished the sentence.

'Yeah, that's right. How did you know?'

'Where I come from, Vanka, they're called Singularities. They're classified as high-performing psychopaths.' What Ella declined to add was that the Singularities had been deliberately seeded into the Demi-Monde for the express purpose of making sure that the place was a cauldron of bigotry, hatred and violence.

'Yeah, well, de Nostredame's work would have remained just a piece of academic curiosity except for the discovery that Visual Virgins could identify Dark Charismatics by their auras.'

'I ask this question with the greatest of trepidation,' began Norma, 'and I certainly don't want Potty-mouth at the front answering it' – Burlesque blew her a kiss – 'but could you tell me what a Visual Virgin is?'

'They are virgins,' began Vanka, 'who can read auras. The Doge uses them to identify liars and criminals. Apparently Dark Charismatics have a distinctive aura that's a real giveaway when they're examined by Visual Virgins.'

'Virgins reading auras? Only in the Demi-Monde.'

'And once she learned that Dark Charismatics could be identified, then Doge Catherine-Sophia—'

'Mad as a box ov bolts, she is, an' always pissed, to boot,' commented Burlesque helpfully, as he gave another toot on the horn. He was thoroughly enjoying himself.

'—ordered that all male Dark Charismatics living in the Quartier Chaud be castrated—'

'Ouch,' from the front seat.

'—as castration negates their MALEvolent inclinations. The Covenites use the practice a lot too. They call their eunuchs "NoNs".'

'Wot? They chop your willy orf?' This question came from Rivets, who seemed to have gone very pale.

'Yus, they've got this special machine, see. First ov all, they—'

'That's enough, Burlesque,' snapped Ella, having seen how bilious Rivets looked. The last thing she wanted was to have the boy vomiting down her back.

Vanka continued with his explanation. 'Unfortunately, three of the Dark Charismatics identified were senior senators in the Quartier Chaud.'

'Maximilien Robespierre, Tomas de Torquemada and Godfrey de Bouillon.'

'Good guess, Ella.'

'I wasn't guessing.'

'Anyway, these men – the Gang of Three – told the Doge that they weren't inclined to go through the rest of their lives singing falsetto and holed up in the Senate building in Paris where they declared UDI.'

'UDI? Wot's that?' asked Rivets. 'Sounds nasty.'

'It stands for Unilateral Declaration of Independence.'

'You're right, Wanker, that's wot this is all abart. Them three 'ave organised a cup de tea.'

'A *coup d'état*,' corrected Norma.

'Yeah, that as well. I betcha anyfing that these three bastards 'ave thrown in their lot wiv Heydrich, opened up the Hub Bridge an' sold Venice darn the river as part ov the bargain.'

A silence descended in the steamer's cabin, as everyone pondered on what Burlesque had just said. Unlikely though it seemed, it was the only logical explanation for what they were witnessing. The Medi had apparently surrendered to the ForthRight without a shot being fired.

'But we can't go to the Quartier Chaud now,' observed Norma, 'Heydrich and his crew will be waiting for us there.'

'Well, we can't go back—' began Vanka.

'We'll go to Venice,' announced Ella after a quick scan of PINC. 'I've always wanted to go to Venice.'

Burlesque nodded and shifted the steamer down a gear, almost demolishing the gearbox in the process. 'Good idea! Once we're over the Thames, we'll 'ead for the Rialto Gate in the 'ubLand Wall. Wiv a bit ov luck, we'll get there before the ForthRight Army.'

They were helped in their escape from the ForthRight by no one wanting to impede the progress of a Checkya steamer, especially a Checkya steamer flying Beria's pennant, especially a Checkya steamer that didn't seem to have any brakes. But still, such was the press of men and matériel trying to cross Hub Bridge Number Two that it took them hours and a great deal of shouting and swearing just to get over the river and into the HubLand that bordered the Quartier Chaud. Once they were there, exhausted and drained from their adventures of the night before and the excitement of Burlesque's driving, they decided to rest for a couple of hours and to make for Venice as soon as night fell.

It was a bad decision.

By the time darkness came, they found their path to Venice blocked by the cordon sanitaire the ForthRight Army had thrown up along the wall separating the Quartier Chaud from the Hub, with hundreds of armoured steamers standing between them and Venice. Worse, all the refugees streaming into the Sector from the ForthRight – and by Ella's guess, several thousand had crossed the Thames during the day – were being bustled towards Paris, and away from Venice. They had no choice now: they had to take a chance on getting to Venice through Paris.

They abandoned the steamer about a mile from the wall itself, after the crowd of refugees became so dense that it was impossible even for someone as homicidally inclined as Burlesque to drive it any further. When they arrived at Porte Saint-Martin – the main gate giving access to Paris from the HubLand – the scene that greeted them was like a madhouse, with hordes of displaced people trying to enter the city, and the Quartier's GrandHarms being equally resolute in their determination not to let them in. Not even Vanka's guineas, Burlesque's bluster or Rivets's pleading could get them through the gate, and it was a tired and dispirited Ella who found herself standing in the middle of the crowd, leaning on Vanka and trying to think how they might connive their way into Paris.

And that was when Fate took a hand.

'Look, look,' came a shout from the edge of the crowd, 'it's the Lady IMmanual!'

It took a moment for Ella to register that she was the 'Lady IMmanual' being referred to, and when she belatedly looked around, standing there not twenty-five yards away from her was William Penn and the rest of the disciples who called themselves 'the Twelve'.

'Bollocks,' whispered Vanka in her ear, 'I thought we'd lost that lunatic back in the ForthRight.'

Ella smiled and bowed towards William Penn, who went bright red with excitement. 'This, ladies and gentlemen,' he shouted as he spun around to address the crowd, 'is the Messiah. This young girl is the divine saviour sent by ABBA to save the poor souls trapped in Warsaw by that personification of evil Reinhard Heydrich. This is the Lady IMmanual who performed the Miracle of the Boundary. I entreat you, ladies and gentlemen, to kneel before the Messiah.'

There must have been a fair few people fleeing Warsaw in the crowd, because when William Penn dropped to his knees, two or three hundred others in his immediate vicinity did the same. Ella and her four colleagues were left standing, very self-consciously, amidst a sea of genuflecters.

'Shit, Ella, this is really heavy-duty,' said an awestruck Norma Williams. 'Just what the fuck have you been doing since the last time I saw you?'

'It's all a ridiculous misunderstanding, Norma. I pulled a stunt back in the Ghetto and now everybody thinks I'm some sort of Messiah.'

And if Ella felt embarrassed by what was happening, it was an embarrassment tinged with apprehension. She really didn't like the way the GrandHarms who were patrolling the HubLand Wall were staring at her.

# 4

## Paris
## The Demi-Monde: 2nd Day of Spring, 1005

From whence Dark Charismatics came, we might never know. For my part I would postulate that *H. singularis* is a product of a micro-evolutionary event that took place in the comparatively recent past. Indeed, by my reckoning, *H. singularis* may have first appeared in the Demi-Monde at the time of the Fall. I have referred this perplexity to theologians, one of whom – Mage Thomas Aquinas – has opined that *H. singularis* may be an echo of the meddlements performed by Lilith when she sought to usurp ABBA and to remake HumanKind in her image.

*Letter dated 53rd day of Spring, 1002, from Professeur Michel de Nostredame to Doge Catherine-Sophia*

Unlike the vast majority of the GrandHarms working in his precinct, Henri Aroca enjoyed night duty. He wasn't a superstitious man and he wasn't afraid of the goolies, beasties, vampyrs, Grigori or any of the other horrible creatures that were rumoured to infest the streets of Paris when the sun went down.

Whilst his comrades on the force found much to complain about when they were ordered to spend a night patrolling the wall that separated Paris from the HubLand, Aroca was of a different view. He found that invariably there was little work to do other than to rattle gates and test locks, to ensure that the various *apotropes* – the devices Quartier Chaudians used to dissuade and dispel the daemons of the night – were in place, and to accept the refreshment heaped on him by owners of the various late-night kiosks he visited during his perambulations. Even the blood-drunks he was called upon to deal with were, by and large, more merry than dangerous. Having his good friend Pierre Maigny as his partner on these nocturnal tours of duty helped, and many were the pleasant nights they enjoyed saun-tering along the dark, deserted pavements of the Border arrondissement, discussing their principal passion in life: fishing.

Night duty also kept him out of the clutches of his shrewish Current, but this was one advantage Henri Aroca kept to himself. If she was ever to suspect that Henri volunteered for every night duty available in order to avoid having to share a bed with her, there would be Hel to pay. Maybe, Henri thought, there was something in what Senior CitiZen Robespierre was saying. Maybe ImPuritanism had gone too far, maybe it *was* time for men to assert themselves. Maybe he should have put his foot down harder with his daughter, Odette, and told her she wasn't to go on her stupid demonstrations.

It was an interesting thought, but one Henri decided that he would delay implementing. He would do his asserting when he was out of arm's reach of both his Current and his daughter. They were both big women with fists the size of puddings.

Anyway, he didn't know where Odette was any more. Since she'd got involved with the UnScrewed-Liberationists, she'd become a little distant – which he supposed was the best place to be when the Quizzies were after you.

With a doleful shake of his head, Henri brought his atten-tion back to his duty as a GrandHarm rather than as a father. He pushed his eye up against the peephole that allowed GrandHarms to see what was going on outside the city walls, and what he saw did not make a pretty sight. The onslaught of the UnFunnies and their army meant that a whole swarm of refugees from the ForthRight was now attempting to enter Henri's beloved Paris. As he had been so forcefully advised by his ridiculously stupid commander, Captain Lefevre, these refugees had any number of Suffer-O-Gette assassins, WhoDoo saboteurs and HimPeril agents provocateurs hidden in their ranks, so it was necessary for the GrandHarmerie to refuse them *all* entry. It had been distressing for Henri, a naturally warm-hearted type, to deny these anguished and destitute people sanctuary, but what else could he do? Orders were orders, and if Henri wasn't a particularly effective GrandHarm, he was at least a dutiful one.

Now, finally, after three hours of shouting, screaming, shoving and general unpleasantness, the crowd surrounding the Porte Saint-Martin checkpoint had settled down into a sort of discontented stupor. Exhaustion and cold had triumphed over desperation.

But even as he watched the crowd, something very strange happened. At the very moment Henri was about to abandon his surveillance and sample the wine and the oven-hot pastries that Pierre had brought to sustain them during their vigil, the crowd had fallen to its knees and begun to worship a small group of bedraggled people who were standing rather awkwardly a hundred metres or so from the gate. What the crowd was doing made Henri nervous: ImPuritanists like him weren't big on worshipping and grovelling – unless, of course, the worshipping and grovelling was part of some ImPure sexual ritual. And that, as best he could judge, was not the case with these people.

His nervousness was such that he pulled his revolver out of its holster and checked that it was loaded. At the start of their watch, the captain had insisted that the GrandHarms be armed, which at the time had seemed to Henri to be a trifle excessive.

But now, as the mood of the crowd became more intense, Henri was glad that he had heeded his captain's orders. The people worshipping beyond the walls were becoming more febrile by the minute, so much so that Henri was obliged to send a runner to persuade their captain to abandon the cosy bar he was occupying, and do some work for a living.

When a grumbling Captain Lefevre arrived five minutes later, he took Henri's place at the peephole and spent almost a minute studying the scene developing beyond the wall. 'You . . . Sergeant Aroca,' the captain shouted towards him, 'what's happening out there? Why are all these people praying?'

'I don't know, Captain.' Henri shrugged. 'One minute they were just standing there, and the next they were on their knees. I think they're praying to that Shade girl wearing the LessBien trousers.'

Cautiously the captain edged open one of the gates, pulled a spyglass out of his jacket pocket and used it to survey the scene. Then, with a frown, he snapped the telescope shut and bellowed at Henri: 'Go out there, Aroca, and tell them to stop this nonsense. It is an affront to UnFunDaMentalism.' Automatically Henri's eyes checked the right lapel of the captain's jacket. Sure enough there was a small, gold Valknut badge pinned there announcing that the captain was a newly converted UnFunny. 'Don't you know that there's a new law in the Medi that bans all non-UnFunDaMentalist rites and rituals being performed within the borders of the Quartier?'

Henri did know: it had been one of the first things Robespierre had done after the Great Schism with Venice. But he also knew that there were a couple of thousand desperate people gathered around the Shade girl, and he had a sneaking suspicion that they would be mighty pissed off if he tried to interrupt their devotions.

'*Me* stop them? I don't think they'll want to stop, Captain. They might get nasty.'

'Order them! Do your duty as a GrandHarm, Sergeant Aroca.'

*You rotten cowardly bastard*, thought Henri Aroca, as he reluctantly snuck through the checkpoint's gate and, with the ever-faithful but bloody frightened Pierre Maigny at his side, began to lizard his way through the kneeling throng towards the girl and her companions.

Ella watched nervously as the gate, set in the wall protecting Paris from incursion from the Hub, swung open and a fat GrandHarm sergeant, brandishing a huge pistol in his right hand, and his equally tubby companion armed with an enormous rifle stood for a moment under the famous sign over the gate – 'Liberté, Egalité, Fornication' – and then walked towards them. The two GrandHarms were wearing rather jolly uniforms made from a material that alternated broad stripes of lemon and fuchsia, but from what Ella could see of the sergeant's face under his half-mask, he looked far from jolly. His florid face was dressed with a dour expression that showed he was a very resolute and very unhappy, man. She had a sneaking feeling that unless the discussions with him were conducted in a diplomatic manner, the situation could rapidly degenerate into violence.

'Why's this twerp wearing a mask?' asked Norma. 'Who does he think he is: the Lone-fucking-Ranger?'

Ella shook her head; PINC had already given her the answer. 'Everyone in the Quartier Chaud wears a mask when they're out in public, Norma. It's an ImPuritan custom designed to help people more readily assume a sexually enfranchised personality. The idea is that when their real identity is hidden, CitiZens won't feel embarrassed or awkward when they're indulging in casual sex.'

Norma made a moue. 'Sounds like a good idea. Some of the guys I've dated would have looked better masked . . . but then, some of them would have looked better decapitated.' She leant forward to get a better view of the GrandHarm. 'And isn't his codpiece a little large?'

'Not if Beria's bin banging on his nuts, it ain't,' commented Burlesque, with real feeling.

A smiling Vanka stepped forward to deal with the glowering GrandHarm sergeant but he was elbowed aside by Burlesque. 'I'll deal wiv this Frog, Wanker. I spraken their lingo bon.'

Vanka made a desperate grab for Burlesque's arm to stop him, but it was too late.

'Bon jour, Mon-sewer le Frog. Je suis Burlesque Bandstand, purveyor de beverages alcoholiques et impresario extraordinaire.' Burlesque thrust out a filthy hand, which caused the GrandHarm to flinch back in alarm.

The sergeant peered down his long nose at Burlesque and Ella saw his nostrils tweak as though he was offended by a bad odour, which was, of course, the case. Burlesque stank of cordite, neglect and several other unmentionable – even unimaginable – substances.

Only when he had regained his composure, and presumably his sense of smell, did the GrandHarm deign to address Burlesque. '*Pourquoi toutes ces gens sont-elles à genoux devant cette fille?*' ('Why are all these people bowing down to this girl?') He nodded in Ella's direction.

'Par ce que elle est une . . . prophetess.' Burlesque glanced towards Vanka. 'Oi, Wanker, wot's Frog for "prophetess"?'

'It's *voyante*,' answered Vanka. 'Look, Burlesque, I really think it would be better if I . . .'

Burlesque shooed Vanka's protests away. 'Elle est un beaucoup de important voyante. Vous savvy bon, Mon-sewer?'

Amazingly the GrandHarm did seem to 'savvy bon'. '*Une voyante? Comment s'appelle-t-elle?*' ('A prophetess? What is her name?')

'The Lady IMmanual.'

The name obviously carried some resonance with the GrandHarm. '*C'est la Dame IMmanual? C'est la fille qui a ouvert la Couche Limite?*' ('This is the Lady IMmanual? This is the girl who opened the Boundary Layer?')

'Wee, wee, c'est vrai, Mon-sewer. Je suis elle's manager. Elle est beaucoup de best Physicalist dans le Demi-Monde. Elle only puts art pour current guineas pour un sorry.'

Ella's eyebrows arched in surprise: her price had gone up. Forty guineas for a soirée was a mighty advance on the ten guineas she'd been getting only a few weeks ago.

'*Son agent, vous? Vous mentez, Monsieur. Comment une aussi belle créature peut-elle avoir pour agent le gros porc que vous êtes?*' ('Her manager? You are lying, Monsieur: how can such a beautiful creature as she have such a fat pig as you for a manager?')

Burlesque paused for a moment as he interpreted what the GrandHarm had just said. ''Ere, 'oo are you callin' a fat pig?'

'D'you wont me to put wun on 'im, Burlesque?' Rivets asked helpfully, as he rolled the sleeve of his jacket up over his forearm. 'I always wanted to give wun ov these fairy Frog fucks a smack.'

Henri Aroca scuttled back to the checkpoint to report to the captain. He wasn't quite sure what language the fat and very smelly vagabond had been speaking, but he had understood enough to know that out there was the Lady IMmanual. He also knew that pinned up on the noticeboard of the precinct head-quarters was an instruction – signed by Grand Inquisitor de Torquemada no less – to the effect that all officers were to be on the lookout for the Shade girl known as the Lady IMmanual, and that if she was discovered she was to be immediately handed over to the Inquisition.

*Poor cow.*

Since the Great Schism with Venice, the CIA – the Central Inquisitorial Agency – of Tomas de Torquemada had been charged with bringing the Medi into the loving – and often very painful – grip of UnFunDaMentalism. The more liberal and, Henri had to admit, enjoyable pleasures of ImPuritanism had been banned by the Inquisition, and though some of the trappings of ImPuritanism – especially the wearing of masks and the sordid delights of Fleshtivals – were proving tenacious, there was no denying Torquemada's efficiency in having any HerEticals, RaTionalists or zadniks found within the Quartier summarily exCommunicated.

*ExCommunicated.*

Now that was a word that chilled the SAE of Henri Aroca. ExCommunication was a punishment reserved for those who denied the Sacred Truth of UnFunDaMentalism. And as the Grand Inquisitor saw it, if you didn't have your tongue then you were much less inclined to continue denying.

'It's the Lady IMmanual,' squeaked a breathless Henri. 'That's who they're praying to.'

'The Lady IMmanual? You're sure?' The captain snapped open his telescope and examined the group of Anglo refugees again. 'Which one is the Lady IMmanual?'

'The good-looking Shade.'

The captain thought for a moment and closed the telescope. 'Then you'd better go and arrest her.'

Henri Aroca's eyes widened in astonishment at the stupidity of this order. He'd seen the way the dwarf, who seemed to be the bodyguard of the fat Anglo, had wanted to hit him. The fucker might be small but he'd looked very dangerous. And then there was the crowd of IMmanualists surrounding the girl; the thought of being torn apart by an enraged mob of religious fanatics did not appeal.

'With all due respect, Captain, fuck that. I go out there to try to handcuff the Lady IMmanual, and my Current will have to reassemble me before I can be buried.'

'I am giving you an order, Aroca.'

'And I'm giving you the finger, Captain. I'd sooner be banged up in the Bastille than end my days as a human jigsaw puzzle.' A thought struck Henri. 'If you want her arrested, why don't *you* go out there and do it?'

The captain obviously considered that a ridiculous suggestion; ridiculous and dangerous. 'It would be undignified for a man of my rank to perform such a trivial duty,' he answered stiffly. 'So what do you suggest, Sergeant? We can't just ignore her. The Grand Inquisitor says she is one of the foremost enemies of UnFunDaMentalism.'

'Well, we could call up the Quizzies and let them do their own dirty work.' A scowl from the captain showed what he thought of *that* idea: no one – no one sane anyway – wanted to have anything to do with Torquemada's gang of maniacs. What they were rumoured to do with red-hot pokers was nobody's business. 'Or we could let *all* the refugees in, and nab her in the confusion.'

'But that would be in violation of our orders to keep the refugees from entering Paris.'

'Oh, I don't think they're *refugees*, Captain. I'm guessing that most of them are Quartier Chaudians who've been living and working in the ForthRight and who just want to come home now that war's been declared. Anyway, it's either that, Captain, or you go out there and let those Anglo bastards beat you to death with one of your own legs.'

The GrandHarm captain made a megaphone announcement that, by the unprecedented magnanimity and unparalleled charity of Senior CitiZen Maximilien Robespierre, the Government of the Free UnFunDaMentalist Medi had granted sanctuary to all refugees of good character now gathered beyond the walls of Paris. As the great doors were dragged

open, the result was predictable. The thousands of people –
all of whom deemed themselves to be of requisite 'good character' – gathered around the Porte immediately abandoned
their devotions, leapt to their feet and, panic-stricken lest the
captain change his mind, pushed and shoved their way
towards what they saw as a safe haven from the ForthRight
Army.

As the crowd degenerated into a shouting, screaming mob,
Ella saw the GrandHarm sergeant, accompanied by five large
and heavily armed colleagues, sneak out of a side exit and kick
and bully their way towards her. It didn't take a genius to deduce
that they were intent on arresting her. For a moment she
thought about making a run for it, but the GrandHarms were
armed and she doubted she'd get very far before she took a
bullet in the back. Anyway, if they started blasting, a lot of innocent people would get hurt. Better, she decided, to go quietly
and wait for a chance to escape later.

'I have a feeling, Vanka,' said Ella quietly, 'that everything is
about to get a whole lot more difficult.' She turned to the rest
of her little party. 'So, ladies and gentlemen, if things go pear-
shaped and we become separated, I suggest we all meet up on
the Bridge of Thighs in Venice. Go there at twelve noon every
day.'

'*Mademoiselle*,' interrupted the red-faced sergeant, as he
barged his way up to Ella. '*Je vous arrête pour agitation religieuse.
Je vous prierai de n'opposer aucune résistance à cette arrestation, sinon
je me verrai dans l'obligation d'employer la force.*' ('I must arrest you
for being a religious agitator. I would entreat you not to protest
this arrest, otherwise I am empowered to use force.') And for
emphasis he waved his pistol vaguely in her direction.

Ella smiled. '*Employer la force ne sera pas nécessaire, Monsieur le
GrandHarm*,' ('Violence won't be necessary, Monsieur le
GrandHarm') she replied in her flawless French. '*Mes amis et moi*

*allons venir tranquillement.*' ('My friends and I will come peaceably.') But when Ella turned around, she saw that Burlesque and Rivets had already vanished.

Then things really took a turn for the worse. As the GrandHarm sergeant moved to grab Ella by the arm, a group of infuriated IMmanualists began to hurl stones at him. Unfortunately, their aim didn't match their piety. One of the stones they hurled missed the sergeant and instead hit Ella full on the forehead. Everything went black . . .

Rivets watched as an unconscious Miss Ella was carried away, and Vanka and Norma were bundled into the back of a steamer. This had really aggravated the crowd, and for a minute it had looked like things might have really kicked off, but when the GrandHarms started shooting into the air everyone had quickly calmed down. Still, Rivets had the suspicion that abandoning his friends in their hour of need wasn't a terribly noble thing to do.

'Bit ov a coward's way, ain't it, Burlesque? Deserting our comrades and everyfing.'

'Nah,' said Burlesque, as he rammed his way past the swirl of humanity pressing around the gate giving access to Paris. If there was one person who was going to get into Paris, that person, Rivets reckoned, was Burlesque Bandstand. 'You know the old saying, Rivets? "He 'oo fights and runs away . . ."'

'"Lives to fight another day"?' suggested Rivets.

'Nah, "He 'oo fights and runs away don't have a red-hot poker jammed up his jacksie, courtesy of the Quizzies."'

# 5

## Venice
## The Demi-Monde: 2nd Day of Spring, 1005

PreScience describes and plots the irresistible cyclical
trajectory of history; of how events roll through time with
the power and the predictability of ABBA-inspired temporal
avalanches. These avalanches are propelled by the big and
muscular events of history: wars, the discoveries made by
science, and the actions of crowds. These are the 'macro'
events of history. As such, they are immutable and follow
the tenets of Determinism . . . of *Macro*-Determinism, the
philosophy that underpins preScience. There is no free will
evinced here. A temporal avalanche is Macro-Deterministic
in that it is a prisoner of its own momentum and its own
historic inevitability.
  **A LayPerson's Guide to preScience: *Nikolai Kondratieff,***
  ***Future History Institute Press***

In the humble opinion of Docteur Nikolai Dmitriyevich
Kondratieff, the artist who had been responsible for the deco-
ration of the ante-room of the Doge's Palace, where he was
currently standing, had either been possessed of an over-
wrought imagination or had been smoking something
decidedly illegal. The confection of overblown angels, cherubs
– well, Kondratieff assumed they were cherubs, since his
angelology was a little shaky – and ABBAs swirling around the

walls and ceiling of the vast room was a trifle overwhelming.

But this, he supposed, was the point: the size of the room, the opulence of its furnishings and the artistically excessive nature of its frescos were all designed to place the Doge's supplicants in a mood of awed humility.

Kondratieff judged himself to be summarily humiliated, but if he had been asked he would have admitted – and Kondratieff was a naïvely truthful man – that he found the expressions on the faces of the painted ABBAs more indicative of imminent flatulence than omnipotence, and that the state of undress of a number of the female angels was a tad excessive. He took a moment to polish his neat wire-framed spectacles, then popped them back on his long nose and made a careful scrutiny of a jar decorated with the image of a pair of naked angels struggling with a female Grigori blessed – if Grigori could be blessed – with a particularly impressive pair of mammaries.

As his nose came close to the jar he was enveloped by the stench of garlic. This was obviously a weapon against Grigori who, so tradition had it, were allergic to the stuff. Since coming to the Quartier Chaud, Kondratieff had been amazed by the natives' obsession with vampyres; everywhere he went entrances were protected by garlands of garlic, hawthorn and wild roses and by seeds spread over doorsteps, and virtually every CitiZen wore a silver amulet of some description. Quartier Chaudians seemed obsessed by bloody Grigori. Most odd.

It was at the very moment when Kondratieff was bent in close examination of these diabolical tits, trying to discover how the stereoscopic effect had been contrived, that the Doge's chamberlain chose to make his entrance. 'Docteur Kondratieff? Her Most Reverend Excellency the Doge Catherine-Sophia will see you now,' the flunky announced with a sniff, obviously having decided that Kondratieff's interest in female anatomy was, even for an ImPuritan, excessive. Placing the jar back in its niche, Kondratieff dutifully trotted after the chamberlain into what he assumed was one of the Palace's more informal reception rooms. Informal it might have been, but it still managed to be enormous in scale and decorated in a manner that was, if anything, even more frenzied than the antechamber. The room was a visual cacophony of cream and gold, and the number of tits and bums on display was, by any measure, overindulgent.

The Doge was sitting on a couch in the centre of the room, though it took a moment for Kondratieff to spot her. The room was bedecked with shadows and as the Doge was wearing her habitual widow's weeds, she wasn't so much dressed as camouflaged. But despite all her efforts to merge into the background, Kondratieff could still see that the Doge was a handsome woman. For a woman in her fifties – how far into her fifties was a state secret – she was still attractive, albeit in a somewhat excessive sort of way.

*Excessive.*

Yes, Kondratieff decided, excessive was an excellent adjective to apply to Doge Catherine-Sophia. She was, after all, excessively astute and possessed of an excessive appetite for both the pleasures of the flesh *and* for political intrigue, all of which made her an excessively able Doge. Correction: *had* made her. Sadly, since the death two years ago of her beloved Current, Grigori Alexandrovich Potemkin, the woman had gone into Solution-fuelled decline. The half-empty bottle that stood on the side table was mute testimony to how she was dealing with her bereavement.

The Doge roused herself and tried to sit up a little straighter. It was an awkward manoeuvre as the woman was drunk and the décolletage of her bodice was excessively . . . well, excessive.

'Docteur Nikolai Dmitriyevich Kondratieff,' announced the chamberlain in a loud voice, 'Head of the Department of preScience at the University of Venice, and President of the Future History Institute.'

The Doge acknowledged Kondratieff's bow with a fluttering wave of her hand, which she then directed towards her chamberlain. 'You may leave uz now, Chamberlain, as I vish to have confidential discourse mit zhe good Docteur.'

Kondratieff almost laughed, but then the Doge's accent was a standing joke in the Sector. It was an accent developed during the woman's somewhat peripatetic childhood, which involved her father dodging around the Demi-Monde to avoid his many creditors. Whilst this had given the Doge fluency in all the languages of the Demi-Monde, it had also resulted in her acquiring a terrible accent in every one of them, even her native Anglo.

'But, Your Most Reverend Excellency . . .' spluttered the chamberlain in protest.

'Oh, don't fret yourzelf, Chamberlain, I have zhe most capable of protectors votching over me, should Docteur Kondratieff choose to attack my poor veak body.' She gave Kondratieff a salacious wink, and then nodded towards a dark corner of the room.

*Now this* is *a surprise*, decided Kondratieff, and then cursed himself for using the word 'surprise'. PreScientists were never 'surprised' . . . well, they never admitted to being anyway. The business of preScientists was divination, prognostication and 4Telling, and being able to accurately predict the future meant that 'a surprise' was another way of saying 'a mistake'. But even Kondratieff had to admit to being – *sod it* – surprised to be meeting a Visual Virgin. They were, after all, semi-mythological creatures, and the girl who stepped out from the shadows wasn't just *any* Visual Virgin. This was, unless he was very much mistaken, the most famous Visual Virgin of them all, Sister Florence, the Auralist who had identified the Gang of Three, who had discovered the nest of Dark Charismatics the Quartier Chaud had been nurturing in its bosom – or in its Senate, to be more accurate.

*This is one to be very careful of*, decided Kondratieff, especially today when he would have to be very economical with the truth.

As the chamberlain made his reluctant departure, the Doge effected the introductions. 'Docteur Kondratieff, I have pleasure in introducing Zizter Florence, Zenior Auralist in zhe Zacred unt All-Zeeing Convent of Visual Virgins here in Venice.'

The Sister did not disappoint. Kondratieff guessed her to be in her late teens: though she was veiled it was obvious from her body that she was in the prime of life, and, being so very tall, there was certainly a lot of body to be primed. What was more, thanks to the transparent habit she was wearing, he had an almost uninterrupted view of *all* that wonderful body. The garment was made from a delicate red organza that didn't so much cover her naked body as tint it.

The girl moved nearer to Kondratieff, her bare feet making nary a sound on the marble floor. As she approached him, the feeling of almost intoxicating eroticism that flowed around her grew stronger. Though never one to evince a particularly dynamic sexuality – most of his lovers had classed him as *mezzo-piano* or moderately capable – even he felt the unmistakable stirrings of lust. Sister Florence was *that* desirable. Deliberately desirable.

*She's reading me*, decided Kondratieff, and to do this she was arousing him. He had heard that Visual Virgins were adept in fiduciary sex, the technique of being able to sexually arouse their subjects without touching them. This was a key weapon in an Auralist's armoury: when a subject was aroused, their auras became easier to read and their innermost secrets more openly displayed.

Sister Florence bowed to Kondratieff, giving him a coquettish little smile as she did so, knowing damned well the effect she was having on him. 'Verily, I am much pleased to meet with thee, Docteur Nikolai Kondratieff.' The girl spoke in Old French, and Kondratieff presumed that that was how Visual Virgins conversed with each other behind the walls of their convents.

He took a moment to recover his inner calm. This calm didn't last very long. The Doge patted the couch next to her, indicating that Kondratieff should sit beside her.

*Oh dear . . .*

'I have brought you here, Kondratieff,' the Doge slurred, 'to discuss zhe Institute's most recent 4Telling.' She paused to take a sip of her Solution. 'But first, perhaps, you could explain zhis preScience mumbo-jumbo ov yours to zhe good Zizter?'

It was a simple enough request made slightly disturbing by the way the Doge edged closer to Kondratieff and nudged a breast provocatively against his arm.

'Certainly, Excellency.' He smiled towards Sister Florence, who took a seat on the couch opposite the one Kondratieff was sharing – rather too intimately – with the Doge. 'The Demi-Monde is a sealed world, a closed system – this being a consequence of the Confinement – where the majority of economic inputs are regulated by ABBA, and where the population is broadly fixed. This makes it ideal for mathematical modelling using the techniques of preScience. By this modelling, it has been proven that the Demi-Monde is a largely Deterministic world, where effect invariably follows cause, and hence that our future is capable of very accurate prediction. And that is the purpose of the Future History Institute, of which I am President: to take the insights into the future given to us by preScience and to apply them in the service of Venice. The accuracy of these 4Tellings has enabled us to direct the workings of the Bourse to maximise earnings from its trading and financial ventures, and this, in turn, has made Venice the wealthiest of all the city-states in the Demi-Monde.'

'You must understand, Zizter Florence, zhat by knowing zhe future Venice is able to *manipulate* zhat future.' The Doge paused, then gave Kondratieff a rather predatory smile. 'Iz zhis not zo, Docteur?'

*Careful.*

He had to give no hint as to *who* was now actually manipulating the future of Venice, or why.

'Of course, Your Most Reverend Excellency. One of history's great preHistorians, George Santayana, said that without a belief in Determinism – that history signposts the future – Venetians are for ever condemned to repeat the mistakes of the past. PreScience allows us to avoid making such unnecessary blunders.'

Sister Florence gave a nod of understanding. 'Thou sayest, good Docteur, that the Demi-Monde is a *largely* Deterministic environment. Mayhap there be manifestations and contrivances in our world that suffer it to be *In*Deterministic?'

*Careful! The girl's sharp.*

'You are correct in your surmising, Sister. There are two elements in the Demi-Monde which are InDeterministic, and somewhat cloud our otherwise impeccable vision of the future. The first is the one with which you are most familiar: Dark Charismatics. These singularities of nature seem to have been placed in the Demi-Monde by ABBA to make our world a more uncertain and dangerous place, this, we are told by theologians, to better challenge HumanKind's faith and courage. But now, thanks to your remarkable abilities as an Auralist, Dark Charismatics can no longer lurk amongst us unseen. As a result, I am confident that their disruptive and InDeterministic influence on Demi-Mondian affairs can be mitigated and, of course, better integrated into our calculations.'

'Thou art too fulsome in thy praise, good Docteur. By the grace of ABBA, I am blessed with the power to see the Shadows of Evil that suffuse the auras of those foul creatures known as Dark Charismatics.'

The Doge raised her glass in salute to the Sister. 'Jah, knowing who zhe fuckers are iz a big step forward in being able to deal mit zhem. Mitout your good offices, Zizter Florence, ve vould not have known zhat Robespierre, Torquemada unt Godfrey de Bouillon vere plotting against Venice. Ve vould not even have known zhey vere Dark Charismatics.'

*Not that knowing this will do Venice much good*, thought Kondratieff as the Doge's hand wandered somewhat alarmingly up his thigh.

'Thou sayest, good Docteur, that the base and baleful Dark Charismatics are but *one* of the InDeterminate elements in the Demi-Monde. Pray, what is the second?'

'The second are the Daemons which from time to time torment our world. Of these Lilith, the Seidr-witch who caused the fall of the Pre-Folk, is the most famous. Daemons, as you know, Sister, are visitors from the Spirit World, though the frequency of their manifestations has fallen of late.'

'Mit vun notable exception,' Doge Catherine-Sophia muttered, 'unt zhat is vhy I have called you here today, Docteur Kondratieff. We must consider how Venice should deal mit zhe Lady IMmanual.'

'The Lady IMmanual is a very interesting phenomenon,' he admitted, and in view of who he suspected the Lady to be, the word 'interesting' was a masterpiece of understatement. 'She is the first Daemon since Lilith to impinge upon Demi-Mondian Future History in a strategic rather than in a tactical way. By performing the Miracle of the Boundary, she profoundly distorted the Future History of our world.' Kondratieff really didn't want to remember the week of long days and nights he and his computators had laboured to reprogram the Institute's difference engines to incorporate the impact of the Lady IMmanual's tinkering. 'But even the actions of the Lady IMmanual are not wholly InDeterminate: her coming was, after all, 4Told in the nuJu Book of the Profits.'

'Only if we accept zhat zhe Lady IMmanual *iz* zhe Messiah, unt zhis iz somethink which must be verified. If she iz zhe Messiah, zhen her coming indicates zhat ve are entering Ragnarok – zhe Time ov Revelation az it iz called by zhe nuJus – unt zhat zhe Final Days are at hand. If zhis iz truly zhe case, Docteur, zhen it iz important zhat you advise me az to how best to deal mit zhe voman.'

'She must be brought to Venice,' was Kondratieff's emphatic answer. 'Once she is here, we will be able to study her and influence her. Only in this way can her intentions be understood and incorporated into HyperOpia, our 4Telling program. Only in this way will we be able to calculate her full impact on the OutComes of Future History. Without such input, we preScientists are blinded by her and the future is once more veiled.'

'Jah, you are correct, Kondratieff, ve must bring zhe Lady IMmanual here to Venice. Ve are most fortunate zhat in fleeing from zhe ForthRight she chose to run to the Quartier Chaud. My cryptos tell me zhat she has come to Paris.'

'That is what HyperOpia predicted, Most Reverend Excellency, ascribing a confidence index of 99.7 per cent on that event occurring.'

'Excellent, excellent,' the Doge congratulated him, as she ran a finger around his codpiece.

More than a little nonplussed by the Doge's blandishments, Kondratieff shuffled on his seat, but protocol and good manners necessitated that he do nothing to dissuade the Doge's burgeoning ardour. The teachings of ImPuritanism were very strict regarding matters of sexual etiquette.

'My cryptos believe she is now being held in zhe Bastille, but zhis intelligence is merely speculative. I have already dispatched my most trusted agent, Machiavelli, to Paris to discover her vereabouts, unt tonight Zizter Florence vill leave to join him. It vill be her responsibility to verify zhat zhe girl is zhe Messiah, unt if she is, to assist Machiavelli in escorting her safely to Venice. Zhat I am villing to place such a treasure az Zizter Florence in harm's vay indicates zhe importance I give to having zhe Lady in my power.'

Kondratieff kept his expression as bland as he was able, but it was difficult. It was unbelievably naïve of the Doge that she should think *she* would have power over the Lady IMmanual, when the very reverse would be the OutCome, HyperOpia having predicted that the Lady IMmanual would assume mastery of Venice within ninety days of her first entering the Quartier Chaud. The Doge Catherine-Sophia's time was over, and now was the moment for all good men to put their efforts into saving the true Messiah from the Beast.

Not that he would ever allow the Doge to see *those* predictions, or the Temporal Interventions he and de Nostredame were executing to try to defeat the Beast. The Doge could not and *must* not understand what the future held for her, otherwise she would seek to alter the OutCome. In Temporal Interventions secrecy was everything.

The Doge flicked a smile towards Sister Florence. 'Machiavelli has secured a place for you in zhe Convent in Paris, good Zizter, which fortunately has not yet been closed by zhat evil bastard de Torquemada. You are to go zhere immediately unt vait for his vord.'

Sister Florence stood up, bowed to both the Doge and Kondratieff, and then silently exited the room.

'Zo all iz zettled,' said the Doge in a misty voice, once she and Kondratieff were alone. 'Unt now I feel somevhat enervated, Docteur, unt in need of stimulation. All zhis political manoeuvring is most tiring.' Almost casually she drew open her bodice. 'You may attack my body venever you vish, Docteur.'

*What wouldn't a man do to serve his Doge?* Kondratieff

wondered, as he began his dutiful nuzzling of the woman's breasts.

Michel de Nostredame blew on his hands. It was bitterly cold but, having been pre-warned by HyperOpia about how cold a Spring it would be, he was at least wearing his fur coat. It would take more than a little early morning frost to deter him from his rendezvous with the Column.

*The Column.*

As dawn's light spread along the drained section of the Lagoon, de Nostredame gazed up at the Column. Column with a capital 'C'. It seemed almost blasphemous to use the generic term 'column' when describing something so awe-inspiring. The Column, he knew instinctively, had the potential to change the Demi-Monde and to reshape the way Demi-Mondians thought about their ancient forebears, the Pre-Folk, about the Confinement and about Ragnarok.

The problem was that if he couldn't find a way to decipher the runic writings covering the Column's six sides, it was a potential destined to be unrealised. The fear tugged at him that, renowned preScientist and runic scholar though he was, he would be unable to translate the Column's message.

De Nostredame stroked his long grey beard as he puffed his pipe back into life. Only when the noxious smoke was haloing around his head did he resettle his gaze on the runic riddle-me-ree that was etched on the Column. He was so lost to the world that he hardly noticed the water seeping up through the duck-boards he was sitting on. Squatting there, enjoying his pipe, de Nostredame's subconscious had clearly decided that the message hidden in the tightly written runes was of such import that a little dampness of the arse was hardly a matter of note.

He was drawn to the use of the word 'remarkable' when cogitating on the Column.

It was *remarkable* that the Column had been discovered in the first place. It was sheer serendipity that the Doge had, for the first time in a hundred years, given permission for building works to be undertaken in Venice, works which required part of the Venetian Lagoon be drained and the Mantle-ite piers that studded the bed of the Lagoon to be exposed. And it was utterly, profoundly *remarkable*, once this part of the Lagoon had been walled and pumped dry, that they should find there, standing unsullied by five thousand years of submersion, the miracle that was the Column.

The Column was a Mantle-ite pillar, which accounted for its perfect state of preservation, since Mantle-ite was impervious to wear and tear, but not, of course, to the wiles of the Pre-Folk who had managed, ABBA only knew how, to carve the stuff. It was six metres tall with six flat sides, each of which tapered down from a width of around three metres at the top to two metres at the bottom. The Column sat on a hexagonal base, each edge of which – as best de Nostredame could see through the clinging mud – was four metres wide. Along the full length of each of the ascending sides of the Column were carved two serpents coiling and spiralling around one another. In a perverse way, these snakes reminded him of the caduceus, the symbol adopted by those working in the field of medicine, but that was as far as his speculations had taken him. Regarding which pre-Confinement deity was symbolised by these somewhat disturbing pairs of snakes, he could only guess.

*Lilith?* Now *that* was an interesting thought. The naked girl shown on the final side of the Column *could* be Lilith, but why would the Pre-Folk have created a monument to commemorate their greatest adversary? It didn't make sense.

Intriguing and indecipherable though these embellishments were, they paled in comparison with what else was carved – or stamped, or moulded, or etched; who knew – into the Column's sides. Whilst the Column was an impressive piece of art in itself, it was these lines of enigmatic runic writing that made it possibly, probably, *certainly* the most remarkable archaeological find ever made.

*Remarkable.* That bloody word again.

Despite the objections of his aged muscles, of his numbed arse and of his creaking joints, de Nostredame groaned up onto his feet and walked across to the Column. Reaching up, he reverently ran his tobacco-stained fingers along the tightly packed lines of infuriatingly opaque script. He had no idea what they said, but he touched them anyway in the forlorn hope that by doing so he might somehow be able to decipher the meaning hidden there.

*Translation by osmosis, perhaps?*

This was the real paradox of the Column. All the inscriptions carved into its sides were made in Pre-Folk A, the undeciphered language of the Pre-Folk, those long-lost ancients of the Demi-Monde. It was the language he had dedicated his long life to unBabelising, a dedication that had yielded nothing but failure.

Perhaps that was a *little* harsh. He could tell from the symbols used on the column, that the inscriptions made up an Eddic poem attributed – deep-breath time here – to Loki himself: the crossed emblem atop the sixth face of the Column, above the naked Lilith was Loki's mark. He smiled ruefully. No wonder Loki was called 'the Trickster'; the whole damned Column was one huge practical joke. Loki had sent a message down to them through time and yet had written it in a way that made it impossible to read.

He felt the presence of someone standing beside him and turned to find his friend and fellow expert in the esoteric world of preScience, Nikolai Kondratieff, gazing up at the Column. He studied Kondratieff for a second: the man looked a little peaky, his cheeks were flushed, and his normally immaculate suit was a trifle dishevelled.

'Good morning, Nikolai, so good of you to attend me. But I must say, you look a little out of sorts.'

'I have just come from an audience with the Doge.'

There was no other explanation necessary. The Doge was famous for her ability as a *fortissimo*-class love-maker. No man was safe in her presence.

'You have arrived at just the right moment, Nikolai. We are about to try to lift the Column from its resting place here in the Lagoon.' De Nostredame glanced over to the engineer in charge of the lifting. 'Are we ready, CitiZen de Lesseps?'

'We are ready, Professeur.' De Lesseps nodded to the thick cables tethered around the Column, these cables threaded through massive pulleys and connected to a huge steam-powered winch. 'I would be grateful if you and Docteur Kondratieff would stand to one side, Professeur. I don't want either of you hurt when we hoist the Column free.'

De Nostredame and Kondratieff did as they were asked, and once de Lesseps was confident that the area was clear, he signalled to his winch operator. The ropes tightened and the steam engine began to chug, but the Lagoon refused to give up its prize easily. It took almost ten minutes of pummelling and puffing before the base of the Column swung free of the tenacious hold of the Lagoon's mud. As soon as it did, de Lesseps called out an order to a group of men holding hoses, and great jets of water scythed through the muck decorating the Column's plinth. In a matter of moments the pristine and flawless Mantle-ite was revealed, and like the flanks of the Column, the base was swathed in carved writing. But unlike the flanks, this wasn't rendered in Pre-Folk A.

For a moment de Nostredame could hardly breathe. He was choked with excitement. He felt dizzy. As he looked at the words written before him, he knew he was destined to be one of the most famous men ever to have lived in the Demi-Monde. What was written on the base of the Column gave him the key to deciphering Pre-Folk A. Now he would finally be able to translate this cryptic message sent from the furthest depths of Demi-Mondian history.

# 6

## Paris
## The Demi-Monde: 3rd Day of Spring, 1005

Oddly and uniquely in the biological record, it would appear that all Demi-Mondians have traits of both H. *sapiens* and H. *singularis*, that is, they are simultaneously both Human *and* Dark Charismatic. In every one of the many hundreds of subjects I have examined during the course of my enquiries, there lurked the trait of H. *singularis*, this pernicious parasite, this malevolent cuckoo, striving endlessly and indefatigably for the opportunity to take command of its host's soul.

*Letter dated 53rd day of Spring, 1002, from Professeur Michel de Nostredame to Doge Catherine-Sophia*

Father Donatien, Chief Inquisitor in the Central Inquisitorial Agency, hated Spring the most. During the Winter all the refuse that an uncaring CitiZenry tossed so disdainfully aside, all the rubbish which fell from the backs of wagons and steamers, and all the effluent emitted from the rear of animals as they trundled through the streets of Paris, pulling carts or meandering to the slaughterhouse, was frozen and buried by the snow. Then Spring came, the snow retreated, and, centimetre by centimetre, these forgotten wonders, in all their noxious glory, were revealed. Spring was a shitty season.

But such was the urgency with which Donatien scuttled

across the Place de Grève, en route to the Hôtel de Ville where Robespierre had his offices, that he couldn't be too careful where – or into what – he stepped. It was an urgency propelled by his hatred and fear of Robespierre.

No, that was wrong.

It was a sad fact that Donatien's fear of Robespierre considerably outweighed his hatred of him. A sad fact but, with regard to the importance Donatien placed on remaining attached to his head, a vital one. The pre-eminence of his fear over his hatred was, he supposed, the reason why he had survived so long, and why his previous and very disreputable life as a Venetian courtier had been so conveniently overlooked. His fear made him cautious, and his caution made him dutiful, recognising, as he did, that Robespierre demanded unwavering dutifulness above all things. So Donatien, in order to survive, had become the most servile of men, and hence Robespierre had spared him, which, considering Donatien had been working for Robespierre for over a year – all through the Great Schism – was something of a miracle.

The people who survived more than a year in proximity to Robespierre could be counted on the fingers of one hand; before, that is, said fingers were removed by the Great Inquisitor, Tomas de Torquemada, in retribution for some minor transgression against the Revolution or for some inadvertent comment denying the joys of UnFunDaMentalism. The death and torment these two beauties had visited on the CitiZens of the Medi made the SAE creep.

Not *Donatien's* SAE, of course. He found the thought of torture incredibly arousing, which was one of the reasons he had agreed to become an Inquisitor in the first place. If ever there was a man whose work was his pleasure it was Father Donatien. He just had to stay alive long enough to enjoy these dark pleasures, and being late for an audience with Robespierre was not conducive to attaining old age.

Donatien almost ran across the square, and as he ran he tried to ignore the looming presence of the guillotine standing to one side of it, and the foul stench of decaying Solidified Astral Ether coming from the severed heads standing on pikes decorating it. How many 'enemies of the Revolution and of the Rapprochement with the ForthRight' had Robespierre sent to their doom here – a thousand? Two thousand? Three thousand? All he really cared about was not making it three thousand and one.

He arrived at the Hôtel de Ville, sweating and panting, with just minutes to spare, though the GrandHarms guarding access to the place were as aggravatingly fastidious as ever. But finally, ten minutes after he had first presented himself, Donatien was brought to a halt outside a door guarded by a uniformed member of the Special Corps of GrandHarms, a brute who searched him in the most impolite and personal manner.

Satisfied that Donatien wasn't carrying anything 'offensive', the GrandHarm knocked, and, receiving the command 'Enter,' announced in a loud voice, 'CitiZen Father Donatien, Chief Inquisitor, to meet with His Excellency, Senior CitiZen Maximilien Robespierre, Head of the Committee for Public Safety.'

As he stepped past the oak door, Donatien frowned. It appeared that the GrandHarm had made the announcement to an empty room. Standing, marooned, in that vast and seemingly deserted office, he shivered: the room was icy cold, and this despite a huge fire roaring in the hearth. Donatien wasn't surprised. It was a peculiarity of Dark Charismatics that had intrigued him ever since Robespierre had been unmasked as one of these mysterious creatures by Sister Florence: they seemed to suck the heat from any room they were in. Enter a room occupied by a Dark Charismatic, even during the hottest day of Summer, and the room would feel chilly. This phenomenon had led Donatien to the very unscientific conclusion that the inherent power of Dark Charismatics was so profound that it chilled the soul of all who stood near them. Unscientific it might be, but it was a damned persuasive hypothesis.

As he looked about him, Donatien realised that the room, though cold, was not, in fact, empty. Robespierre was sitting, disguised by shadows, behind a huge desk set at the end of the room. Automatically Donatien bowed, and Robespierre waved a negligent hand in acknowledgement.

'Come over here, Donatien. I wish to interrogate you.'

The word 'interrogate' sent a shiver of cold, clammy fear trickling down Donatien's spine. 'Interrogate' was resonant with the infliction of pain and torture, neither of which Donatien was especially fond, except, of course, when it was him doing the inflicting. With guts churning, Donatien walked like an automaton the twenty metres or so across the polished wooden floor, until his toes touched the line painted precisely one metre away from the desk. Robespierre disliked his visitors coming *too* close to his person.

Robespierre closed the report he had been studying and dabbed a silk handkerchief to his prissy mouth. Donatien knew the man was only in his mid-thirties, but there was nothing young about him. His pale, thin face was heavily lined and he had deep shadows under his weak eyes, though these were almost hidden behind his green-tinted glasses.

The remarkable thing was that, though Robespierre was obviously in one of his most ferociously unhappy moods – the malicious sparkle in his eyes attested to that – his opening question was surprisingly mild.

'Tell me, Donatien, what is your opinion of my spoken French?' he asked conversationally. His voice, as always, sounded weak, barely more than a whisper.

'I am sorry, Senior CitiZen?'

Robespierre groaned. 'You see, Donatien, this is my dilemma. I ask what I perceive to be a very straightforward question, and people, for whatever reason, fail to understand what I am saying.' He smiled, and Donatien almost fainted. Robespierre only smiled when he was about to do something truly horrible, like chop someone's head off. He had been doing a lot of smiling recently. 'Perhaps, Donatien, your wound has addled your thought processes?'

Instinctively Donatien touched his fingers to the vinegar-soaked bandages that swathed his head, covering the gunshot wound he'd suffered when he'd tried to arrest that bitch Aroca.

'No, Senior CitiZen, it is only a graze.'

'So, let me try again. How good do you believe my spoken French to be?'

'Why, it is excellent, Senior CitiZen. Your pronunciation is impeccable. Your accent—'

'So,' interrupted Robespierre sharply, 'there is no reason, as a consequence of impaired phonetics, why people should not understand my instructions?'

Donatien nodded, the centime having finally dropped. 'No, Senior CitiZen, none whatsoever.'

Robespierre rose from his chair, picked up his cup of coffee au gore and sauntered lackadaisically around the desk, coming to a halt just a half-metre in front of Donatien. 'This being the case, Inquisitor Donatien,' he said quietly, 'perhaps you would be so good as to explain why, after more than one whole Season of endeavour, you have not yet perfected the galvanicEnergy Interrogation Engine? Why, after more than a Season, is the Revolution still denied the means to scientifically determine who of those denounced as Enemies of the Revolution are genuinely hostile to the Revolution, and those who have been falsely accused and are the unfortunate victims of political calumny?' He flicked a hand towards the stack of dossiers piled by his desk. 'The matter is pressing, Donatien. I *must* have a means by which the delinquent chaff can be separated from the virtuous wheat . . . of better determining who should live and who should die. And as we have now established that it cannot be that you were unable to comprehend what it is I demand of you, then I can only attribute this failure to either incompetence or wilful disobedience. If it is the former, I have no further use for you. If it is the latter, I have no further use for you.'

As Donatien stared into those empty cold eyes, he knew that his life now hung on the next sentence he would utter. 'Senior CitiZen Robespierre,' he began, desperately trying to still the quaver in his voice, 'everything has been done as you ordered, but the intelligence regarding galvanicEnergy is amongst the ForthRight's most closely guarded secrets. However,' he added hurriedly, 'I am now able to *guarantee* success in this endeavour.' The word 'guarantee' had its designed effect and Robespierre's tight lips twitched into a smile. 'Indeed, I am pleased to inform you, Senior CitiZen, that Vice-Leader Beria has finally acceded to our several requests that the ForthRight provide us with an expert skilled in the use of galvanicEnergy. This expert will be here in Paris within a matter of days.'

'This is excellent news.' Robespierre took a long sip of his coffee. 'The triumph of the Revolution depends upon our being able to find and destroy the Spies and Seditionists trying to Traduce the Virtuous.'

*This prick*, Donatien decided, *is the only man in Paris who can speak in capital letters.*

'Only by the use of force – public force – can we cut this canker from the sweet body of the Medi. Yes, CitiZen Chief Inquisitor, we must cut, cut, cut.' The tic pulsing in the corner of Robespierre's right eye became worse. 'But although we must act swiftly and resolutely, we must act surely. Do you not understand, Donatien, that in this matter you are commanded by the Supreme Being, by ABBA Himself?'

*No*, decided Donatien as he watched a line of spittle dribble from the corner of Robespierre's mouth, *in this matter I am commanded by a fucking maniac.*

'And now that we have the Lady IMmanual within our grasp, it is more important than ever that you are successful. The Lady IMmanual is perhaps the most pernicious and dangerous enemy of UnFunDaMentalism. I wish you to use the wonder of galvanicEnergy to delve into the deepest recesses of her mind, to secure her darkest secrets. We must know how she has done what she has done. We must know how she worked her miracles. So I ask again: in this most sacred matter, CitiZen Chief Inquisitor, am I *truly* able to rely on you and your talents?'

*The Lady IMmanual!* So his employer – his *other* employer – had told him the truth.

Donatien took a second to compose himself. He was being given the honour of interrogating the Lady IMmanual. This was a moment he had dreamed of all his life: to have a Daemon at his mercy. Now he would be able, at last, to obtain empirical evidence that the whole concept of ABBA and of supreme beings was the arrant nonsense he had always conjectured it to be. Now he would be able to torture ABBA in His guise of the Lady IMmanual, to torture her using the miracle of galvanicEnergy. And by doing so, to receive a full pardon from the Doge.

Of course, he had been offered more – much more – if he would connive in the Lady IMmanual's assassination, but that would risk his being unmasked as a crypto and being executed. Better a smaller reward than the risk of death. Death was not a condition Donatien aspired to.

'Yes, Senior CitiZen Robespierre, you may rely on me.'

Ella came to reluctantly, consciousness seeping only slowly through her bruised body. With her head aching like the very devil, she relinquished her grasp on comforting oblivion unwillingly. Even the slightest, most tentative of movements sent a shiver of suffering through her head, and thence down through her body. Consciousness seemed to offer nothing but pain and nagging discomfort.

How long she had been unconscious Ella was unable to tell, but the rancid taste in her mouth and the stiffness in her limbs told her it had been a long time. Long enough, obviously, for her to have been removed from the Hub and brought . . .

She referenced PINC, which told her that she was now in a cell in Paris's infamous prison, the Bastille. This somewhat disturbing piece of news prompted her to try to open her eyes, but the headache sizzling across her forehead dissuaded her. Instead she pressed her eyelids tighter shut, trying to squeeze out the pain that made it impossible for her to think clearly.

As she lay on the hard narrow cot, her other senses kicked in; especially her sense of smell. The cell she was being held in stank of urine and damp, but there were other competing fragrances, notably the tart smell of tobacco smoke and the heavy, cloying fragrance of cologne. This told her that she was not alone.

Gingerly, Ella eased open her eyes.

'I am pleased to see you have returned to us, my Lady IMmanual.' The voice drifted towards Ella from what seemed like a thousand miles away. It was a man's voice, cultured and languid.

Turning her head carefully towards the voice, Ella braved her headache and cautiously opened her eyes. There was a only single oil lamp burning in her cell but it provided enough light for her to see the man addressing her. He was sitting on the other side of the cell, idly puffing on a cigarette and sipping from an enormously large glass of Solution. Clad, as he was, in an uncomfortable-looking dark grey habit made of rough wool, he made an incongruous sight. He looked like a rather pious debauchee.

As her eyes became used to the semi-darkness, Ella saw that he was small, young – she judged him to be in his mid-twenties

– and quite attractive in a nondescript sort of way, though his best feature – his blond, curly hair – was cut in an unfortunate tonsure and partially hidden by the thick bandage which circled his head. Attractive he might be, but there was still something unpleasant about him. His sharp blue eyes and full mouth were of the type Ella associated with petulant children, and he possessed the sort of podgy hands forever destined to be caught picking over the contents of a chocolate box.

'I am Chief Inquisitor Donatien,' announced this strange man, 'commanded by Senior CitiZen Robespierre to prepare you for the Ordeal of Interrogation.'

'Interrogation?'

'Why, yes, Senior CitiZen Robespierre has instructed me to delve deep into your mind and discover all your secrets, especially those involving the performing of miracles.' Donatien gave an airy wave of his cigarette and took a long slurp from his glass. 'You should feel honoured, my Lady; because for the first time in the history of the Quartier Chaud the wonders of galvanicEnergy will be employed to unpick the secrets of a mind. It will also, of course, be the first time a living, breathing Daemon has been put to the question. Believe me when I tell you that I am excited at the prospect of working with you – or perhaps that should be, working *on* you? In just a few days' time I will know whether the precepts that have until now underpinned my life and my philosophy are validated.'

'I don't understand.'

'How disappointing. I had expected the Lady IMmanual – the Messiah – to be all-knowing, but no matter. What is life if not a collection of disappointments? To explain: my entire philosophy has been predicated on there being no such thing as ABBA, no such thing as the Supreme Being, and no such thing as a Messiah. And now I am being given an opportunity to put that belief – that *disbelief* – to the test.'

Ella shook her head in protest, but all she succeeded in doing was to incite a spasm of pain to shoot across her forehead. She groaned and clenched her eyes shut again.

'I think if you lie still, my Lady, the pain and the nausea will pass a little more quickly. It was quite a blow you took to the head. Your disciples were very firm in their defence of you, but also very inaccurate.'

'You think I'm the Messiah?'

'Well, that's how you've been billed by your very vocal exhorters, the IMmanualists. Of course, people claiming to be the Messiah are ten a penny, but your Miracle of the Boundary does set you apart from the common herd.' Donatien took another long drag on his cigarette. For a man dressed as a monk to be smoking and drinking as he was, suggested there was something decidedly not right about him. 'Miracles are what separate the men from the boys when it comes to testing divinity and as all miracles have a depressing tendency to wilt when subjected to the scrutiny of scientific enquiry, I have had to conclude there is no such thing as ABBA.'

'But you're a man of God . . . of ABBA.' Ella nodded to the Valknut badge pinned to Donatien's habit, which proclaimed him to be an UnFunDaMentalist.

'This badge?' Donatien gave a disdainful sniff. 'A flag of convenience, my Lady, nothing else. UnFunDaMentalism is the religion of hypocrisy, as it must be, given that it teaches that all virtue is linked with chastity. But the powers that be in the Medi demand a certain cosmetic devotion, and for the sake of my neck I am willing to participate in their charade. The reality is that I am far from being a proponent of theism – quite the opposite, in fact.'

'You're a RaTionalist?' The question was slurred and distorted by her gummed mouth and leaden tongue. Ella swallowed, trying to suck away the taste of bile.

'Tush, nothing so mundane. Rather, I am a libertine. That's

"libertine" in its original rather than its more modern and somewhat sulphurous connotation. I regard myself as a freethinker and, of necessity, a free-doer. A libertine is one who surrenders to instinct . . . one who is loyal only to himself and his desires.'

'You're a libertine who nevertheless seems to set great store by miracles.'

'Because, my Lady, I do *so* wish to believe. Man is addicted to the pleasure derived from the marvel and astonishment engendered by experiencing and believing in ABBA, and miracles are proof that He exists. And that is why a true, honest-to-goodness miracle providing irrefutable evidence of His actuality would come as such a relief. That's what makes *your* miracle so very exciting.'

Although the fog that clouded Ella's thought processes was beginning to ease, she was still beset by a disturbing sensation of unreality, as if she were participating in some darkly abstract farce. Nothing seemed to make sense. 'Water?' she asked, hoping that if she could drive the fug from her brain and the taste of bilge from her mouth, she might have a better chance of making sense of what Donatien was saying.

'Oh, how remiss of me.' Donatien stood up from his chair and poured a glass of water from a jug resting on a shelf, then stepped across the cell to hand the glass to Ella. She made to take the glass, and it was only then that she realised her right wrist was manacled to a steel hoop fixed to the wall. Disbelievingly she pulled at the unyielding chain, rattling it, trying to tug her wrist free. It was no good: the chain, the manacle and the wall fixing were heavy and substantial.

'Why?' she asked.

'Why are you manacled? Isn't that obvious? To protect me from you and, of course, to ensure that you don't escape. Reinhard Heydrich believes you're much too important to lose, and whatever Heydrich thinks, invariably Robespierre agrees with.'

With a rueful shrug, Ella reached out her untethered left hand and took the glass of water from the man. She drank it in one long gulp, not having appreciated just how parched she was. Somewhat revived, she swung her legs off the cot and slowly sat up.

'You say I'm dangerous? I don't understand.'

'Then you are a very naïve Messiah. You are seen as that most dangerous of things, a threat to Certainty. The promotion and broadcasting of UnFunDaMentalism as the only true religion in the Demi-Monde is vital to both Heydrich and Robespierre. By puffing themselves as the Defenders of the Faith, they proclaim themselves to be blessed by ABBA, and are thus able to hoodwink the hoi polloi, who are universally stupid and ignorant, into obeying their commands no matter how ridiculous they might be. But to do this effectively they have to promote a Certainty – to evince a lack of doubt – and you and your miracles challenge that Certainty.'

'That is a very cynical view.'

'Oh, thank you. I am delighted to be called a cynic, because cynicism denotes a frame of mind whereby all the morality and precepts governing life are held in derision. And that is what I have striven all my life to do. But enough of this chit-chat. I will now leave you to contemplate the pain and the torture to come.' He reached over to take Ella's glass, and as he did so their hands met. That single touch was enough to allow PINC to tell her who this man was.

'You're the Marquis de Sade,' she gasped.

Donatien bowed. 'A somewhat obsolete title now since I am *persona non grata* in Venice, but I suppose the answer is yes, I am indeed Donatien-Alphonse-François, the Marquis de Sade.'

# 7

## The ForthRight Ministry
## of Propaganda: The Rookeries
## The Demi-Monde: 4th Day of Spring, 1005

Ah, Spring comes to the Quartier Chaud, when the sap rises, loins are girded and an ImPuritan's thoughts turn to what they should be wearing to this Season's Fleshtivals. And my advice? For men: stripes, stripes, and more stripes! Trousers should be skintight and striped, with a contrasting codpiece in gloss shellac (red or yellow for preference). Hats should be at least three inches taller than was currently en vogue, and decorated with polka dots. For the ladies, it is the nipple that takes centre stage this Spring. Breasts should be covered – or is that *uncovered*, ladies? – by voile, and the nipples varnished a colour that complements the gown. And as for masks: white leather leavened with a haze of sequins remains de rigueur for both the man *and* the woman about town.

'ImPure Modes': Frederick Worth,
UnVague Vogues Monthly, *Spring 1005*

Comrade Vice-Leader Lavrentii Beria felt that fortune was smiling on him. He had learned from his agent in Paris that the Lady IMmanual was now incarcerated very securely in the Bastille, so he had dispatched his foremost expert in the use of galvanicEnergy – together with one of his precious Faraday

Thermopiles – to that benighted city to tease out all her secrets before she was sent off to be topped by Madame Guillotine. If the Doctor couldn't find out how she had opened the Boundary Layer, then Beria was damned if anyone else would be able to.

The army's occupation of the Medi was going smoothly, too, so much so that Beria had bowed to the pressure imposed on him by the Great Leader and had taken the unprecedented decision to travel to Paris himself, so he could supervise its subjugation personally. And while he was there, he could ensure that the one remaining loose end in this whole sorry Lady IMmanual saga could be tied up, the loose end called Burlesque Bandstand.

The man's treachery had to be punished. Treachery was like cancer: if it wasn't destroyed quickly, it had the nasty habit of infecting everything – and everybody – around it. The destruction of Burlesque Bandstand was therefore a matter of some urgency, and hence deserved the use of his best man – or rather his *worst* man – to secure his demise. Beria would, of course, have preferred to inflict Bandstand's punishment personally, but such was the pressure of work that he had had to forgo this pleasure. He just hoped that Zolotov's description of how he killed the fat fool would be moderately diverting.

Beria leant over and pulled a bell cord that hung from the ceiling and a moment later a liveried servant scurried into the room. 'Comrade Zolotov should attend me immediately.' As the flunky scuttled off, he took a moment to pour himself a glass of Solution. He would need a drink; meetings with Zolotov were always trying occasions. The man was an effective assassin and an utterly charming bastard, but he was inclined to be disrespectful, never quite having thrown off his Royalist inclinations. Once a count always a count seemed to be Zolotov's motto.

*

There was a knock on the door of Beria's drawing room, and a lithe, elegant man was announced. A lithe, elegant and very *arrogant* man: unlike all other supplicants, Andrei Zolotov failed to bow and to avert his eyes when first ushered into the presence of the Vice-Leader. He didn't even bother to remove the cigarette that hung so casually from his lips, though he did have the good grace to doff his top hat.

Louche and careless, he stood with one hand tucked stylishly in his jacket pocket and an amused smile on his face. For a man being driven from St Petersburg, penniless and bereft of *blat*, friends and influence, Zolotov seemed irritatingly sanguine. Rascal though he was, Zolotov was a *charming* rascal. Beria was certain his agents would need to have both guile and amiability to be able to find and assassinate Burlesque Bandstand in an ImPure Quartier Chaud. And Zolotov had guile and amiability in abundance; he was after all, the man who had inveigled himself between the legs of Lady Irma Dolgorukova, and, knowing the frosty reputation of that frigid bitch, this was an amazing accomplishment. Of course, Comrade Commissar Dolgoukov had been less enamoured of Zolotov's dalliances with his wife and had threatened to reciprocate the favour by getting between *Zolotov's* legs and castrating him. Which was why Zolotov was now *persona non grata* in St Petersburg and would be amenable to a holiday outside the ForthRight.

'Good evening, Comrade Zolotov. My thanks for attending me so promptly.'

Carelessly Zolotov hitched a buttock up onto the side of a table, draping his rangy body back over the polished walnut. 'I am beholden to you for my room and board, Comrade Vice-Leader, and such largesse deserves to be rewarded with a certain appreciative alacrity.'

Beria studied the young man for a moment. He really was

the most impudent of rascals but, contrarily, there was something likeable about him. He was not yet twenty-one, though
his long blond hair and thin moustache made him look even
younger than his years. There was an air of innocence about
him that was almost endearing, but it was a somewhat specious
innocence, Zolotov having long since corrupted himself by a
surfeit of whoring, duelling, gambling, drinking and other, even
more malevolent, mischievousness. It was a mischievousness
well known in society circles, and Zolotov's reputation went
before him, matrons in St Petersburg doing their best to ensure
that their daughters were kept out of his clutches, though many
of them had been less careful regarding their *own* involvement
with the very beddable Zolotov.

'Speaking of largesse, Comrade Zolotov, it would seem that
you have been utilising the services of my tailor.'

An infuriating little shrug of the boy's strong shoulders.
'When one is of royal blood . . . oops, forgive me, Comrade Vice-
Leader, I did, of course, mean to say *Aryan* blood, it behoves one
to maintain appearances.' He brushed a piece of delinquent fluff
from the trousers of his immaculately cut suit. 'I have to concede
that your tailor is a master, Comrade, though I am forced to
criticise your choice of bootmaker.' Here he lifted a foot so that
Beria might better admire the shiny leather items he was
wearing. 'These new boots of mine pinch like the very devil.'

'I am delighted that you find my tailor is of an adequate standard, though I am less enamoured with your habit of charging
your purchases to my account.'

If Zolotov was at all disturbed by the rebuke, he certainly
didn't show it. Instead he offered a small smile by way of
apology. 'When one is as impoverished as I am, Comrade Vice-
Leader, one has to swallow one's pride and take assistance and
charity where one finds it. You have been very generous.'

'So at least you have the good grace to acknowledge the extent of my generosity, Zolotov. This is gratifying, as I have in mind a service that will extinguish the debts you owe me.'

Andrei Zolotov stopped swinging his leg and for the first time gave Beria his undivided attention. 'I really do hope, Comrade Vice-Leader, that you are not assuming the hectoring tone so beloved by my father, and suggesting that I join the military or, even worse, take up a diplomatic post in some ABBA-forsaken Sector whose language I would be unable to pronounce unless I had a mouthful of phlegm. If you are, I would counsel you that I have an aversion to authority.' Zolotov pronounced the word 'authority' as though the very thought of it made him nauseous.

'And also to hard work, according to your father. No, Zolotov, the task I have in mind is much more attuned to your natural talents of treachery, chicanery, seduction and murder.'

'This being the case, Comrade Vice-Leader, I am all ears.'

'You have heard, no doubt, of the Lady IMmanual.'

'Wasn't she the witch who performed that Miracle of the Boundary? I seem to remember hearing something about her.'

Beria took a long, deep breath. The youth of today never failed to amaze him by its lack of interest in the world about them. 'Yes, that's the girl. By the use of WhoDoo magic she managed to open the Boundary Layer, thereby allowing three million nuJus to leave Warsaw and escape into the Great Beyond. She is the same girl who performed, in her guise of the mambo Laveau, at Dashwood Manor. You were in attendance of the Great Leader that evening. Do you remember her now? She is a Shade.'

Zolotov shook his head. 'No, I was otherwise engaged when the séance took place.'

*Otherwise engaged with one of the Dashwoods' serving girls, no doubt,* decided Beria.

'But that is not to say I haven't met her. Several of my meetings with ladies have been very brief, and the conversation enjoyed inclined to a certain breathless aspect. And as these meetings invariably take place in the dark, her skin colour would have been lost on me.' He gave Beria an anxious glance. 'She wouldn't happen to be pregnant, would she?'

Beria laughed. 'No, she is not pregnant. But what she most certainly is, is very dangerous. So dangerous that she has been designated by the Great Leader as a major threat to the ForthRight. Following the events in Warsaw, she escaped to the Quartier Chaud where she is now in custody – her escape being facilitated by a rogue named Burlesque Bandstand.' Beria waved a piece of paper in Zolotov's direction. 'I have here a death warrant authorising Bandstand's assassination – an assassination I wish you to perform.'

'What type of man is this Bandstand of yours, Comrade Vice-Leader?'

'Bandstand runs a pub in the Rookeries.'

A laugh from Zolotov. 'A pub operator, you say. Dangerous chaps these landlords, eh? Death by short measure, perhaps?' Zolotov took a long drag on his cigarette. 'Not that I'm overly surprised: it's impossible to trust anyone these days . . . even bootmakers.'

Beria was genuinely shocked by Zolotov's whimsy, and he began to wonder if the man had sufficient gravitas to undertake a mission of the importance he was proposing. 'Reports have it that this villain Burlesque Bandstand is now in Paris, where he plots the destruction of the ForthRight.'

An exaggeration, of course, but necessary if Beria were to avoid the rumour spreading that he'd been foxed by a nobody like Bandstand.

Although Beria imbued the words with as much portent as he was able, Zolotov was unmoved. Instead, he just sat on the edge of the table, puffing his cigarette and swinging a leg in an indolent, carefree manner.

'I would have thought my services were a little too . . . expensive to be employed in disposing of a nonentity like this Bandstand chappy of yours.'

Beria skewered the young man with a vicious look. 'You cannot refuse, Zolotov. This is a deadly service that I ask you to undertake for your Fatherland.' There was no response, so Beria was obliged to prompt one. 'You do think yourself capable of killing the man, don't you?'

Zolotov chuckled. 'The question, Comrade Vice-Leader, is not if I am *capable* of killing the man, but whether I am *willing* to kill the man.'

'Surely a loyal man of royal blood . . . of Aryan blood,' Beria quickly corrected himself, 'would have no hesitation in performing any service that will help preserve the sanctity of the ForthRight?'

'The problem here is that the adjective "loyal" is, in my case, substituted by the word "indigent".'

'But I have supported you in a manner appropriate to your rank. I have permitted you to dress yourself—'

'My dear Comrade Vice-Leader,' interrupted Zolotov with a negligent wave of his hand, 'if you imagine that I am inclined to murder in exchange for a couple of suits and a pair of ill-fitting boots, then we have a fundamental difference in understanding when it comes to evaluating the worth of my services.'

'What do you want?'

'I want Commissar-Comrade Dolgorukov called off. He has threatened to have his bully boys chop off my cock, and as I am inordinately fond of that particular piece of artillery, I want him deterred. I want to be reinstated in St Petersburg society. The Rookeries are all very fine in their way, but the women here are rotten with syphilis. And finally, I want all my debts extinguished; my nuJu moneylenders in Venice are becoming very insistent.'

'I am aghast at your bourgeois attitude.'

'Bourgeois or not, are my terms agreed?'

'Agreed.'

'That being the case, I am your man.'

Beria tossed a leather-bound file to Zolotov. 'This contains all the information you might require regarding Burlesque Bandstand.'

Zolotov made a quick, lazy flick through the pages of the file. 'It's terribly thick.'

'I note your aversion to study, Zolotov, but I suggest you peruse it diligently. Make no mistake, Burlesque Bandstand will be a doughty opponent.'

'Do you have a picture of the man?'

'Unfortunately not, Zolotov, but I have this . . .'

He signalled to a flunky and moments later a very strange-looking individual was ushered into the room. Enormously fat and decked out in an amazingly tatty suit, the fellow looked for all the world like a very large rubbish heap with legs. 'This man is a former associate of Burlesque Bandstand.'

'Indeed?' said Zolotov, as he raised a quizzical eyebrow. 'I would ask if it has a name, but I fancy this . . . *thing* has yet to evolve the power of speech.'

'Come on man,' prompted Beria, 'tell us your name.'

'My name is Maurice Merriment, Comrade, Your Majesty, Vice-Leader, sir. I am an entertainer.'

'Really?' mused Zolotov. 'And what do you entertain, apart from the lice which no doubt call your verminous person home?'

'I am a comic, sir.'

'I am amazed by what the lower orders find amusing.'

Beria decided to interrupt this rather irritating exchange. 'But you know and can identify Burlesque Bandstand?'

'Oh yes, sirs, I'd know that thieving bastard anywheres.'

'Excellent. Then I suggest, Zolotov, that you take this creature with you to the Quartier Chaud and use him to help you track down Bandstand.'

Zolotov seemed less than impressed. 'Generally I prefer as my accomplices those who are at least *partially* simian in origin, and who don't smell in *quite* such a pungent manner.' He shook his head. 'Indeed, such is the pong emanating from this wretch's breeches that I am unsure, Comrade Vice-Leader, whether he has risen from the primordial ooze, or is still living in it.'

'Oh, that's the dogshit,' said Maurice Merriment helpfully. 'I am resting between engagements at the moment and 'ave found gainful employment in a tannery.'

'Well, there goes my chance of surprising this Bandstand person,' said Zolotov, as he dug a scented handkerchief from his pocket and held it to his nose. 'If he doesn't spot us first, he'll be sure to smell us. I'll have to attack him from down-wind.'

# 8

## Paris
## The Demi-Monde: 13th Day of Spring, 1005

The conclusion is inescapable: all Demi-Mondians possess the *potential* to be Dark Charismatics, although in the vast majority of mankind this potential is unrealised. The internal conflict resulting between *H. singularis* and *H. sapiens* produces, in more extreme cases, the condition known as schizophrenia. Fortunately, for the sanguinity of the Demi-Mondian race, the malicious traits ascribable to *H. singularis* are latent – its true, horrific nature only being stimulated into blossom by accidental excitements.

*Letter dated 53rd day of Spring, 1002, from Professeur Michel de Nostredame to Doge Catherine-Sophia*

Ella was frightened. She had been through a lot in the Demi-Monde, but the ten days she'd spent as a prisoner in the Bastille was the worst experience of them all. The Bastille was a horrible place – dark, dank and oppressive – and its inhabitants were similarly vile. The waiting for something to happen had been nerve-shredding. But now it seemed her waiting was at an end.

The mysterious 'Doctor' – the ForthRight's expert on galvanic-Energy, as PINC told her electricity was known in the Demi-Monde – had finally arrived in Paris, and Ella was being marched through the prison's foetid corridors to meet the man.

Despite the attendance of de Sade and a Sergeant-Inquisitor,

Ella had never felt more alone. Being separated from Vanka hadn't done anything for her peace of mind: she'd come to rely on his indefatigable optimism to carry her through the scrapes they'd been involved in together, and without him at her side things now seemed decidedly bleak.

Very bleak.

She was now in the power of the Marquis de Sade, one of the Real World's most famous sexual delinquents, the man who had given his name to the practice of sadism. And, from what Ella had gleaned during the several tête-à-têtes she'd had with him, the man was most certainly off his rocker. The way he described it, he just *loved* torturing people.

She felt de Sade edge closer to her. 'The device we will be using to test you, my Lady, is perhaps one of the most remarkable of *all* engines, in that it is driven by galvanicEnergy, a phenomenon newly discovered by Comrade Scientist Faraday. Unfortunately, this engine is so temperamental that it must be operated by an expert on secondment to the CIA from the ForthRight. I warn you now that this expert is an uncompromising individual, so I offer you this advice: speak the truth and speak it quickly. In this way you will avoid at least *some* degree of unnecessary pain. Unlike mine, his passion for cruelty is promoted by an inclination towards the bestial, and he possesses none of my finer feelings or sensitivities.'

*Fucking hell.* If the *Marquis de Sade* was warning her that the man she was about to meet was beyond the pale, then he really must be a thoroughgoing badnik.

They came to a halt in front of a heavy door, which de Sade opened, ushering Ella into the large, whitewashed laboratory beyond. The room was stiflingly hot – sauna-hot – and the reason wasn't difficult to see. In the far corner of the laboratory bubbled and popped what looked to be a huge copper boiler, perhaps ten feet tall and maybe five feet or so in diameter, its outer edge decorated with serrated fins – probably, Ella decided, to help cool the thing down. Various pipes snaked out of the contraption to disappear off into the walls, and two black cables trailed from terminals set atop the device to drape themselves over the arms of the huge high-backed chair that stood in the middle of the room.

Ella found the chair more disturbing than anything; it reminded her of pictures she'd seen of electric chairs. A dreadful feeling of foreboding descended over her.

A man and a woman, both dressed in white laboratory coats, were standing beside the chair watching her. It was the man – ruddy-cheeked and wearing a wide smile that showed off his gapped teeth – who stepped forward to greet the arrivals. 'Ah . . . Chief Inquisitor Donatien, I am delighted to meet you again.' The two men shook hands and then the ruddy-cheeked item turned his attention to Ella. 'And this, I presume, is the subject that First CitiZen Robespierre wishes examined.'

'It is, Doctor. This is the Shade witch known as the Lady IMmanual.'

'Excellent. And how old are you, young lady?' asked the doctor.

'Eighteen.'

'Good. And you seem fit and healthy, too.' He stepped nearer to Ella, pushing his face to within inches of hers, swamping her with the smell of engine oil and disinfectant that clung to him. He peered at her in the same way a farmer might assess a prize cow. 'Do you suffer from any congenital weaknesses?' he asked, and then added, 'Apart from your obvious racial degeneracy, that is.'

Ella bristled. 'No. And I do not regard my skin colour as an indication of any inferiority. Compared to the lighter skin of an Aryan intent on torture, I have a feeling it indicates quite the opposite.'

'Hah! The girl has both intelligence and spirit, Chief Inquisitor, and as such will make a wonderfully resilient subject for our little experiment.' He turned to his assistant. 'I would be grateful, Miss Godwin, if you would unshackle the girl. I need to weigh her and then take a number of measurements.'

As the chains fell from her wrists, the doctor smiled at Ella. 'You have a great deal of hair, young lady . . .'

They bundled Ella into the chair and used leather bands to strap her wrists and ankles, so that she was obliged to sit helpless while the doctor's assistant shaved her scalp with a cut-throat razor.

Then, for the next half-hour, the doctor examined Ella. Peculiarly, he spent a great deal of time measuring her head, checking the angle of slope of her jaw and her forehead and, for a few truly horrible minutes, fondling her skull, fingering every bump and gully. Unfortunately, such was the thickness of the rubber gloves the doctor wore whilst he worked that PINC could give Ella no information about the man, but then PINC wasn't the only one to be puzzled.

'Most peculiar,' mused the doctor as he stood back and eyed Ella carefully. 'I would explain the aberrational results of my examination but I doubt whether one of your racial inferiority would be familiar with the science of phrenology?'

Oddly enough, Ella *was* familiar with it. As part of her psychology course back in the Real World she had written a paper regarding the influence of bogus science on the growth of racial prejudice. Phrenology – the theory that by examining the shape and size of an individual's head, scientific conclusions could be drawn about their personality and intellect – had been one of the main topics she had discussed.

'I don't know it as a "science",' answered Ella, 'rather I know it as a *pseudo*science. It's just nonsense used to promote racist twaddle about certain people being inferior to others. As a medical technique, it was pronounced flawed many, many years ago.'

A frown crossed the doctor's brow. 'How can this be? Phrenology is a discipline at the very forefront of medical and scientific enquiry, therefore it is impossible for it to have been pronounced flawed "many, many years ago".' After a moment's silence he began to nod slowly, and then gave Ella a complacent little smile. 'Ah, I see, this is a ruse to render me intellectually off guard. Clever. It is a subtlety I never expected from one of your primitive provenance, but it is at one with the unusual findings I have made about you.'

He clapped his hands and his assistant handed him a clipboard which held a sheet of paper thick with numbers. These the doctor studied for a few moments. 'You know, Chief Inquisitor Donatien, when I was told my subject would be a Shade, I had anticipated finding evidence of the atavistic stigmata that Lombroso describes as typical of UnderMentionables. But in this girl I see no prognathous jawline, and her forehead is almost parallel to the vertical axis of her skull. This is most atypical of her race. You will also be interested to learn that the measurements of her skull's latitudinal and longitudinal girth are all soundly in the upper quartile and, contrarily, point to her possessing a mind of superior size and performance.' He shook his head, and then turned to Ella. 'It would seem, young lady, that you are one of those recidivists who do not manifest the physical deformity of your race.'

'Or it could be that your theories regarding racial profiles are just junk,' Ella shot back. 'Could it be, Doctor, that my race does not manifest your so-called physical deformities, because it is *not* deformed? You lambaste people because they appear different from your Aryan ideal, but you never pause to consider that it might be the Aryans themselves who are deformed . . . deformed spiritually.'

'Foolish, stupid, UnderMentionable scum,' sneered the doctor. 'Well, we will see how argumentative you are after treatment.' He nodded to his assistant, who placed an inch-wide steel circlet around Ella's head. The circlet was already connected by the two wires to the machine bubbling and burping away in the corner of the room.

'As I have already discussed with you, Chief Inquisitor, the device in the corner is an example of the newly invented Faraday Thermopile, a machine designed to convert heat energy into galvanicEnergy by the use of the thermocouples which radiate out from the engine's central spine.'

The doctor used a pencil to tap the fins of the thermopile, which were now glowing red-hot. 'A marvellous machine, is it not, Chief Inquisitor? It is my conjecture that the mind of a Demi-Mondian functions by the transmission of sparks of galvanicEnergy within the Solidified Astral Ether housed inside the cranium. By the application of the galvanicEnergy generated by this thermopile, I am able to interrupt this process, the amount of galvanicEnergy needed to commandeer a subject's mental process being directly proportional to the subject's intellectual capacity.'

With that the doctor began an intensive examination of the settings of the various valves and taps that decorated the surface of the machine. 'Shall we make a start? For this particular experiment we will use the nomenclature "Mengele Experiment Forty-Seven" . . .'

'You're Josef Mengele?' asked Ella, in a shaking voice.

A querulous frown from the doctor. 'You know my name?'

'Yes, I know who you are – and *what* you are. You're the Angel of Death, the monster who killed all those poor people in Auschwitz.'

Mengele shook his head dismissively. 'Ridiculous. I have no idea what you are talking about, young lady. I have never been referred to by such a melodramatic sobriquet, and I have never been to a place called Auschwitz.' He turned back to his assistant. 'We will begin on setting number two.'

Ella saw the lever being thrown.

And then her head exploded.

# 9

## INDOCTRANS Headquarters, Fort Jackson
## The Real World: 16 August 2018

The Lilithi were the priestesses of Lilith, dedicated to passing the knowledge and wisdom of the first Lilith down through the generations. Exclusively female, the Lilithi were a species of woman physically and mentally superior to all other species of HumanKind: they were *Homo perfectus*, the apotheosis of life in the Demi-Monde. Indeed there is an opinion amongst experts that the Lilithi may not have belonged to the genus *Homo*. The Lilithi were perhaps more than human, being reputed to possess Atavistic Thought Inheritance, a mysterious ability named but never described.

**Myths and Legends of the Demi-Monde:**
*Lucien Lévy-Brühl, Quartier Chaud Imprints*

Bole sat alone in his office at INDOCTRANS, sipping a glass of warm honeyed water while trying to settle his mind and body after an unusually taxing week. Unfortunately, today Septimus Bole was not destined to achieve the tranquillity of spirit he craved: the emergency warning light flashing on his desk saw to that.

'Bole,' he intoned.

'Professor Bole, this is Nurse Green at the storage facility. Doctor Andrews has just reported abnormalities with one of our biPsychs.'

'Which one?' It was an important question. Including Ella

Thomas there were eighteen biPsychs stored in in the facility, seventeen belonging to the neoFights the US military believed to have been captured by ImPeril agents working for Shaka Zulu and held as prisoners in NoirVille. Bole suppressed a smile: it had always amused him how easily the military had swallowed this piece of fiction, but then, he supposed, they were only Fragiles.

'BiPsych Thomas.'

Septimus Bole had never thought it possible to cover so damned quickly the ten floors from his office to the facility where the bodies of those Real Worlders active in the Demi-Monde – the biPsychs – were held. And once there, a breathless Bole headed straight for the monitoring station, where a very grim-faced Dr David Andrews, the medic in charge of biPsych storage, stood poring over computer read-outs.

'Report,' barked Bole.

'It started ten minutes ago: first biPsych Thomas became agitated, and then her readings went all to hell.'

Bole glanced through the observation window toward the ranks of TIS-swathed bodies lined up on gurneys in the storage hall. Ella Thomas's body was easy to spot, bucking and writhing as two nurses tried ineffectually to keep it still.

'She's still in the Demi-Monde?'

'Yes, her body is still dormant.'

It didn't look dormant. In Bole's experience, dormant bodies didn't spasm in quite the way this one did.

Taking a deep breath to help him maintain focus, Bole examined the dials scattered across the control panel. Andrews was right, the readings were all to hell. Her blood pressure had soared, her heart was pumping like a trip hammer, her REMs were off the dial, her body temperature had rocketed – and, most worryingly of all, the composition of her blood was wrong, and getting wronger by the minute.

'What have you done to control the situation?'

'We've pumped her full of DayRapturePlus, enough to sedate an elephant, but it's done no good. There's something happening in the Demi-Monde that's causing her extreme agitation.'

Bole rechecked the dials, and could hardly believe what he was seeing. If the pressure readings coming from the straps tethering the girl's wrists and ankles were correct, the force she was placing on them was almost double the maximum a human subject was considered capable of exerting. There could be only one explanation: the girl was mutating!

But that was impossible. It *had* to be impossible!

He had verified that, unlike all the other Dupes, Thomas didn't carry the Grigori gene. And the alternative – that she was a latent Lilithi – was absurd. Anyway there was no electricity in the Quartier Chaud to provoke a mutation.

Bole froze. There *was* electricity in the Demi-Monde. He had allowed it in order to facilitate the work on the Plague, to provide Boyle, Cuvier and the other scientists working in the Institute with everything they needed to develop the ultimate eugenical weapon. But that had been a recent amendment and there was no way Faraday would have been able to disseminate the technology beyond the ForthRight so quickly. Or was there? He had told Beria to keep the knowledge of galvanicEnergy a secret, but Beria was a politician, and politicians would do anything to secure an advantage over their enemies.

From far away, Bole heard the voice of Dr Andrews talking to him. 'As best we can make out, it seems that the Dupe of biPsych Thomas is being subjected to extreme electro-shock treatment. I'm having ABBA make estimates now.' He tapped a computer display screen. 'Jesus! ABBA's saying that her Dupe is being subjected to shocks of over two hundred milliamperes. She should be burning by now.' There was a warning *ping* from the control panel. 'Ah, fuck, that's her PINC flat-lining.' Even as the words left the doctor's mouth, several of the screens carrying data from Ella Thomas's Dupe suddenly went blank.

Bole did his best to mask his annoyance; without PINC he wouldn't be able to track the girl inside the Demi-Monde.

Dr Andrews turned and pressed his face hard against the observation window. 'Why isn't she dead? No human can stand that amount of abuse!'

The doctor was quite right: nobody *human* could withstand that level of shock. But then, Bole had a sneaking suspicion that Ella Thomas might no longer *be* human. As he watched her writhing on the gurney, he decided that the girl had been elevated from an irritant to a major danger.

She was now the worst enemy of the Dark Charismatics . . . of the Grigori. She was now one of the Lilithi.

Bole scuttled back to his office, dived into his chair, took a long calming breath and then turned towards the Flexi-Plexi.

'ABBA, I wish to interrogate you regarding Section 51.'

'Please insert your pass code, Septimus, and then provide me with three bioSignatures.'

Bole did as he was asked, simultaneously irritated by the delay caused by the security measures necessary to access this oh-so-secret area of ABBA's database, and yet pleased that they meant no one else could interrogate the machine on the oh-so-delicate subject of Grigori and their by-blows, Dark Charasmatics.

'Security checks are satisfactory, Septimus. I am now able to provide advice regarding Section 51 of my memory.'

'Have you analysed the reaction of Ella Thomas to the stimuli she has been subjected to in the Demi-Monde?'

'I have, Septimus.'

'And what were your findings?' prompted Bole testily, angry with himself for having asked a closed question in the first place. ABBA was very pedantic regarding such matters.

'It would seem that Ella Thomas is possessed of a dormant inclination to Lilithianism, and that the excitements she has been subjected to in the Demi-Monde have woken these aspects.'

'Why didn't you advise me of Ella Thomas's potential as a Lilithi when we were screening her?'

'You will remember, Septimus, that the constraints imposed on the divulging of Section 51 data mean that I am unable to discuss, to acknowledge or to imply the existence of Grigori, of Dark Charismatics, of Lilithi or of Kohanim, unless specific security protocols have been executed. Your failure to do this when Ella Thomas was being evaluated for deployment in the Demi-Monde resulted in my inability to alert you regarding her proclivity towards Lilithianism.'

Bole snorted. 'And the reason I did that was that all surviving Lilithians were meant to have died when Cavor's research facility on Krakatoa exploded in 1883.'

*Meant to . . .*

'I have examined the genealogical records of Ella Thomas, Septimus, and it would appear that she is a distant relation of Margaret Jekyll who, you will be aware, was herself Lilithian. It would seem that she passed her genetic idiosyncrasies down through her line to Ella Thomas.'

Margaret Jekyll, now there was a name to chill the blood of any Dark Charismatic. When the meteor had landed in 1795 and bathed those gathered in Bole Manor in its strange radiation, not only had Sir Augustus Bole mutated but also that witch, Hortense Steele. But rather than Bole's Grigorian aspect, it had been the girl's latent Lilithianism that the meteor had resuscitated, a trait she passed down to her granddaughter, Margaret Steele . . . or as she had become, Margaret Jekyll, her full powers revived by that interfering wretch, Edward Hyde. It had been Margaret Jekyll that had almost done for the Grigori, it had been Margaret Jekyll who had destroyed the TiME facility on Krakatoa in 1883, sacrificing herself – and his ancestor, Cornelius Bole – in the process.

'But Margaret Jekyll died childless, he protested. 'The Lilithian strain died with her when Krakatoa exploded.'

'Not so, Septimus. She had a daughter, Lily, who was raised by the Petrov family in Russia. Lily came to the USA to escape Stalin in 1923, changing her name to Thomas in the process. It was in this way that the Lilithian trait, attenuated to be sure, was passed down to Ella Thomas.'

Bole knew this was not a time to despair or to panic. He tried to clear his mind. The Lilithi might be the ancient enemy of the Grigori, but Ella Thomas was still only a girl. Or was she? What if there were others? 'This Lilithian trait of Ella Thomas', is it manifest in any others?' he asked ABBA, fearful of what the answer might be.

Bole slumped back in his chair; the shadows of the past were once more falling over the present.

'Unfortunately, Septimus, I have access to the DNA data relating to only 73.45 per cent of the world's human population, therefore my answer must be balanced with certain caveats.'

'Never mind the caveats, ABBA. Just tell me how many of these Lilithi are out there.'

'Only one, Septimus. Ella Thomas is the last of the Lilithi.'

Bole smiled. Just one of them, and that one would soon be very, very dead. And then the line stretching back all those thousands of years to the first Lilith would be finally ended.

It was time for the Grigori to be deployed in the Demi-Monde.

# 10

## The Bastille: Paris
## The Demi-Monde: 13th Day of Spring, 1005

What can we glean from the scant historical records regarding the character of Lilith? That she was an erotic woman is a given: every religion describes her as a woman who used her beauty and her sexual wiles to beguile and to control her subjects and to bend her enemies to her will. Legend has it that Lilith was the greatest exponent of fiduciary sex ever to walk the Demi-Monde, able to enslave a man or woman with just a glance. Strangely though, there is not one account of her being in love – there is no *grande passion* in the life of Lilith – indeed she seems a somewhat frigid and aloof character. And this surmise is reinforced by the many tales of brutality associated with her: the manner in which she dispatched rivals is utterly cold-blooded. She was an unemotional, single-minded and fearsome shaper – *re*shaper – of HumanKind.

**Lilith: a Biography:** *Doctor Jezebel Ethobaal,*
*WhoDoo Books and Periodicals*

Ella looked down at her body lying forlorn on the cot in her cell, knowing that her spirit had soared free of her corporeal form. Indifferent to the chains that bound her, her spirit writhed like smoke through the Nine Worlds, her thoughts blown hither and thither by the Chorus of the Kosmos. Around her light looped and spun, spewing gobs of flaring sunlight that gybed with the shadows of Nothingness. Onward and deeper into the Kosmos she floated, urged on by the whispers from times long ago, whispers giddy with excitement.

Time passed – though it seemed nebulous, twisting and turning, mutating and merging the Now with the Then, with the Never-Was, with the What-Might-Have-Been and with the That-Which-Is-Yet-To-Come.

Suddenly she was still. In that instant her spirit settled, condensed back into a place that was just a sliver of her imagination, and gazing out into the Nothingness she saw herself gazing back.

Herself in the form of Lilith.

'I am come, Ella,' said Lilith, her unvoiced words heavy with foreboding. 'This is your Awakening. The fires damped within you are now rekindled. You are Lilith reborn.'

'Lilith? But Lilith is just a myth.'

'A myth now made flesh: Doctor Mengele, by his meddling, has unleashed that which you had imprisoned inside yourself. It is time for you to finish the work which I – which *you* – began those many centuries ago.'

'I don't understand.'

'You are no mere Fragile, Ella: you are a woman with powers and abilities denied those primitives. You have inherited the talents of the first Lilith, the Goddess born eleven thousand years ago in the now forgotten past, the first person ever to manifest *overt* powers of zoological heredity.' Lilith sensed Ella's befuddlement, 'She was able to convey her ancestral memory and experiences to her daughters *intact* and by this gift of Atavistic Thought Inheritance, the whole of the knowledge and the experiences of that first Lilith were visited upon her daughters, who in turn passed this knowledge, supplemented by the knowledge they themselves acquired in their lifetimes, to their daughters and so on. You, Ella, are the last of the Lilithi, and within you carry the accumulated wisdom of five hundred generations of our race. The voices you hear clamouring in your head are the voices of your long dead sisters demanding that you listen to them. That is why I say to you: you are Lilith reborn . . . you are *all* the Lilithi reborn.'

Ella was silent. What Lilith was saying was simultaneously ridiculous and persuasive, persuasive because even as she lay there it was as though a veil was slowly drawn back from a previously hidden part of her mind, that suddenly she understood things that she could never believe it was possible to understand. But still her rationality provoked her to protest. 'This is wrong. There isn't any such thing as Atavistic Thought Inheritance. Genetics has shown it to be impossible.'

'Forget genetics and listen to your own instincts . . . listen to your soul.'

'But if I am Lilith reborn, why can't I remember? Why don't I have this race memory?'

'You will, Ella, you will. It is held fast within you by pain, the pain of the loss of so many of your sisters when our world was destroyed by the Deluge. Thanks to Atavistic Thought Inheritance, the Lilithi created amongst themselves what de Chardin called a noösphere, a community bound together by a collective consciousness, and the result was that the Lilithi were so traumatised by the communal deaths of their sisters in the Deluge that they suppressed their racial memories . . . they forced themselves to forget. But through the serendipitous meddling of Mengele you are awoken. Soon your race memory will return to you and then you will know that the Lilithi were Goddesses who used their powers to better the lot of the Fragiles, who uncovered the secrets of life, of sex and of evolution . . . who were the first to domesticate the beasts of the field and tame the grasses of the plains. The Lilithi gave these miracles to humankind and a grateful humankind worshipped them as Goddesses, calling the first Lilith Mother Nature and making her divine.

'Divine?'

'Yes, and that is the gift I offer you: the gift of divinity. Look deep into yourself, Ella, and see what you once were, see Lilith standing at the dawn of time, bestriding the world like a colossus . . . a Goddess who remade humankind.'

'But why?'

'Because we had the power to take Destiny into our own hands and because we were dissatisfied by how dilatory evolution was. We sought to mould humankind into something more glorious, more powerful and more intelligent than nature ever imagined. In a time before history and in a land before memory over many thousands of years the Lilithi created their masterpieces. They decreed that there would be three races which would lift the world on their shoulders, three races which would ensure the safety and welfare of the Fragiles. The first of these were the Lilithi: the Priestesses who alone bore the gift of Atavistic Thought Inheritance. The second were the Kohanim: those bred to be the most intelligent of all peoples. And the third were the Grigori: the shield and the sword of the people of the Empire of the Lilithi.'

'You played God.'

'God? An obsolete Fragile concept. But whilst there is no God, Ella, there is a Goddess. You, Ella Thomas, are that Goddess, a Goddess with an obligation to *lead* humankind.'

'Lead humankind where?'

'To lead them to perfection, Ella, to finish the work so rudely interrupted by the Deluge. That is your destiny.'

Lilith fell silent and Ella tumbled into herself, plummeting deep into her unconscious. Only there, she knew, would she find understanding, only there would she be at one with the

Kosmos and the Living. And as she tumbled so she felt herself changing, mutating, the very essence of her being, of her body and of her mind transmogrifying.

Ella could feel power crowding in on her. She felt strong . . . invincible. And as the power grew, she sensed the Living squirm in an ever-more-violent frenzy, twisting and spiralling around one another in a panicking dance. Their Mistress had returned: Lilith *was* reborn.

In the chill black cell where she lay, Ella smiled quietly to herself: how could she resist her destiny? How could she resist such a delicious temptation? Bole had connived to have Mengele release that which had lain dormant within her for all these long years, and now Bole would reap the consequences. This was one djinn that most certainly would not go back in its bottle. Oh, how the Worlds would tremble.

A sound invaded her thoughts, urging her to return to consciousness. She opened her eyes. She listened. They were coming for her. She sensed those in thrall to the Dark approaching. They had come to take her to her death.

*Fools.*

That they were intent on destroying her, she was indifferent to. She had felt Death's frosted breath on her cheek too many times to shudder at its approach. And now, having come to understand that there was no Death, merely a merging with the Living, she was immune to fear. By defying Death, she would defy the Dark Charismatics and their masters, the Grigori.

Until . . .

Until she was ready to conquer them. Until she was ready to make them kneel once more at her command.

Silently she scolded herself for pursuing this perversely enjoyable thought. Now was not yet the time. She was not ready. There was still one who could deny her, one who could thwart her ambitions. Yes, Vanka Maykov had to be destroyed.

Although the Fragile part of her still loved the man and would weep bitter tears at his passing, she knew that he could not be allowed to live. If he ever came to know who he was – *what* he was . . .

No, nothing and no one could be allowed to stand between her and her destiny. There was too much at stake to surrender to Fragile sentimentality, not now that she had been given a second opportunity to fulfil all her ambitions. And ambition was, after all, the most delicious of temptations.

As the Inquisitors bent over her, she lay still, pretending to be asleep. She knew they were afraid of her, sensed that they were frightened of what she had become. Now she could smell the fear of what they might have woken inside her.

*Fools, if they only knew.*

They shook her awake and then pulled her to her feet, telling her it was time for her sacrifice, and that she must take her place with the Living by becoming as one with the Dead. Then they manacled her wrists to heavy chains. She made no protest. Her fate wasn't to be resolved here. Her destiny required her to be the dutiful prisoner . . .

For now.

And when she wished to be free, no manacles made by Fragiles could hold her. *Fools. I am the tear you never shed, the nightmare that haunts your dreams, the silent scream that echoes in your memory. I am ferocious fantasy made flesh and blood. I am Lilith come again.*

# Part Two
# The Storming of the Bastille and Escape from Paris

You have been taught | to scorn Daemons.
To slight | Monsters
Giants | and Gods.
To rely | on the ignorance of crowds
On the certainty of stupidity.

But I counsel you | listen.
I give you warning | I ride the wind
I thirst for revenge | I yearn for Blood.
You have become | important enough
To be my enemy.

Know you | Seidr lives.
The most powerful | of all Dark Magicks.
Riddled | Runes
Hidden near | the deepest roots of Yggdrasil
It lives.

You sneer | There are no witches.
Seidr died | But in the emptiness of Doubt
In the husk | of a forgotten Past
I ferment nightmares. | Remember
The fate of the Vanir.

Look inwards | to lost Vanaheimr.
Look to the unending river | for forgotten Vanaheimr.
There lived | the Vanir
The Elvish godlings | who sweetly ruled
The Demi-Monde.

Fair and fertile | was Vanaheimr.
Gentle | and slow to chide
Were the Vanir. | Their women
The soft hand | staying
The sword.

But look now | in vain
For the Vanir. | They are but Shadows.
Formless | Phantoms
From a Time before | from a Time that is
Gone.

Came the Lady | cunning in Seidr.
Wanton | perverse
Knew she | the arcane
Lore of Runes | that Od
Died to possess.

None were | as beautiful
None as reckless | as Lilith.
None were as skilled | in the arts
Of love. | Lie with her
And despair.

*Diagram and translation reproduced by kind permission of Snore Igbolinn, Cartographer-General to the Court of Her Most Reverend Excellency, Doge Catherine-Sophia*

# THE EDDIC OF LOCI 2: THE VANIR REMEMBERED
## PLATE 2

# 11

## The White House: Washington DC
## The Real World: 17 August 2018

PanOptika is the ABBA-platformed program which links
all surveillance apparatus (whether private or state-operated), all eyeSpies (whether private or state-operated) and
all databases (whether private or state-owned) to produce
a full 360° cyber-portrait of individual citizens. PanOptika
was developed by ParaDigm CyberResearch for the British
government and subsequently adopted (albeit reluctantly
and only after extreme pressure from Britain) by the US
government after the 12/12 atrocities.

*iSuccess in GCSE-Dip: A Revision Guide to British*
*History, ParaDigm Publications*

As the Humber Sentinel limousine swept around the drive
leading up to the White House, Septimus Bole sat back in the
cosseting luxury of the passenger compartment and tried to
bring order to his thinking and calm to his frazzled nerves. But
it was difficult. The metamorphosis of Ella Thomas had been
a monumentally unsettling event and one which threatened to
derail all his carefully laid plans. Moreover, it couldn't have
come at a worse time. The meeting he was en route to constituted one of those moments the historians at the Bole Institute
of History termed a Nexus Point: the instant when the
Postulated TimeStream veered off in a new direction.

He could not – must not – allow himself to be distracted.

*Perhaps just a taste of blood?*

Angrily he pushed the temptation away. Blood dependency was one of the defining traits of all Grigori and though he was only a Dark Charismatic, and hence genetically impaired by the contamination inherited from Fragile broodmare, he was still pure enough to have inherited their lust for blood. And blood did have such an invigorating effect on his spirits. But this, he knew, wasn't the time for such indulgence.

He tried to control his thoughts, not wanting to dwell on the failures he'd suffered since Ella Thomas had been introduced into the Demi-Monde, a list of failures that was embarrassingly long. This girl – this Lilithian – had led a charmed life but now, it seemed, luck had finally deserted her. Captive in the Bastille and with Semiazaz and the other Grigori poised to enter the Demi-Monde, soon she would be dead. Even if de Torquemada failed him, Semiazaz most certainly would not.

With a determined effort Bole wrenched his attention back to the task at hand. Today his mission was nothing less than the remodelling of history. And the intriguing thing was that no one other than Aaliz Heydrich could even begin to appreciate what he was attempting, and even she was a mere pawn in the complex game of historical chess he was playing. And as for the President and his acolytes . . .

*Bloody Americans.*

Ever since their political and economic demise, following the end of the Second World War in 1946, the US had been desperately trying to climb back up the greasy pole of world domination.

*Pathetic.*

Unfortunately, their being reduced to the status of a second-class nation had done nothing to diminish their arrogance. They still treated Bole as a powerful but servile apparatchik: as a mere boffin. Clever certainly – too clever by half, according to General Zieliéski – but still hated as a Brit . . . as one of the Master Race.

Not that Bole was particularly concerned about this. As a Dark Charismatic, he was genetically conditioned to hate all Fragiles, and anyway, soon the Fragiles would be swept away. Today marked the beginning of the end of this *ancien régime*; from today all Fragiles would be nothing more than a super-annuated anachronism, a species destined to go the same way as *H. neanderthalensis*. And today, with Bole's help, they would take their first step on the road to extinction.

Skidding on the pristine gravel, the Humber came to a halt in front of the great house and an impeccably uniformed Marine sergeant stepped up to open the door. Bole ignored him, pausing for a moment to settle himself and to ensure that the counte-nance he would present to the President was calm, cool and collected.

Only when he was certain of his inner and outer sanguinity did Bole secure the wide-brimmed hat on his head – to ensure that it fully protected him from the afternoon sunshine – and allow himself to be led into the White House for his rendezvous with destiny.

As Bole entered the huge oak-panelled Kenton Room, all conver-sation stopped. The group of three men and one woman clustered around the large fireplace turned to examine their visitor and their vinegar expressions spoke volumes about how popular Professor Septimus Bole was with President Samuel Williams, his wife and his Chief of Staff, Nathaniel Armstrong. The antipathy was mutual: as far as Bole was concerned, each of them wore an aura of sanctity and moral certitude which he found repulsive. Since Williams had managed to tear the White House from the tenacious grip of the Kenton clan – and they could thank the impact of the 12/12 atrocity for that – he and his minions had come to view themselves as the bringers of hope and salvation to the people of America. These misguided fools had dedicated themselves to making the USA a fairer and a less divided land, where the strong protected the weak and everyone was ready to stretch out a helping hand. They wore their political piety like haloes, but Septimus Bole knew of only one word which adequately encapsulated his feelings towards such asinine aspirations. Twaddle!

For a second or two, Bole stood looking silently at the President, who in turn stood staring silently back. In Bole's opinion, the President looked like a dyspeptic solicitor, his weakness signalled by the ridiculous way he was clinging to the hand of his wife, Mary, an excessively thin and habitually depressed individual much given to hysterics. She was dwarfed by the figure standing protectively behind her: the hugely fat and hugely obnoxious Nathaniel Armstrong.

It was the President who broke the ice. 'Ah, Professor Bole, so good of you to attend us.' He crossed the room to shake the Professor's hand, which Bole extended with the greatest of reluctance. Touching Fragiles was something he found utterly distasteful; despite their love of perfume and cologne, they stank abominably. 'I believe you know my other guests.' Mary Williams and Nathaniel Armstrong nodded a begrudging greeting. Bole was indifferent to their lack of politeness; he was simply relieved he didn't have to shake their hands, too. 'If you would take a seat, Professor.' The President gestured towards the single empty chair on one side of the long, narrow boardroom table, facing the row of three chairs which the other attendees were obviously intent on occupying. This layout suggested it would be a very confrontational meeting, with Bole on one side of the table and his inquisitors on the other.

*Excellent.*

*

Once everyone was settled, the President began. 'As you know, Professor Bole, my daughter was returned to us two weeks ago, after her unfortunate sojourn in the Demi-Monde. During this time, Norma has undergone a full-spectrum medical evaluation at the Walter Reed Hospital, and the doctors there are satisfied that physically she is in remarkably good shape.'

'I am delighted to hear it.' Bole smiled at the President.

'However, although Norma is *physically* fine, she does seem to be suffering from some kind of post-traumatic stress disorder.'

'And how does this manifest itself?'

'In profound amnesia.'

Bole shrugged. 'This isn't unusual, Mr President. Our experience with neoFights returning from the Demi-Monde is that almost 30 per cent suffer from some form of amnesia. They find the rather visceral ambience of that world somewhat overwhelming, and their minds adopt a defensive posture, shutting out those memories that are found most distasteful. In most cases, this memory degradation is merely a temporary phenomenon.'

'This isn't a "memory degradation", Professor,' Mary Williams protested. 'Norma can't remember *anything*. She doesn't remember her friends or family. She's got no memory of the White House or her school. She can't even remember her *dog*.' The First Lady paused to dab a tear from her eye. 'Even her accent has changed. If I didn't know better, I'd say that she wasn't the same girl.'

Bole tried to imitate sympathy. 'This does seem rather profound.'

The President took his wife's hand in his and gave it a comforting squeeze. 'As you might imagine, Professor, this has been a very trying time for my family. And with you being the expert on the Demi-Monde, I've invited you here today in the hope that you might be able to help Norma.'

Bole sighed and spread his hands to indicate his helplessness. 'It is standard operating procedure that all neoFights back up their pre-deployment memories using PINC technology.'

There was a gasp from the First Lady. 'But aren't PINCs illegal in the USA?'

'They are,' said Bole airily, 'but for the US military to utilise the Demi-Monde, their use is essential.'

The President shuffled uneasily in his chair. 'I gave permission for their use.' He looked nervously at his wife. 'That's classified information, Mary, and not for dissemination outside this room.'

Mary Williams looked decidedly unhappy about this piece of news, which didn't surprise Bole. The majority of Americans, conditioned by sixty years of Kentonesque religious propaganda, believed PINC to be the Mark of the Beast, citing Revelation 13: 16-18, that the Antichrist, before the Day of Revelation, would persuade everyone, small and great, rich and poor, free and slave, to receive a mark on his forehead, so that no one could buy or sell unless he had the Mark of the Beast. And as most Americans thought ABBA was the Beast, then the First Lady's trepidation was understandable . . . ridiculous, but understandable.

'In cases of post-traumatic-stress-induced amnesia,' continued Bole, 'we use these to kick-start memory deficits. It's a technique that has proven most successful in cases similar to that of your daughter. However, as Norma entered the Demi-Monde by an unconventional route, we have no such PINC data on file.'

'Yeah, how did she do that?' snapped Nathaniel Armstrong. 'How did Norma ever get into that cyber-cesspit of yours, Professor?'

'I really have no idea.'

'Well, I think you should have. It's because of this goddamned ABBA thing of yours that the President's daughter is now in the state she is.'

Bole refused to be perturbed by the President's pit bull. In his opinion, the man had the intellectual capacity of a salad. 'As a politician, Mr Armstrong, you have a natural inclination to leap to conclusions, therefore I shall ignore your somewhat emotional outburst. For your information, ABBA is merely a machine – a particularly capable machine, admittedly – but like all machines, whenever it malfunctions this is invariably a consequence of human error or human mischievousness.'

Armstrong glowered at Bole. 'Yeah, and I think I've a pretty good idea as to which human made the error.'

'Gentlemen, please,' interjected the President, 'I'm not interested in the why or the what. All I'm interested in doing is helping my daughter. So the question, Professor Bole, is can you do anything to help repair Norma's memory?'

'Possibly.'

The face of the First Lady brightened.

'Since the signing of the Anglo-American Accord on the control of political delinquents, the US has adopted ParaDigm's PanOptika program to monitor its citizens. PanOptika – platformed as it is on ABBA – allows the agglomeration of the data collected by *all* surveillance devices in the US, and intermeshes them with the results secured by the use of ParaDigm's BaQTraQ data-mining package.'

Bole paused for a moment to allow his audience's sluggish brains to assimilate this information. 'As a consequence, the US government has full-scope information regarding all actions and movements made by each and every one of its citizens, plus records of all their conversations, and detailed analysis of their physical and emotional characteristics, personality traits and predilections. We thus have available a full 360-degree cyber-portrait of every man, woman and child in the country, including, Mr President, your daughter.'

'Whilst this is all very interesting, Professor—'

Bole ignored Armstrong. He hated to be interrupted by lesser intellects, which, of course, meant that he hated to be interrupted by *anybody*. 'Anticipating the thrust of this meeting, Mr President, I had ABBA consolidate all the available data regarding your daughter. We are fortunate that a sizeable proportion of her life has been experienced post the adoption of the PanOptika System by the US in 2014, and as a result, ABBA has access to all the surveillance data gathered at her school, in her classrooms, in her dormitories and during her time living in the White House. These data have been supplemented by cross-referencing the data streams emanating from her friends and family. ABBA is now in a position to create a faux-memory for your daughter comprising 77.3 per cent of all her recent life experiences. This will allow her to function quite normally until her biological memories reappear and usurp the ABBA-contrived ones.'

'But surely this faux-memory won't be able to ape the real thing,' the President said. 'There'll still be gaps, won't there?'

'You are quite correct, Mr President. It is to be regretted that those misguided politicians drafting the US Patriot Protection Act believed it essential that individuals were granted some space wherein they could be guaranteed freedom from surveillance. This they christened the "Domestic Curtilage". Actions and activities taking place within this Domestic Curtilage were deemed to be off-limits to PanOptika scrutiny. Because of this oversight, we have no data regarding what Norma did in washrooms or toilets or in her bedroom.' Bole shook his head dolefully to signal his disappointment with regard to the excessively liberal attitude of US lawmakers.

'Then this faux-memory *will* have holes in it,' persisted an anxious President.

'None which are meaningful, since ABBA will fabricate – to a high degree of accuracy – what might have happened during these time gaps.' Bole took up the glass of water that had been set before him by a steward, examined it carefully, then put it aside. Bole was fastidious regarding cleanliness, which obviously the presidential staff were not. 'Indeed, in terms of clarity of recall, Norma's faux-memory will in many ways be better than the real thing.'

'Will this procedure . . . will this introduction of a faux-memory be painful?' asked the First Lady.

Bole shook his head. 'Not in the slightest. All the data are contained on a PINC which is designed to adhere painlessly to your daughter's brain. I have it here with me.'

'Is it safe?'

'Totally.'

'That's what you said about the Demi-Monde,' sneered Nathaniel Armstrong.

It took Bole a moment to quell his irritation. 'I made no such claim. The Demi-Monde was never *meant* to be safe, Mr Armstrong. Nothing so challenging could ever be safe. "Safe" is a chimera sought by an effete society which has become increasingly passive and risk-averse. Everything has an element of risk, the trick is to balance the risk with the benefits and this is what the US military did with regard to the Demi-Monde: they judged the benefits in the shape of improved operational effectiveness of neoFights in Asymmetrical Warfare Environments outweighed the impact the Demi-Monde might have on a player's psyche.'

Armstrong obviously wasn't impressed. 'Well, that don't matter a hoot. We're gonna be shutting the Demi-Monde down.'

Bole took a deep breath. It was vital that the Demi-Monde wasn't shut down.

'Impossible,' he sneered. 'Do that and Ella Thomas and the other Real Worlders held captive in the Demi-Monde will be reduced to a vegetative state. And,' he added slyly, 'you, Mr President, should appreciate that shutting down the Demi-Monde will mean that I am unable to guarantee the effective functioning of your daughter's faux-memory. Destroy the Demi-Monde, Mr President, and this could lead to the traumatic and irreversible destruction of your daughter's biological memory.'

A gasp from the First Lady.

'You can't threaten the President of the United States,' said Armstrong darkly.

'I do not threaten. I merely inform.'

A silence descended on the room, as those who sat facing Bole cogitated on what he had just said. The President broke the silence. 'There is no question, Professor Bole, of the Demi-Monde project being terminated. Now, regarding my daughter . . .'

Bole was shown to the darkened bedroom Aaliz was occupying, the girl sitting in an armchair by the window – the drapes tightly drawn – looking small, thin and unnaturally pale. When Bole and her mother entered, she glanced towards them in a languid, almost absent-minded fashion.

'Good afternoon, Norma, darling,' crooned the First Lady. 'I've brought Professor Bole here today. He believes he might be able to help you recover your memory.'

'Yes, Mother,' replied the girl in a faraway voice, as she idly pushed her fingers through her thick mane of black-dyed hair.

'I would appreciate it if I was left alone with Norma,' said Bole. 'My experience is that patients respond better to the PINC implant when it is administered on a one-to-one basis.' As the First Lady stiffened in preparation to protest, Bole added, 'You will, of course, be able to watch and hear what happens via the eyeSpies.' He nodded towards the four SurveillanceBots hovering near the ceiling, one in each corner of the room.

'I would much rather stay,' protested the First Lady.

'And I would much rather you didn't,' countered Bole.

'Mother, please, I'll be fine.' Aaliz gave her 'mother' a desperate smile.

It was a decidedly unhappy First Lady who kissed her daughter, gave Bole a venomous look, and finally left the room.

'ABBA,' said Bole, as soon as the door closed behind her, 'suspend all surveillance of this room and substitute counterfeit footage Code 3247ReViewAH.'

The instant the order was given, each of the eyeSpies floated gently back to their perches and their red eyes dimmed to black.

Satisfied they were no longer being watched, Bole turned to the girl and smiled. 'Your room is now fully surveillance-sealed, Miss Williams.'

'My name is Aaliz Heydrich.'

'Not in the Real World.'

The girl was obviously unused to being corrected: all the vagueness left her face and for a moment her eyes sparkled with petulance. 'Very well, Professor,' she said through gritted teeth, 'let it be "Norma Williams". So might *Norma Williams* ask if you have brought blood?'

Bole suppressed a smile. That the girl's desire for blood was so strong was a vindication of the Demi-Monde, after all, one of its aims – its *real* aims – was to resuscitate the latent Grigori gene, MAOA-Covert, present in the Fragiles duplicated in that virtual world. The rigors these Dupes were subjected to there – the extreme stress of permanent war, the perverse leadership of the Dark Charismatics, and their enforced addiction to blood – would make their Grigori gene ripe for awakening in the Real World. If Aaliz Heydrich was typical then the Demi-Monde was going to plan.

With a nod, Bole delved into the inside pocket of his jacket and extracted a small sealed bottle full of crimson liquid. The girl snatched it from his hand, snapped back the stopper and drank down half the contents in a single swig. This done, she slumped back into her chair, closed her eyes and sat for a full two minutes in silent contemplation. 'Chink blood, if I am not mistaken, Professor,' she said finally. 'The donor was young, female and athletic. I can tell this by the bouquet and by the piquant aftertaste. Excellent quality and vintage, though I must confess to having a preference for Medi blood. It is somewhat sweeter with a less tart finish.'

'I will endeavour to find a source.'

'I would be most grateful. And my thanks for your consideration thus far: I feel reinvigorated already. Seventeen days without blood, Professor – I never thought I could survive so long. The temptation to ravage and drain my nurse was almost overwhelming. But I have resisted.'

'Indeed. And now to business, Miss Williams. I have here an implant which will provide you with all the background memories you will need to carry through your subterfuge effectively. If you would lay your head back and open your eyes wide.'

The girl did as she was asked, and Bole took a phial of clear liquid from his case and, using an eye-dropper, placed a single drop into her left eye. 'It will take the PINC contained in the solution only a few seconds to fuse with your brain and for the data it carries to be fully meshed with the rest of your memories. When you review these you will discover that there is one blank area: that relating to how Norma Williams came to be in the Demi-Monde. Rather than concoct a back-story that would be susceptible to challenge, it is better you feign continued amnesia regarding this subject. If you are interrogated on this matter, your lack of recall will be assumed to be caused by psychological trauma associated with the Demi-Monde.'

'Very good,' murmured Aaliz. 'Now, Professor, when we met in the Demi-Monde you intimated that you had a plan as to how I might proceed here in the Real World.'

'My plan is that you – that *Norma Williams* – should undergo something of a spiritual rebirth post-Demi-Monde: a divine revelation akin to that experienced by Paul of Tarsus on the road to Damascus.'

'Yes, I met Paul de Tarsus in NoirVille. He was an unimpressive little man. Everyone thought him quite mad.'

'Well, in the Real World he is revered as a saint, therefore by aping him you will make your volte-face believable. So I suggest you throw over the trappings of a wayward and rebellious teen and embrace Christian fundamentalism. You are experienced in the leading of the ForthRight's RightNixes, so I thought it appropriate that we utilise that expertise here in the Real World. I am intent on introducing you to the Reverend Jim Kenton, who is the foremost evangelist in America and who owns and operates Believers' Broadcasting, the most influential of all the religious broadcasting networks. Your proposition to him will be that you wish to become the head of Kenton's youth league – the Young Believers of America.'

'An excellent idea, Professor, but as I'm the President's daughter, won't Kenton object to my involvement? I understand from PINC that the President and Kenton are somewhat at odds politically.'

'Fortunately, I have some leverage with Kenton in the shape of footage of him engaging in activities that Believers' Broadcasting would consider decidedly inappropriate for a minister . . . they might even think it inappropriate for a veterinarian. To keep this secret, Kenton will do precisely what you tell him to do.' Bole gave Aaliz a broad smile. 'And anyway, how can he refuse you? You'll be the girl who can perform miracles.'

# 12

## Paris
## The Demi-Monde: 13th Day of Spring, 1005

```
TO DR JEZEBEL ETHOBAAL HEAD OF THE JAD INSTITUTE OF
METAPHYSICS PO BOX 11/11 + + + GREETINGS + + + AS U R
THE DEMI-MONDE'S 4MOST EXPERT ON LILITHIAN LORE I HAVE
TAKEN THE LIBERTY OF SENDING BY SEPARATE CONFIDENTIAL
COURIER A COPY OF THE TXT OF EDDIC OF LOCI INSCRIBED ON
MANTLE-ITE COLUMN RECOVERED FROM VENETIAN LAGOON + + +
ALSO OLD FRENCH RENDERING OF SAME + + + I WD B SO BOLD
AS 2 SUGGEST THIS WILL ASSIST IN UNBABELISATION OF THE
FLAGELLUM HOMINUM NO COPY OF WHICH IS EXTANT IN VENICE
+ + + KONDRATIEFF
```

*Copy of PigeonGram message sent by Docteur Nikolai
Kondratieff on 12th day of Spring, 1005*

Her recent run-in with the Quizzies had made Odette more determined than ever to lead her regiment when the UnScreweds
marched on the Bastille. So, once she had found a place to hide
out – her uncle was a very understanding man and had given
her use of his house while he was away on business – she had
made contact with her three lieutenants to tell them to pass the
word that it was business as usual, and that the demonstration
was most certainly still going ahead. After that, it had just been
a question of keeping out of sight and waiting very impatiently
for her chance to give the Quizzies a bloody good kicking.

When the evening of the 13th finally rolled round, Odette had been so eager to begin that she and her three friends – Adélaide the plump shoe-maker, Sabine the rather obstreperous flower girl, and the ever-popular Sophie who sang and performed in the Maison d'Illusion – found themselves early for the demonstration. And being early presented them with a problem: the orders from the UnScrewed Committee were that demonstrators should gather in front of the Bastille at nine sharp, and that under no circumstances should they arrive before then. The concern of the Committee was that any early birds would alert the GrandHarms standing guard on the Bastille that something was going down.

Odette found the naïveté of the women who made up the Committee simply breathtaking. For them to imagine that they could organise a demonstration, involving several thousand women, without the GrandHarms and the Quizzies getting wind of it showed a removal from reality which smacked of middle-class arrogance. As far as she was concerned, it was a racing certainty that the Quizzies knew the UnScreweds were coming, so she had made damned sure that she and her regiment would come properly prepared. If it all ended in a tussle, Odette and her market girls would give as good as they got.

But the problem remained that Odette and her three comrades *were* early for the demonstration and, with each of them togged up as Liberté, it was a centime to a franc that walking around Paris *tits al fresco* they would be spotted as being UnScreweds, and arrested by the Quizzies. So, having half an hour or so to kill, Odette had readily agreed to Adélaide's suggestion that they stop off en route to enjoy a bracing glass of Solution. Unfortunately, the bar Adélaide chose was not one of their regular haunts and even as the four girls pushed their way inside, Odette sensed that it might not be a particularly welcoming one. She had the uncomfortable feeling that things might be scheduled to kick off a little earlier than the Committee had intended.

*

Since his illicit entry into the Quartier, Rivets had fallen into the habit of having his supper in a bar just off the 4th arrondissement. It was a nondescript sort of place but being popular with the non-Medis living in Paris meant that Rivets didn't look quite so out of place. And as Burlesque had warned that the Inquisition were now, in all probability, on the lookout for him, he was grateful for any anonymity the city could offer. Anyway, it was a better class of pub than those he usually frequented back home in Stepney, with the sawdust on the floor being changed once a week whether it needed changing or not. It even had an outside lavvy.

Yeah, it was a good bar and Rivets found he liked mixing with the tradesmen and small-business types who constituted the evening clientele. At least they didn't take the piss out of him when he pulled his book out and read for the ten minutes or so it took him to scoff his pasty and down his pint. Not like the chancers and hooligans who drank in the dens around Stepney. Those bastards ragged him something fierce about his liking for a good read.

Rivets enjoyed reading. Since Vanka had employed a teacher to school him for two hours a day in his letters, Rivets had discovered he possessed a real hunger for a good story. He was currently devouring *Gregory the Grigori*, which, he freely admitted, was succeeding in scaring the shit out of him. He was so lost in the novel that he failed to notice the man approaching his table. Fortunately for him, his visitor was a friend.

''Ello, Rivets, 'ow you 'anging?'

Rivets looked up and studied the very big and very florid-faced man who was addressing him. It took a moment for Rivets to identify him as Burlesque Bandstand, the red leather half-mask and the new beard combining to provide a very effective disguise.

'Stone me, Burlesque, you gave me a start. I thought you'd scarpered back to the Smoke, or sumfink.'

Burlesque raised a finger to his lips. 'Keep yer voice darn. Remember we're 'ere on the QT.' With that, Burlesque pulled up a chair and sat down as close to Rivets as decency permitted.

To Rivets's astonishment, Burlesque smelt almost fresh. The aroma of smoke, soot and shit that perfumed everyone in London was gone and, worse, Burlesque's new-found cleanliness was augmented by a floral fragrance.

'Gor, Burlesque, you look Sunday-fied an' then some. An' you pong a bit flowery, as well. You ain't gone light on your loafers, 'ave you, Burlesque? You ain't turned zadnik, 'ave you?'

Burlesque blushed. 'Nah, I 'ad a wash.'

'A wash?' gasped Rivets. 'Blimey, Burlesque, that ain't natural. You wanna be careful lessen you wash away all your skin's goodness. Yer 'air might drop art, or sumfink.'

Burlesque nodded in disconsolate agreement. 'That's wot I fink, but there ain't no tellin' these Frogs. They're always washin' themselves. Got so I 'ad to 'ave a bath and buy some fresh linen, ovverwise they'd 'ave spotted me for an Anglo, sure as eggs is eggs.'

With a shake of his head, Rivets communicated his sympathy with Burlesque's plight. 'Any'ow, you look well, Burlesque, and I like the Charlie.' He gestured towards Burlesque's incipient goatee. 'Makes you look distinguished. Is it meant to be a disguise from the Peelers?'

Burlesque nodded, as he fingered the first sproutings of a beard that decorated his chin and upper lip. 'Yeah, I reckon by now Beria'll 'ave 'is cryptos out an' about in the Quartier, looking for me. I did 'im a bad turn, and Beria ain't the sort ov rotten bastard to let a bad turn go unpunished.'

'You fancy a swill?' asked Rivets, waving to the barmaid to order two more glasses of Solution even before Burlesque could reply. He poked a finger towards the meat pie he'd been chewing on. 'I'd offer you a chonkey, but they're a bit iffy. Full o' mystery meat, though I've an inkling it went "meow" when it was in the land ov the living.'

Once the drinks were served, Rivets was prompted to ask the question that had been worrying him ever since he'd arrived in Paris. 'So wot's to do, Burlesque? We can't hang around 'ere in Frogland for the rest of our naturals. You 'eard anyfink about Vanka? 'E owes me a wonderment ov money 'e does.'

'Word is that Miss Ella, that snotty cow Norma Williams and Wanker 'ave bin banged up in the Bastille.'

'Then they're fucked, Burlesque. Bollocks, bang goes me inheritance.'

Burlesque gave a nod of understanding. 'Yeah, there ain't nuffink we can do for them now, so I wos thinking ov taking Miss Ella's advice an' headin' for Venice. I might start up a bar or sumfink there. I lost everyfink when Beria arrested me, but I ain't on me uppers. I've got a nest egg tucked away in Venice from a job I did for Wanker that'll set me up a treat.' He took a long sip of his Solution and winced. 'Fucking hell, this Frog Solution's crook. It tastes like rat's piss.'

'Yeah, they don't make it wiv vodka like proper Solution. They make it wiv stuff called absinthe.'

'*Absence*? Good name for it, iffn you ask me, given there's fuck all alcohol in it.'

The pair of them were quiet for a moment as they contemplated the horrors of Frog Solution. It was Rivets who broke the silence. 'You mind iffn I come along wiv you to Venice, Burlesque? I don't fancy staying 'ere livin' wiv the snail-eaters, an' it's a bit lonely all on me ownsome.'

There was no reply, and when Rivets looked up he saw that all of Burlesque's attention was focused on four large girls in funny hats and very revealing frocks who had just entered the bar.

'Gor,' said Burlesque quietly, in an awestruck tone of voice, 'will you look at the charms on that one.'

'Crikey,' added an astonished Rivets, as he studied the girls, 'they've 'ardly got any clobber on at all.'

'I'll say this for these French birds,' said Burlesque, his gaze never leaving the very big girl with the long brown hair, who was parading around with one of her breasts bared, 'they really know 'ow to dress. You'd never get wun of them Rookerie tarts wiv 'alf as much *dunno-say-qua* as they 'ave.'

'Dunno say what?' queried Rivets.

'It's Frog for "fuckability",' explained Burlesque. 'You know I might even be inclined to chance me arm wiv that tall wun – the wun wiv the *really* big jugs. I've always 'ad a weakness for birds I 'ad to look up to.'

'You can't do that,' protested Rivets. 'You're married.'

'Nah, I ain't. Cow divorced me, didn't she, after I got banged up by the Checkya. Seems iffn you're classified as an Enemy ov the ForthRight, it's grounds for instant divorce. I fink the cow only did it to get 'er 'ands on the Prancing Pig before Beria's bailiffs moved in.'

Explanation given, and with a wink to Rivets, Burlesque rose to his feet, hitched up his codpiece, sucked in his gut and turned towards the girl who had taken his eye. He wasn't quick enough off the mark. Before he had even started across the floor of the bar, an ugly-looking Frenchman had already sauntered over to the girls' table.

The girls' drinks had only just been served when a man – old, pox-marked, unkempt and with an UnFunDaMentalist badge stuck in the lapel of his soiled jacket – materialised alongside Odette. 'Your kind ain't welcome here,' he said in a voice he must have thought was menacing, but which in reality was almost as unsteady as his stance. The man had obviously shipped a lot of Solution.

Odette eyed him unconcernedly, and the truth was she *wasn't* concerned. She was bigger than this man was, stronger than he was, and a lot more sober than he was. What was more, he probably didn't have his hand curled around a half-kilo steel knuckleduster like the one she had hidden in the pocket of her cloak.

'Why's that, CitiZen?' Odette asked equitably.

''Cos yous all ImPuritan whores, that's why,' slurred the man. ''Cos it ain't natural for women to flaunt themselves in public, and display their bits for men who ain't their husbands.'

'Bollocks, CitiZen,' Odette said with a smile. 'The Charter of Responsibilities says that CitiZens of the Quartier Chaud are permitted to seek JuiceSense by engaging in sexual pleasure – of whatever description – free from abuse, violence or coercion. It also says, CitiZen,' and here Odette's voice took on a harder edge, 'that it is the responsibility of all CitiZens to refrain from censuring, curtailing, impeding or compromising another's sexual pleasure, except when such sexual pleasure mitigates their own. And I think that's what you're doing, CitiZen, censuring me.' She smiled again. 'So why don't you just fuck off while you're still capable of fucking off?'

That comment persuaded the man to shuffle on his feet, as he tried to make himself look bigger and more dangerous. Odette thought it made him look ridiculous, but her grip on the knuckleduster tightened, anyway.

'You can't talk to me like that. I'm a bloke and women 'ave got to *heed* blokes. That's wot UnFunDaMentalism says.'

'I'm not an UnFunDaMentalist, I'm an ImPuritan.'

'ImPuritanism's crap, that's wot it is.'

Despite her feeling that this conversation would inevitably end in fisticuffs, Odette did her best to carry on in the same careless manner. It was mildly amusing, and anyway she had nothing better to do with her time. 'You're wrong, CitiZen. ImPuritanism's the best thing that ever happened to the

Quartier Chaud. For five hundred years ImPuritanism has kept MALEvolence in check, and has brought peace, happiness and wealth to the Quartier Chaud. And why did this happen? Because the Quartier Chaud has been run by women, that's why, and women's inclination to violence is considerably weaker than men's. Women are more peaceable than men, CitiZen. Now fuck off before I thump you.'

'It's not right. Women should do what men tell 'em. And mark my words, when Robespierre brings UnFunDaMentalism to the Quartier, scrubbers like you are in for a real shock.' He made a grab for Odette's exposed breast, but she knocked his hand away. 'Then you women are gonna know what your proper place is. Feeding, breeding, and menfolk-heeding.'

Odette sensed that the man was fast running out of control, and that it would be necessary to deck him. But just as she was hauling herself up onto her feet, she became aware that another man had come to stand by her table.

'Est-ce que cet homme est un pain-dans-le-arse, Mademoiselle? Desirez-vous que je put un sur son?'

If the interloper had been a Quartier Chaudian, Odette would have berated him for being a patronising, chauvinistic bastard and told him to fuck off. But he wasn't. As best Odette could tell from his garbled French, the newcomer was an Anglo. Not, admittedly, a very prepossessing Anglo: he was quite fat, had horrible teeth, and his bruised and battered face made him look like he'd been in a recent altercation with a steamer. But unusually for an Anglo, he smelt almost clean. He was also – and this Odette would never share with her friends on the grounds that they would quite rightly take the piss out of her – being gallant. And gallantry *was* an old-fashioned, even an obsolete concept.

The protocol associated with gender equality in the Quartier Chaud meant that it was considered impolite for a man to come to the aid of a woman. But despite Odette's espousal of ImPuritanism and its teachings, she had to admit that it was quite refreshing to meet a man who still seemed beholden to the concepts of knightly love so wonderfully described in the penny-dreadful romances she was addicted to. In this regard the fat Anglo was a real throwback. In fact, judging by the slope of his forehead, Odette suspected that he must have been thrown back to the dawn of time. She made a quick check to see that his knuckles were actually clear of the floor.

Yes, much as she hated to admit it, such a show of chivalry made her feel almost girly. She had never been treated as a damsel in distress before, and she was enjoying it. Ignoring the giggles coming from her friends, she smiled sweetly at the chivalrous Anglo and decided to let love take its course.

What had prompted him to go to the girl's rescue, Burlesque wasn't sure. He had never been much of a romantic – actually, he had never been a romantic at all – so he couldn't for the life of him decide what had inspired him to play the knight errant and walk over to the girl's table to enquire if she needed his assistance.

Whether she did or did not have need of his assistance swiftly became academic, as the Frog who had been berating her now turned his ire upon Burlesque.

'*Va te faire foutre, sale Anglo de merde*,' ('Fuck off, you piece of Anglo dogshit') the man snarled at Burlesque, and though the latter didn't fully understand all the man had said, he understood enough to know that he wasn't being particularly friendly. He didn't like the shove on the shoulder the Frog had given him, either.

Fuck offez vous aussi, Mon-sewer le Frog. Par-ce que, iffn vous doesn't, je will smackez vous sur votre tête très fort. Capiche?'

The man's brow furrowed as he disentangled Burlesque's strange patois. Once he had, he drew a large and very businesslike knife from the back of his belt and brandished it in Burlesque's direction. Immediately there was a scraping of chairs as the bar's patrons politely moved back to afford the combatants more room.

Burlesque sighed. The last thing he wanted was to get involved in a fight, because fights attracted attention. But with this Frog tart looking on, Burlesque was buggered if he'd back down. He'd come over here to defend her honour – though, looking at how she was dressed, he didn't suppose there was much honour left to defend – and defend it he would.

Although he had his Webley holstered beneath his coat, Burlesque decided that he'd use something a little more subtle and a little quieter to subdue this truculent Frog. Something that wouldn't bring the Coppers running. And he had the very thing hidden up his sleeve: a length of rubber tubing filled with a pound of lead shot and fashioned into a blackjack. As he shook his arm, the blackjack slid into his hand, and he used said blackjack to planish the Frog's head. The Frog, quite under-standably, sank to the floor with nary a peep of complaint.

To Burlesque's delight, the girl proceeded to boot the man in the nuts. Here was a woman after his own heart!

Odette was impressed. This funny Anglo had dispensed with the drunk very, very efficiently. He must, she decided, have had a lot of experience in running bars, where, as she understood it, the philosophy for maintaining an orderly house was to hit miscreants just once, but to hit them first and to hit them so hard that they ceased being a problem.

Certainly the Anglo was physically . . . well, odd. Odette toyed with the word 'repellent' for a moment, before deciding that that was a little *too* harsh. But he obviously liked her and, as her success with men of late had been dismal, she decided that she would be accommodating. She gave the man an encouraging smile and a jiggle of her bare breast.

'Je suis Burlesque Bandstand,' said the man after being suitably encouraged. He then made a rather flamboyant bow.

'*Vous êtes très galant, Monsieur. Je suis Mademoiselle Odette Aroca.*' ('You are very chivalrous, Monsieur. I am Mademoiselle Odette Aroca.') She held out her hand, and allowed the Anglo to plant an excessively damp kiss on it. '*Et, Monsieur, des sentiments si délicats et une inclination si noble méritent une récompense.*' ('And, Monsieur, such delicacy of feeling and noble inclination deserves a reward.') Odette had to boot Sabine under the table to stop the silly girl's tittering. This done, she delved into her pocket, extracted a piece of paper, wrote down her address and then handed it to the Anglo. '*Je serais ravie de vous recevoir à toute heure.*' ('I would be pleased to have you call on me at any time.') Then she stood up and enveloped the Anglo in a huge hug, and such was the disparity in their heights that the man's face found its way quite wonderfully between her breasts. Amazingly, the silly Anglo blushed.

Burlesque watched entranced as the vision that was Odette Aroca left the bar, this magnificent piece of Frog womanhood blowing him a kiss as she went. His body clock went pit-a-pat, and for the first time in his sordid life he understood what it was like to be in love. He was so smitten that when, an hour later, he and Rivets rose, a little worse for Solution, to leave the bar to journey to Rivets's lodgings, his instinct for self-preservation – usually so acute – almost failed him. But even pissed, even with his mind befuddled by thoughts of the marvellous Odette, Burlesque was still sharp enough to spot an old chum of his, Maurice Merriment, sitting in a shadowed corner of the bar.

And as he stepped out into the night air, Burlesque suddenly found himself stone-cold sober. The prospect of being knifed in the back always had that effect on him.

# 13

## The Convent of the Sacred and
## All-Seeing Order of Visual Virgins: Paris
## The Demi-Monde: 13th Day of Spring, 1005

Auralism is the ability to perceive and to 'read' the multi-coloured halo that surrounds a Demi-Mondian's body. It is believed that auras are associated with radiations emanating from the soul which suffuses a Demi-Mondian's Solidified Astral Ether. Careful examination has confirmed that each aura is distinct and unique, and in the Quartier Chaud, where the wearing of masks is de rigueur, aural analysis is the only certain way in which individuals may be identified.

**Seeing Is Believing: Auralism and Its Role in Preserving ImPuritanism**: *Sister Florence, Venetian Books*

'Sister? Sister Florence? Art thou rousèd?'

Florence felt a hand on her shoulder as Sister Bella desperately tried to shake her from sleep. She heard the urgency – the incipient panic more like – in the Sister's voice, but she refused to signal that she was already awake. Using all her considerable self-control, Florence continued to feign sleep, lying unmoving on her cot, determined to keep her eyes tightly closed until she was satisfied that all her powers – mental, physical and, most importantly, metaphysical – were fully under her control before she rejoined the wakeful.

In a world beset by turmoil, in a world gripped by evil, in a world where the slightest error could lead to the triumph of UnFunDaMentalism, it was vital that she was always fully composed, always prepared, always on her guard. Whilst ABBA might be all-merciful and willing to forgive transgressions, the Inquisition under Tomas de Torquemada most certainly was not.

Satisfied that she was now in a sufficiently sanguine frame of mind to face whatever alarms were troubling Sister Bella, Florence slowly opened her eyes.

'Sister, I beseech thee, make all haste,' Sister Bella whispered, trying to keep her excitement under control, and not to wake any of the other Visuals sleeping in the dormitory. 'Thou art to attend Abbé Niccolò himself. He desires to have much question with thee.'

*The Abbé Niccolò di Bernardo dei Machiavelli? That means he has found the Lady IMmanual.*

Florence kept her face bland and expressionless, but it was difficult. Machiavelli was the right-hand man to the Doge, Plenipotentiary Extraordinary of the Venetian Republic, and – whisper it quietly – head of the Venetian secret police, the infamous Signori di Notte. He was also, according to the Convent grapevine, the most cunning, conniving and downright duplicitous bastard in the whole of the Quartier Chaud. Venice was lucky to have him on its side.

'Sister Bella, I prithee but allow me a moment to dress.'

'Verily, I beg thee with all my soul, Sister Florence, that thou should bustle. I am implored to bring thee to the bureau of the Abbé with all convenient speed.'

Florence refused to bustle. Bustle and you were just one short step from panic, and panic was the handmaiden of disaster. Better to proceed cautiously and deliberately; better and safer. She rose from her cot and arched her long, toned body, stretching to rid her muscles of sleep. This done, she selected her most ephemeral habit – it was the Abbé Niccolò she was to attend, after all, and hence it was appropriate that *all* her talents be on display – and slipped it over her nakedness.

'Speak thou, gentle Sister Bella, wilt it be His Excellency the Abbé Niccolò alone I am to attend, or mayhap others are to be in assembly?' It was an important question, and the answer would determine which mask Florence would wear.

'Forgive me, Sister, I am much in error. I was bidden to advise thee that thou alone wouldst be in gracious attorney of His Excellency.'

*Alone? Then dirty work is afoot.*

'I am beholden to thee for thy sage intelligence.' She would wear her simplest and most alluring concealment; Abbé Niccolò warranted nothing less. So decided, she buttoned a white veil to her wimple and let it fall over her face. A veil was perfect for such a clandestine assignation, as it combined mystery with just a hint of the uncanny.

And all the while she dressed, Sister Bella prattled on. 'I am informèd that there thou wilt make most conceal'd study of the Grand Inquisitor himself.'

The Grand Inquisitor, Tomas de Torquemada. Sister Florence knew she would have to take care: the Dark Charismatic hated her above all Visual Virgins.

Sister Bella obviously took Florence's silence for indifference. 'Art thou not much afeared, Sister? My own soul shivers at the very uttering of the Grand Inquisitor's name.'

'Why should I be afeared, Sister?'

'Why, good Sister Florence, because I have seen the cruel proofs of this man's work, how he doth rend and ravage the SAE of those who stand against him in defiance of that most foul and misbegotten creed UnFunDaMentalism. It is said that the Lord Torquemada can look into the soul of a woman and see the darkness and the imprudent desires which dwell there.'

'ABBA does this every moment of my life, Sister Bella, and if I am content to let ABBA do thus, and be not dismayed, then I can have little disquiet regarding the more mechanical enquiries of Lord Torquemada.'

Sister Bella peered at her in the flickering candlelight, obviously searching for connivance. 'Thou must be right wary of thy tongue, Sister Florence. The Lord Torquemada is a man even the most devout would do well not to take lightly. He is ImPuritanism's most fierce and unrelenting foe, and is merciless in his defence of the Deviationist Church and of the non-Sacred Catechisms of UnFunDaMentalism.'

Florence bowed her head to acknowledge her understanding of what Sister Bella said, but the truth was she wasn't frightened of Torquemada; she was *excited* by the prospect of meeting him and besting him. 'Fear not, good Sister, I will heed full well thy sage counsel and will strive to be submissive before both ABBA *and* the Lord Torquemada.'

She took a final glance in the mirror and then undid a button holding the neck of her habit. What did the old adage say? When a woman is intent on seduction she should undo every button she dares . . . and then one more.

Sister Bella led Florence deep into the private wing of the Convent, until she came to a large walnut door flanked by two heavily armed Guardian Angels, who cast a wary eye over the tall, slim figure of Sister Florence. She must have passed muster, as the Angel standing to the right of the entrance rapped twice on the door.

'I must leave thee now, Sister,' said Sister Bella quietly. 'Fare thee well, and may the good angels guard thee from the Inquisitor's annoyance.'

'And may ABBA's grace go with thee, Sister,' intoned Florence as the door opened and a uniformed steward bowed her through into the room beyond.

The Abbé's study was swathed in harsh light, and for a moment Florence had to stand blinking as her sensitive eyes adjusted to the glare.

'Sister Florence?' greeted a voice from behind the lamplight, a voice rich as mahogany and deep with solemnity.

By dipping her head to avoid the dazzling light, Florence was able to see the silhouette of the Abbé Niccolò seated behind a huge desk situated at the end of the room. 'Verily I am Sister Florence, Your Grace, Senior Maiden of the Sacred and All-Seeing Convent of Visual Virgins, and bound by ImPuritan faith and conscience, and by vows of obedience, to do the work of ABBA in fair furtherance of the prosperity and tranquillity of the Holy See of Venice.'

'ABBA bless you, my child. Would you come a little closer?'

Florence did as she was ordered, walking slowly over the white marble floor, all the while practising her skills in the amorous art of fiduciary sex. Like every Visual Virgin, she had been taught to employ her unsurpassed beauty to distract and disarm her prey and to provoke their auras into revealing their innermost secrets. Instinctively Florence shortened her steps so as to make her movement across the room graceful and languorous, announcing that she was a desirable woman – desirable but unattainable.

Visual Virgins never surrendered themselves to men or women; rather they permitted themselves to be conquered by their prey's imagination. And as all Visual Virgins knew, the imagination was the most powerful aphrodisiac of them all, souls being more easily snared by a fantasy than by a net.

As she walked, she saw how the Abbé Niccolò was studying her both assiduously and appreciatively. She stifled a smile of triumph: few men truly appreciated how weak they were, how easily their will could be controlled by a woman.

She came to a halt in front of the desk and for a few silent moments the Abbé and Sister Florence examined one another. The Abbé was wearing a simple leather half-mask, allowing Florence to see that he wore his sixty-nine years lightly. His hair was still black, his teeth even and white, and his skin taut. Outwardly he seemed vital and energetic, but his aura was thin and ephemeral . . . the aura of a man weighed down by worries.

Florence bowed, indicating her submissiveness, feigned submission being a potent element in any seduction.

The Abbé smiled. 'You have served ImPuritanism and the Holy See dutifully and well, Sister Florence. The Doge speaks very highly of you. Your powers as an Auralist, Sister, are of the first rank, and you have proven yourself to be a valuable weapon in the sacred struggle with the enemies of Venice and the disciples of Loki.'

Sister Florence bowed again. 'I thank thee for thy most gracious flattery.'

'But now I have a new and important duty for you, one of great importance in the True Church's battle against the forces of UnFunDaMentalism.'

'I stand ready to serve the True Church in any manner I am able, Your Grace.'

Machiavelli stood up from his desk and moved towards her. 'You have been advised,' he said in a low voice, 'that the Inquisition has taken captive and intends to put to the question the Lady IMmanual, the girl that many claim is the Messiah.'

'Claim?' Sister Florence asked.

'Indeed. She has been brought to the Bastille for interrogation. If this girl *is* the Messiah, then we must do everything in our power to free her from the grasp of Torquemada and his

Inquisitors. But before we act we must know that she is truly the Messiah, and that necessitates the use of your esoteric powers.'

Without waiting for a reply, Machiavelli walked over to a wood-panelled wall, pressed one section, and immediately the panel folded back to reveal a secret passage. 'This gives me entrance to the very centre of the world of the Dark Charismatics, to the very centre of the Bastille. If you would follow me, Sister, I will take you to where you can observe the Lady IMmanual's interrogation by the Grand Inquisitor, and having seen the girl you will be able to pronounce upon the authenticity of her divinity.'

# 14

## The Bastille: Paris
## The Demi-Monde: 13th Day of Spring, 1005

UnFunDaMentalist criticism of ImPuritanism was led by Otto Weininger, who claimed – correctly in my view – that '*the perverse and unnatural philosophy that is called ImPuritanism seeks to transform and corrupt the ABBA-prescribed relationship women have with men*'. Weininger goes on to observe that as women are devoid of any sexual appetites (William Acton, *Dead from the Waist Down, an Objective Assessment of Female Sexuality*), coercing them into performing erotic acts (as ImPuritanism does) compromises their reproductive potential and leads to them being rendered unfit for child-bearing. Moreover, female eroticism presupposes that women are possessed of an independent spirit. This is wrong: as Biological Essentialism teaches us, women are only happy when they are being commanded by men. My own view is that the happiness of man is encapsulated in the words 'I Command'; the happiness of women in the words 'I obey'.

**A Student's Guide to UnFunDaMentalism:** *Father Friedrich Nietzsche, 4thRight Press*

It was Vanka's philosophy always to look on the bright side of life, to find hope in the darkest of moments, but even he had to admit that sitting in a squalid, cold, damp cell set under the eaves of the Bastille, there was precious little to be optimistic about. The one good thing he had going for him – other than that he was still alive – was that his guards were eminently bribable. Frozen and worried about Ella he might be, but he could still find comfort in cigarettes and Solution.

Which was just as well, because Vanka couldn't sleep.

No, that was wrong. It wasn't that he couldn't sleep, rather he preferred not to sleep. Sleep, perchance to dream, and that indeed was the rub. In truth, he was frightened to sleep, frightened of dreaming, and of being lost once more in the mystic, mind-torturing mayhem that was the Dream.

And it was a very persistent dream. Vanka had it every night, with the result that every night he woke in the early hours swathed in sweat and with his head pounding with pain and confusion.

Hateful.

He called it his 'Inside & Outside' dream, where he found himself both inside himself looking out and outside himself looking in. At once he was the omnipotent outsider peering down from on high, observing the scurrying world below him, and simultaneously he was one of the objects of that observation, his every act scrutinised and assessed. Lost in his dream, he was both player and audience, fused in an impossible, mind-twisting duality. The impossible made real.

It was a strange and very, very disconcerting experience. Disconcerting because he had begun to wonder if he was suffering from the condition the JAD-based philosopher-scientist Eugen Bleuler called schizophrenia. Could it be, he wondered, that the troubles and the stresses he had endured since he had met Ella had finally – and understandably – driven him to madness? Could it be that he, Vanka Maykov, was now the proud possessor of a split mind, that he was beset by dementia praecox? It was a plausible explanation . . . too bloody plausible for comfort.

Every night two differing personalities, the macro and the micro, struggled for mastery of his mind, the pair only managing to occupy that single space by a sleight of hand that enabled them to avoid decoherence.

He paused in the act of bringing the cigarette he was enjoying to his lips. His hand shook.

*Decoherence?*

Where had that peculiarity sprung from? What in the Demi-Monde was *decoherence*?

He took a swig of Solution to try to calm himself.

Maybe this was the first sign of a crumbling personality, the conjuring from nothingness of whimsical words? Madness signalled by a lunatic lexicon. Maybe he *was* in the first stages of schizophrenia?

Somehow though he doubted it. Apart from this aberration of vocabulary, he still seemed reassuringly sane . . . well, as sane as anyone was in the Demi-Monde. He had experienced no daytime hallucinations, no dives into delirium and he was still as lucid and glib-tongued as ever.

But if incipient schizophrenia wasn't the explanation, what was? Could his dreams be the consequence of too enthusiastic a liking for Solution? Was he on the downward slope to becoming a slave to dipsomania? It was a plausible answer: his consumption had risen prodigiously since he had met Ella.

Ella . . .

Now *that* was a thought that brought him up short.

Yes . . . the uncomfortable fact was that his dreams had begun when he had met Ella. Maybe she'd disturbed the balance of his mind. He gave a wry laugh: if ever there was a girl made to disturb a man's mental faculties it was Ella Thomas. She was the most beautiful girl he had ever met, but more, her physical beauty was matched by the perfection of her soul. She was a *good* person who had persuaded him to abandon his usual suspicions about his fellow Demi-Mondians and rather than standing aloof and cynical – as was his wont – to become *involved* in their sordid affairs. It was because of her that he had worked to help the people of Warsaw and she was the reason why he had consented – much against his better judgement and his instinct for self-preservation – to help rescue Norma Williams from Crowley's grasp. And he had done this because he loved her.

*Loved her . . .*

Another wry chuckle.

Until he had met Ella, love was something he had never experienced and had never wanted to experience. Just a few short months ago he would have laughed at the very idea of him treating a woman as anything other than a pleasant – and very temporary – diversion. But Ella had changed him. She had made the normally cocksure Vanka Maykov unsure and uncertain. Now he felt oddly vulnerable. His decidedly cynical and arm's-length attitude to life had been disrupted.

And it was probably this disruption that was the root cause of his sleepless nights and his bizarre dreams. He loved Ella and he was tortured by the thought of losing her.

He just hoped she was safe. The distressing thought that she might *not* be safe persuaded him to recharge his glass.

What Ella had done, he mused, as he poured himself a generously over-large slug of Solution, was oblige him to stop being an inveterate observer of life in the Demi-Monde and *engage*. He had always prided himself on being the cat who walked by himself, a man with no friends and no lovers . . . just women who enthusiastically satisfied certain lusts he was bedevilled with. Throughout his life – what little he remembered of it – he had steadfastly refused to depend upon anyone and in turn had always been very keen to point out that it was foolish for anyone to rely on him. He was a bystander, mildly amused by the foibles of that peculiar species known as HumanKind.

Love had changed everything.

Despite being locked up in a filthy prison cell, for the first time since she had entered the Demi-Monde, Norma was at peace with herself. This new sanguinity was, she supposed, due to the realisation that now there would be no escape through the portal in NoirVille. Now that Aaliz Heydrich had commandeered her body in the Real World, she had no route home. Now the Demi-Monde was her home. It was a sobering thought that, after weeks of running for her life, she had finally come to terms with the place. Sure, she had had a pretty tough time, and her current situation, locked up in a grim prison cell in the Bastille, wasn't terribly encouraging, but she was still alive and *that* was the important thing. She had survived all that the Demi-Monde could throw at her, and by surviving she still had hope . . .

Hope, but hope for *what*? The answer that came to her was surprisingly simple: hope for change. Hope that the Demi-Monde might be changed from being the frenziedly evil place it was to a world that was at peace with itself. That was the conclusion she'd arrived at after the ten days of enforced meditation she'd endured in the Bastille: that war was utterly stupid, and that intelligent people like her had an obligation to stop it happening. She might be in the Demi-Monde unwillingly, and becoming one of the Kept might have caused anguish to her mother and father and no end of trouble to other people, but she could at least try to learn from her ordeal and to do something worthwhile with her life.

She remembered the words of Shelley, the poet she'd met when she had first entered the Demi-Monde: 'War is the politician's game, the priest's delight, the lawyer's jest, the hired assassin's trade and now, I have come to understand, ABBA's cruel jape.'

*ABBA's cruel jape . . .*

Romantic lunatic – *dishy* romantic lunatic – though Shelley was, he was more perceptive than he knew. Perceptive but ineffective. Shelley was just an armchair revolutionary, long on talking but short on doing.

She smiled to herself: just like her.

Oh, she'd always wanted to be a politician like her father, always wanted to try to do good things, to make people's lives better, but good intentions were cheap. That was one of her father's favourite sayings: 'If wishes were horses, beggars would ride.' And that was all she'd ever done: she'd wished to be the heroine, and ended up playing the victim. She'd been the victim of Aaliz Heydrich's conniving when she was tricked into entering the Demi-Monde. She'd been the victim of Percy Shelley's treachery when he'd betrayed her to Crowley. She'd been a victim of Fate when she had been washed away in the sewers during her abortive escape from Warsaw. She'd been a victim of Aleister Crowley when he had stolen her body in the Real World. And now, imprisoned in the Bastille, she was destined to be a victim of Tomas de Torquemada.

Always the victim and never the hero. It had to stop.

'Vanka,' she called out, in the direction of the cell to her left, 'are you awake?'

'No,' came the gruff answer.

Norma ignored Vanka's sarcasm. 'Why am I always the victim, Vanka? Why don't I ever get to be the hero?'

A groan from Vanka. 'Because you *act* like a victim. Because you're always bemoaning your fate but never trying to *change* your fate. Because you're never willing to take responsibility for your life and the lives of those around you. Because when you

act like a silly, petulant girl you give up on yourself and everybody gives up on you. And most of all, because you're a
natural-born pain in the arse.'

She ignored the gibe. 'So what is a hero?'

'Oh, come on, Norma, it's late, I've got a fucking great lump
on my head, courtesy of the Quizzies, I'm cold and fed up, and
I'm most certainly not in the mood to answer damn-fool questions.'

'Please, Vanka.'

Silence.

'*Please*, Vanka.' For some reason getting an answer had
become important to her.

'Okay, a hero is an inspiration. A hero persuades people to
rise above themselves, to try to be more than they are. A hero
is a wonderful dream made real. A hero shows people what *they*
could be, if only they had the courage . . . if only they could
be persuaded to get out of bed.'

'But what makes a hero?'

'Courage.'

'What sort of courage?'

'The toughest kind: the courage to stand alone.'

*Alone.* Now that was a word that resonated with Norma. 'Go
on,' she said.

'You see, Norma, it's easy to be courageous when everyone
agrees with you, when you've got the mob at your back, but
when a man or a woman stands alone against the mob for what
they believe in . . . that's *real* courage. There aren't many people
who are able to do that. That's what makes a hero and that's
why I've never met one. I don't think they exist outside the
pages of penny dreadfuls.'

'You're such a cynic, Vanka.'

'Not a cynic, Norma, a realist. Look at the Demi-Monde. If
ever there was a world crying out for a hero it's this one, but

all we get are *ersatz* heroes, and *ersatz* messiahs, who fool the people into believing that they're doing ABBA's work when all they're doing is elbowing their way to the trough.'

Norma sat up a little straighter on her cot. She had never heard Vanka sound so impassioned before. 'So what's the solution?' she asked.

'I don't have one, Norma, and I'm no hero. I oppose war and violence by ignoring them. It'll take a *real* messiah to change things.'

Norma was just about to challenge Vanka further when she heard a noise coming from outside of the prison. 'Vanka? What's going on out there? Why are all those people shouting?'

Norma was right: there was a lot of noise coming from beyond the walls of the Bastille. With a moan of protest from his bruised body, Vanka decided to check it out, and as the only window was the tiny one set high up on the back wall of his cell, this required him to stand on his bed, the mattress making a horrible squelching noise under his boots as he did so. The window gave out on the front of the prison and Vanka found himself looking down onto a crowded Rue Saint-Antoine. Much to his surprise, there appeared to be some sort of demonstration taking place outside the prison's front gates. He guessed the demonstrators were members of the UnScrewed-Liberation Movement, that is if their placards were any indication. He particularly liked the ones that read 'Liberty, Equality or no Fornification' and 'UnFunDaMentalism: Fuck No!' He also liked it that the demonstrators were women and that all of them were dressed as 'Liberté' with one of their breasts exposed. Vanka had never realised that political dissent could be quite such an erotic experience.

Unfortunately, the GrandHarms who were attempting to dissuade the women from demonstrating weren't being given much of an opportunity to appreciate such a marvellous display of female flesh. There was a Hel of a lot of UnScreweds pushing and shoving against the police cordon, so many that they were threatening to overpower the fifty or so GrandHarms defending the entrance to the Bastille.

Ever the gallant, Vanka was moved to assist the women. He carried his overflowing slop bucket carefully across his cell, and then spent an entertaining few minutes ladling its contents out of the window and onto the heads of the GrandHarms below. He was pleased to note that the ten days he'd spent as a reluctant guest of the Committee of Public Safety hadn't impaired his ability to pour shit on bastards with unfailing accuracy. He did though feel a moment's sympathy for the poor sod who'd looked up at *just* the wrong moment.

But as always, good things didn't last. Just as Vanka was running out of ammunition, he heard the rattle of a key in the lock of his cell door.

In the opinion of Sergeant Henri Aroca, it was the soggy turd landing slap bang in the middle of Captain Lefèvre's face that turned the mood of the demonstration from one of polite confrontation into one which was decidedly more violent. As the captain tried to wipe the shit from his face with his sleeve – which only succeeded in spreading the ordure around – his expression darkened and his eyes flashed.

'Draw batons! Drive these bitches back!' the enraged captain screamed, and his men dutifully, if reluctantly, did as they were ordered.

Henri quickly decided that this was a mistake. Up until then it had been the rather upper-class women who had so respectfully delivered the petition demanding the release of Jeanne Deroin and Aliénor d'Aquitaine, who had been in control of the mob of women pushing so ineffectually against the line of

GrandHarms protecting the gates of the Bastille. But as soon as the first baton crashed down onto the unprotected head of one of the women, everything changed. Enraged, a knot of UnScreweds hurled themselves at the GrandHarms, using their placards as spears and clubs. It was obvious that these were protesters who didn't spend their time discussing the rarefied nuances of ImPuritan dialectics in the fashionable salons of the Latin Quarter, or reciting the latest lyrical polemic fashioned by a popular troubadour. No, these were working women, who knew how to handle themselves, *and* their fists and their boots.

Such was the ferocity of the attack, led by a particularly vicious cow who looked worryingly like Henri's daughter Odette, that the line of GrandHarms buckled and then stepped back. That was a fatal mistake. There must have been a couple of thousand UnScreweds gathered for the demonstration, and as the GrandHarms retreated the unspoken message radiated out through the crowd of women that victory was theirs. In an instant the demonstrators became an incensed mob, the sheer press of bodies unsustainable. The GrandHarms began to look urgently around for somewhere to run to.

'Stand! Stand!' screamed their shit-faced captain, but then he was felled by a particularly savage blow from a placard – Henri was *sure* it was Odette who had wielded the placard: he felt quite proud – and the GrandHarms' resistance crumbled.

As he held on to the throat of one hellcat who was trying to claw his eyes out, whilst simultaneously defending himself from the blows raining down on his head from another harridan wielding a broken broom handle, Henri realised the game was up. They had to get back into the safety of the Bastille and, with the captain lying broken and busted on the cobbles, Sergeant Henri Aroca was now in charge.

'Back!' he shouted to his men. 'Hold the line and gradually step back.'

'Belay that,' came a rasping order from behind Henri, and out through the Bastille's gates swept a squad of heavily armed and very resolute-looking Quizzies.

Hauled out of her cell, Norma was not a little unnerved by how events were unfolding. She found herself being fitted with manacles, shoved along dark corridors, and then, finally, being pushed unceremoniously into an enormous hall where shadows from burning tapers skittered eerily around the walls. It was bitterly cold in the hall, and she shivered under her thin cotton gown. The stench of garlic was so unbelievably strong in the hall that it took a real effort not to retch: the Quartier Chaudians seamed obsessed with the stuff.

But distracted though she was, she ordered herself to stay alert; she had a sneaking suspicion that, as always in the Demi-Monde, she'd need all her wits about her. The one thing that raised her spirits was the sight of Vanka standing to one side of the hall, guarded by two Quizzies. He might be looking a little worse for wear, but if the wink he gave her was any indi-cation, he was in good spirits.

As her eyes became used to the gloom, Norma realised she was standing facing a man seated on a large wooden throne at the far end of the hall. Although he was partially hidden in shadow, there was enough light for Norma to register that he was a thick-set individual with a boxer's face, a broken nose and close-set eyes that peered out at her from behind a leather half-mask. He was dressed in an all-enveloping black cassock and his hair had been razored into a Roman tonsure.

*God, he's ugly!* If ever there was a man in crying need of a make-over, it was this guy.

A Quizzie edged closer to her and whispered in her ear, 'You must kneel before His Excellency the Grand Inquisitor Torquemada, and abase yourself to his power and his majesty.'

*Tomas de Torquemada!*

Reluctantly dropping to her knees, Norma inwardly cursed herself for not taking more of an interest in her history lessons. She trawled through her memory, trying to remember what she could of the PreLived Tomas de Torquemada. It wasn't much: as best she could recall, he was the maniac who, while he had been Inquisitor General in Spain during the fifteenth century, had tormented and tortured the poor souls deemed to have been the enemies of the Church. And she guessed that like all the other Singularities she'd met in the Demi-Monde, he was a thoroughgoing bastard.

As a chained Vanka was brought to kneel beside her, the Quizzie made an announcement in a loud voice. 'These are the two acolytes of the Daemon and sorceress the Lady IMmanual.'

'I have no use for lackeys and lickspittles . . .' snarled Torquemada.

*Fuck you, too.*

'. . . bring the one who calls herself the Lady IMmanual before me.'

The Abbé Niccolò led Sister Florence through a maze of dusty, dark and cobweb-bedecked passages until, at last, he brought her to what appeared to be nothing more than a blank wall. But then, after signalling that she should be silent, the Abbé carefully eased back a tiny hinged flap to reveal a spyhole. He ushered the Sister forward.

Florence pressed her eye to the opening and found herself looking out onto the infamous Great Reception Hall of the Bastille, the room where Torquemada presided over the spiritual life of the Medi. The Grand Inquisitor was there, seated on a throne not five metres away from her.

It was difficult for any Visual Virgin to gaze upon a Dark Charismatic like Torquemada. Their auras were so bent and deformed, and the colours decorating them so unsettling, that they made Auralists feel physically sick. When Dark Charismatics had first been identified by Michel de Nostredame, there had been much speculation as to what they actually were, de Nostredame theorising that these brutal, unfeeling and ambitious individuals were a separate taxon, a separate species to Man.

But after careful – and nauseating – perusal of their auras, Sister Florence had come to a different conclusion. Dark Charismatics, by her understanding, were actually a mongrel race, something malignant was conjoined with their humanity, polluting all that was good inside them. And Tomas de Torquemada, sitting plump and pompous on his throne at the end of the room, was the archetypal Dark Charismatic. His aura spread wide from his body: a writhing, pulsating concoction of Lokic blacks – only Dark Charismatics had black within their auras – and ravaging reds, signalling that here was a man who delighted in torture.

A monster.

Florence's study of Torquemada was interrupted when the great doors of the receiving chamber were slammed open, and two prisoners were pushed towards the Grand Inquisitor and made to kneel before him. Two vagabonds more like: the woman and the man bundled into the Chamber looked as though they had both been in the wars – which, when Florence thought about it, they probably had. But if they were nondescript physically, then metaphysically they were both quite remarkable.

To the Sister's great astonishment, the slim, long-haired man – this had to be the infamous Vanka Maykov, the Lady IMmanual's companion, and, some suggested, her lover – had *no* aura. For a moment Florence thought there must be something amiss with her powers. *Everyone* had an aura; everyone human that is. She rubbed her eye, then looked again, but still there was no aura.

So everyone in the Demi-Monde had an aura *except* Vanka Maykov? She wondered for a moment if Maykov was such a powerful mage that he could suppress his aura, to prevent even adepts like her reading it. Maybe the reports that Vanka Maykov was a *faux*-spiritualist were in error; maybe he was a *real* magus.

Still perplexed, Florence turned her attention to the pale girl kneeling to Maykov's left. Amazingly, while Vanka Maykov had no aura, this girl appeared to have two! Her body was surrounded by a confusion of light which gave the impression that two personalities – two *very* different personalities – were struggling for dominance over her soul. One was clearly evil, while the other was a confused vortex of colours, though gold predominated.

*Most strange. It's almost as if . . .*

*But that's impossible.*

The hall's great doors swung open, and Ella was escorted into the room.

At least Norma assumed it was Ella.

It wasn't just that her wonderful mane of black hair had been shaved off, or that her head was circled by an inch-wide bruise that left Norma uncertain that this was the girl she knew. She had *grown*. She seemed taller, more powerful, and much more imperious. During their time together in Warsaw Norma had come to associate Ella Thomas with understanding and fairness – she was a *good* person – but the way this Ella looked out on the world was almost disdainful: she looked like the type of person who would run right over you if you got in her way. And whereas Torquemada seemed to suck all the warmth and goodness out of the huge room, Ella seemed to emit a chilling certainty.

'You must kneel before His Excellency the Grand Inquisitor Torquemada, and abase yourself before his power and his majesty,' announced the Quizzie.

Ella replied in a strong, firm voice that reverberated around the room. 'The Lady IMmanual kneels before no man or woman. The Lady IMmanual kneels only before ABBA.'

*Bloody hell!*

One of the guards raised his baton and made to strike Ella, but all she did was point a finger straight at Torquemada. 'Have a care, Torquemada, it is the Lady IMmanual with whom you tryst. Visit hurt on me and I will repay you a thousandfold.'

It was easy for Sister Florence to identify the Lady IMmanual. Men like the Abbé Niccolò might doubt the girl's divinity, but for Sister Florence the evidence was there before her eyes. But whereas she had expected the girl reputed to be the Messiah to be swathed in an aura of gold, this girl was surrounded by a halo of the purest silver. Sister Florence blinked, not quite believing what she was seeing. She had never seen a silver aura before; indeed she had never seen a halo so bright before, so bright that it was impossible for her to detect if there were other colours lurking beneath it. The girl's aura spread out almost three feet from her body, which signalled to Florence that she was gazing on someone very special – someone ordained by ABBA to do remarkable things.

*The Messiah!*

Sister Florence felt her legs go weak with excitement. The people of the Demi-Monde had been waiting so long for the Messiah to come and now there she stood, ragged and dirty to be sure, with her head shaved and bruised, but still proud and determined. Yes, it was her: the Messiah who would lead the Demi-Monde through the final Tribulation and to Revelation.

'Is she truly the Messiah?' the Abbé asked, his voice soft and low to avoid being overheard beyond the thin wall separating them from the Great Reception Hall.

'Verily she is. In this matter there can be not the smallest of doubts, Your Grace. The Lady IMmanual is the Messiah.'

Florence felt the Abbé make the sign of Mannez across his chest, and heard him breathe a whispered 'Hallelujah.'

'And what does her aura tell you about her?'

'Only that she is divine, Your Grace,' admitted Florence. 'Her aura is so bright and so intense that her humanity is quite hidden from view beneath it.'

'Then listen carefully, Sister. It's your responsibility to help me to bring the Lady IMmanual – the Messiah – safe to Venice. And believe me, Sister, there has never been a task so important to the salvation of the peoples of the Demi-Monde. We must rescue her from the grip of the Inquisition and to do this we must beard Torquemada in his den.'

So proud and compelling was Ella's voice, as it echoed around the room, that the Quizzie was frozen by indecision, his baton raised motionless above his head. There was silence for a moment as Torquemada sat transfixed, nervously fingering the large silver cross he had hanging round his neck, obviously trying to weigh Ella up, assessing whether her threat had substance.

He must have come to the conclusion that it had. He waved the guard away. 'Very well, wench, thou mayest stand, though it will make thee no benefit. It has come to our ears, not without afflicting us with bitter sorrow, that thou hast announced most plain and straightforward that thou art the Messiah. More, I am close advised that thou didst, through most devious employment of the foulest magic and maleficia, contrive a most unnatural breaching of the Boundary Layer, and thus offer sanctuary to those spawn of Loki, the nuJus. Speak, Shade, art thou the same wench who is most deceitfully puffed by those benighted and malicious nuJus as the Messiah – as the divine saviour sent by Our Lord, ABBA? I ask thee straight: art thou the Messiah?'

Ella seemed to stand a little straighter. The room tensed, waiting on what she would say. Then, 'Yes, I am the Messiah. I am the one sent by ABBA to free the Demi-Monde from the pestilence of Dark Charismatics such as you, Torquemada, and bring purity to the Nine Worlds. I am the one ordained to contest with the Beast in the final battle that is Ragnarok.'

*Jesus, she's flipped.*

As announcements went, it was a real stunner. There were gasps around the room, and several of the UnFunDaMentalist monks gathered there hurriedly made the sign of the Valknut across their chests to ward off evil.

Ella had changed big time! From what Norma had seen outside the Porte Saint-Martin checkpoint, she had been more embarrassed than anything about being called the Messiah, about being worshipped, but here she was proudly admitting that she was ABBA's right-hand woman. It didn't make sense.

'How canst this be?' sneered Torquemada. 'The holy books speak of the Messiah as being a man – a man who would come to us bedecked in a halo of gold, a man whose very holiness would be such that mere mortals might not gaze upon him lest they be blinded by his piety. How canst thou, a dirty, bedraggled Shade girl, claim to be one blessed by ABBA? Recant thy duplicity. Know thou not that all those who would counterfeit divinity and claim falsely to be the Messiah will be subject to auto-da-fé?'

Now *that* struck a chord with Norma. If she wasn't mistaken, auto-da-fé usually involved burning at the stake. Ella was literally playing with fire.

'Your threats do not frighten me, Torquemada. Know this: ABBA will not allow me to burn. I am here to sweep evil from the Demi-Monde, not to succumb to it. Only ABBA may take me from this world, not you, a lackey of Reinhard Heydrich . . . the Beast.'

Now *that* was an insult that hit home. 'Foul, duplicitous wench, how dare thou imply Great Leader Heydrich is in league with Loki? Cease thy poisonous slander on pain of everlasting torment. Thou shouldst know that the reward for the sin of blasphemy is to be cast to the depths of Hel and there to have eternal torment visited on thy unrepentant soul. I implore thee, do not put thyself in danger of being damned. Admit that thou liest, that thou art just a conniving witch, or mayhap, a most diabolical Grigori,' here the fidgeting with his his silver cross became more pronounced, 'and I will have thee cast into the flames, and by this transitory pain, I will guard thee from everlasting suffering in Hel.'

Norma shivered. Not only was this madman talking about burning Ella at the stake, but he was suggesting that she should thank him for doing it.

'I do not fear for my soul, Torquemada. I am blessed by ABBA.'

'I would that thy spirit was easier for advice, wench, but thy intransigence denotes that thou art a most malicious and malevolent witch. But there is more: my most close and faithful servant, Chief Inquisitor Donatien' – a nod to a curly-haired Quizzie with a bandage around his head, who was standing next to Ella – 'has made deep and devious enquiries regarding thy witchery. And he, with the utmost of conviction, doth relate that thou art possessed of strange and wondrous powers – powers which if not bestowed by ABBA might only be conferred by the Trickster, Loki. Is it not true that thou hast withstood the test inflicted on thee by the galvanicEnergy engine?'

'It is true. And beware, Torquemada, for I possess other powers which will humble you and all of your kind. I say again: I am sent by ABBA to reclaim the Demi-Monde from your foul embrace.'

'Thou liest!' Torquemada screamed. 'Thou art a foul impostor and false prophet, and must be doubly burned, once here in the Demi-Monde and then in the everlasting pyre that is Hel.'

*Ella's toast. All Torquemada wants to do is torch her.*

'By the power vested in me by the Committee of Public Safety and in the full and safe knowledge that I perform ABBA's will, I sentence thee, the Shade known as the Lady IMmanual, to—'

'Be silent!'

Every eye in the room turned towards Ella, and as Norma studied her a change seemed to come over the girl. It was as though she was emitting a power that forced those in the room away from her, that made the hairs on the back of Norma's neck bristle, and her skin pimple with goose bumps.

*Fucking hell.*

Again Ella stabbed a long finger in the direction of the Grand Inquisitor. 'Know this, Lord Torquemada, I am the Lady IMmanual. I am the one who opened the Boundary Layer. I am the one who allowed the citizens of Warsaw to escape to the Great Beyond and from the evil clutches of Reinhard Heydrich. I am the one Mengele tried to cow with his galvanicEnergy, but who survived. I am the Messiah sent by ABBA to lead the people of the Demi-Monde. And mark this well, Tomas de Torquemada, all those who defy me will perish.'

Face red with fury, Torquemada sprang to his feet. 'Take her! Burn her! Burn this abomination of a Daemon!'

# 15

## The Bastille: Paris
## The Demi-Monde: 13th Day of Spring, 1005

And the Master said, 'The Messiah will be the living embodiment of *wu wei*, the action without action that will realign the Kosmos towards the perfection that is Ying, the merging of Yin and Yang.' Then, seeing the confusion on the faces of his students, he explained, '*Wu wei* is like water: yielding, compliant and ever mutable. *Wu wei* is the ultimate expression of Yin, but when roused it has the power to gouge Mantle-ite. Such will be the quiet force of the Messiah: she will be like a flood that will cleanse the Kosmos.'

'And how should we prepare for the flood that will be the coming of the Messiah?' asked a favourite student.

The Master smiled. 'Make fucking damned sure you own a boat.'

*The Fourth Book of the BiAlects, Verse 98*

The Quizzies lived up to their hateful reputation. Armed with steel batons, they waded into the ranks of the UnScreweds, clubbing them down with a savage ferocity, smashing the women to the ground and then trampling on them with their iron-shod boots. They had dogs, too, horrible things that looked like they'd been bred in the darkest part of Terror Incognita, their teeth ripping and tearing great chunks of SAE out of the legs of the women.

For a moment, the UnScreweds – shocked and stunned by the brutality of the Quizzies – nearly broke, but then Odette and her girls from the market counter-attacked. Odette had warned her girls that there was a chance that they would be facing the Quizzies but rather than frightening them, all this had done was stiffen their resolve. They had witnessed what these bastards had done when they had cleared the troubadours out of Les Halles, and were determined not to go to ABBA quite so easily. So they had come well prepared, and now they conjured knives, blackjacks and lengths of chain from their cloaks, fighting fire with fire and steel with steel.

Later Odette could never quite decide who was more shocked by the attack of the market girls: the leaders of the UnScreweds with their petitions and smiles, or the Quizzies themselves. But as the stabbing, spitting, swearing girls smashed into the Quizzies, the shock on both sides was palpable. Now it was the Quizzies who began to crumple to the cobbles, and once they were down there was no getting up. Now the dogs began to howl not with ferocity but with fear as they were stabbed in the eye or had their throats slit by an expertly wielded razor-knife. Now it was the Quizzies' turn to waver.

The colonel commanding the Quizzies obviously sensed that the tide was running against them. Odette saw him haul out his Colt. 'Inquisitors,' he bellowed, 'fire at—'

They were the last words he ever spoke. Odette had come to the demonstration heeled, and now she dragged her Ordnance revolver out from where it was holstered on the back of her belt. She had no chance to take aim, but being only two metres from the colonel she had little chance of missing. She cocked the revolver and squeezed the trigger. The gun bucked and when the mist of powder smoke had cleared she saw she'd hit the man square in the face . . . or what was left of his face after it had been mashed by the lead slug. Without thinking, she turned the gun, cocking and firing it at the other Quizzies.

Outnumbered, outfought and now outgunned, the Quizzies broke ranks and ran towards the open doors of the Bastille, with the enraged women of the Quartier Chaud following hard on their heels. The Quizzies did their best to close the gates behind them, but they were too late. The UnScreweds barged the gates aside, and the horde of screaming, cheering women stormed into the prison.

The Bastille was theirs!

Even as the two guards moved to obey the Grand Inquisitor and arrest the Lady IMmanual, Machiavelli strode into the room with Sister Florence bustling in his wake. Automatically – old habits died hard in the Quartier Chaud – everyone in the room bowed and a goggle-eyed Quizzie announced in a shaking voice, 'Make way, make way for His Excellency, Abbé Niccolò di Bernardo dei Machiavelli, most favoured Emissary of Her Most Reverend Excellency, Doge Catherine-Sophia, and Plenipotentiary Extraordinary of the Venetian Republic.'

Machiavelli acknowledged the greeting with a careless bow. 'I must apologise, Lord Grand Inquisitor, for this interruption, but I am here at the request of the Doge.'

For a moment Sister Florence thought – hoped – that Torquemada would have a seizure, but finally he gained enough control of his anger to splutter out a reply. 'Is there no surpassing thy impertinence and audacity, Machiavelli? Thou knowest, full well and true, that thou art trespassing most griev-ously on both the property and on the good nature of the UnFunDaMentalist Church. By this disdainful act thou hast polluted this sacred Chamber. As a vile and bitter enemy of UnFunDaMentalism, thou art not welcome here. Get thee hence with all haste, lest I unleash my guards on thee.'

Typical man, decided Sister Florence, always so vulnerable to the choleric promptings of MALEvolence. She was just grateful that, standing as she was behind the Abbé Niccolò, she was shielded from the full force of Torquemada's bile and hate, but still it discomfited her.

'As a Plenipotentiary Extraordinary of the Venetian Republic, I have diplomatic immunity,' countered the Abbé Niccolò in a calm voice. 'If you use force against me, it will be viewed as an act of sedition.'

'I care not for thy "immunity", Machiavelli. In this chamber my will prevails, and therefore thou and thy scampering, simpering lapdogs . . .' It was then that he noticed Florence. 'Is't thy intent to royally insult me, Machiavelli? Dost thy depravity know no bounds that thou hast brought that most profane and hateful *Whorealist* Sister Florence in accompaniment of thee?'

Though Sister Florence had expected Torquemada's reaction to her presence in the Chamber to be extreme, even she was taken aback by his anger. A nimbus of bright yellow flamed around his head, signalling his fury. But being a supreme exponent of fiduciary sex, she retaliated by arching her body in order to reveal just a little more naked flesh. Unfortunately, such was the extent of Torquemada's rage that he seemed impervious to her blandishments.

'Knowest thou this, Abbé Niccolò, that the Inquisition has declared all such Whorealist witches to be abominations in the sight of ABBA, and as such, those venturing from beyond the confines of their Convents shall have their heads severed from their bodies, their immoral remains burned and their ashes scattered.' He stabbed a finger towards Sister Florence. 'Guards, arrest this witch.'

'Wait!' bellowed Machiavelli. 'Sister Florence is protected by a warrant granted under the personal seal of Her Most Reverend Excellency, Doge Catherine-Sophia.' Machiavelli conjured a roll of parchment from the sleeve of his frockcoat, and proffered it to Torquemada.

The Grand Inquisitor was less than impressed: he brushed the warrant away with a disdainful flick of his fingers. 'Such warrants are of no import within the Medi . . .'

'Then think on this, Lord Torquemada. Violate this warrant, and the lives of all those Medi CitiZens who are currently residing in Venice will be forfeit.'

*That* stopped Torquemada in his tracks. There were enough Medis in Venice that if the Doge decided to make life difficult for them, then life could be made *very* difficult indeed. The threat found its target. When he spoke next, Torquemada was more conciliatory in tone.

'Verily, then, speak, Abbé Niccolò. What dost thy presence here portend?'

'My Lord, as you know, despite the Great Schism it is still undecided who shall have the final word regarding spiritual matters in the Quartier Chaud. My own opinion is that it is Her Most Reverend Excellency the Doge Catherine-Sophia whose opinion is pre-eminent in these matters, and hence the fate of the Lady IMmanual must be decided by the Doge, and by the Doge alone.'

'Not so,' protested Torquemada. 'This wench is a self-confessed witch, and by the laws of the Quartier Chaud, all of her foul kind must be cast into the fire. And mark you well, Machiavelli, this is a civil matter, not an ecclesiastical one: today has been signed a pact between the Medi and the ForthRight which requires and demands that all fugitives be apprehended so that they might be tried, sentenced and executed. The Lady IMmanual is such a fugitive, a criminal wanted by the ForthRight for the practice of the most base and Lokic of witchcrafts.'

Although his aura showed that he was shaken by this news

that the Medi and the ForthRight were now formally united by treaty, Machiavelli rallied. 'What has the ForthRight got to do with the internal affairs of the Quartier Chaud?'

'By the ForthRight having two hundred thousand soldiers camped outside the walls of Paris, and that should this witch be released into thy care it will be viewed as a *casus belli*. It will be seen as an act of such provocation that the ForthRight will have no alternative but to declare war on the Medi.' Torquemada smiled an evil smile. 'Welcome to the realm of realpolitik, Machiavelli.' He signalled to the guards. 'Take them all. Take them and burn them. Scorch the evil of this witch and her disciples from our land.'

It was at that moment that the doors of the hall smashed open.

Desperately trying to reload her revolver as she ran, Odette Aroca screamed out her orders. 'Adélaïde . . . find the armoury . . . take it . . . distribute the guns to the rest of the UnScreweds.' The huge woman peeled away, taking twenty or so girls with her. 'Sabine . . . search the third and the fourth floors . . . find Jeanne Deroin and Aliénor d'Aquitaine and release them. Sophie' – the dancer from the Maison d'Illusion sprinted up close to Odette – 'you do the same . . . search the first and second floors. Be quick . . . before more Quizzies come.'

Where *she* was going with the rest of her army, Odette had no real idea except that she had read that the most important of the Bastille's prisoners were interviewed in a place called the Great Reception Chamber, so there was a good chance that they would find Deroin and d'Aquitaine there. The problem of where in the muddle of narrow corridors the Chamber was located was solved by a GrandHarm they found cowering in a darkened corner. A quick prod of the point of Odette's razor-knife in his groin and he was only too eager to tell them how they might find the place. He even wished them *bonne chance.*

Five minutes later, Odette's breathless band rounded a corner and found itself facing two huge doors guarded by two huge Quizzies. The guards never stood a chance. With cries of 'Vive ImPuritanism' and 'Liberté, Egalité, Fornication', the women were on them and the great doors were barged open, the sheer momentum of the attack driving Odette right into the room. And there she was confronted by a strange scene. The Grand Inquisitor himself, Tomas de Torquemada, was standing beside his throne at the end of the room, his face purple with anger, pointing towards a tall slim Shade girl standing in the middle of the floor. When Odette smashed her way into the chamber, his mouth dropped open in shocked amazement, and he stood seemingly paralysed in mute disbelief, obviously stunned that anybody could have forced their way into the supposedly impregnable Bastille. He didn't stay stunned for very long.

'Those are UnScrewed terrorists,' he screamed towards the guards stationed around the room. 'Kill them!'

As Odette began blasting away with her revolver, she had to admit to feeling a certain excitement. Storming prisons was a bit like sex: stimulating and sweaty and great fun. Unfortunately, in her case, these two activities had a similar frequency. As she reloaded her Ordnance, she wondered if that funny Anglo she'd met in the bar would be tempted to make a call on her later that evening. That, she decided, would make a perfect end to what had been, in her opinion, a pretty perfect day.

For a moment, as bullets pinged around her ears, Sister Florence stood paralysed with fear and indecision and it took a shouted warning from Machiavelli to shake her out of her fugue.

'The Lady IMmanual is in danger. Protect her.'

Stung into action, Florence reached across, grabbed the girl by the arm and desperately looked around for an escape route. It was then, to her amazement, that an Inquisitor came to their rescue.

'If you want the Lady IMmanual to live, follow me!' the man yelled, pointing to a door he had opened in the wooden panelling of the hall.

For an instant Sister Florence hesitated, unsure whether she could trust a Quizzie. It was the Lady IMmanual who made the decision for her, pushing her towards the door and into the pitch-black corridor beyond. As soon as she, the Lady and Machiavelli were through, the Quizzie barricaded the door behind them and then used a match to ignite a torch.

'This way,' he ordered, and then plunged off into the darkness.

'Hold fast, Inquisitor,' snapped Sister Florence. 'Who art thou, and why dost thou aid thy master's enemies?'

'Don't worry, Sister,' said a breathless Machiavelli as he clutched at his arm, where he'd taken a bullet fired by one of the Quizzies. 'This man is the Marquis de Sade and he's an agent of the Doge.'

Hearing the name, Florence flinched back: the Marquis de Sade was one of the most reviled names in Venice. He was an abomination to ImPuritanism, a man exiled for acts of gross carnal cruelty.

Even in the darkness, de Sade must have seen the expression of disgust on her face. He laughed. 'I am also, good Sister, the man who can lead you out of this place. I'm very adept at negotiating dark, tight and smelly passages.'

When the UnScreweds attacked, Vanka's natural instinct was to get to Ella and spirit her to safety. But as the room descended into chaos he saw her being grabbed by a tall Visual Virgin and bundled towards a door on the other side of the room. He made to follow, but a Quizzie wielding a steel baton got in his way and would have trepanned him if one of the UnScreweds hadn't shot his attacker square in the chest. But in that instant any chance he had of reaching Ella was lost.

Now he had to look out for himself and Norma. It was difficult to see where they should run to: several of the torches lighting the room had already been extinguished, the air was thick with gun smoke, and everywhere around him was a wrestling, gouging, kicking and screaming mêlée of Quizzies and UnScreweds.

In the end it was Norma who saved him. 'Vanka, over there!' she yelled, and when Vanka looked to where she was pointing he saw, not twenty feet away, a side door flapping half off its hinges.

Dodging and weaving, they managed to duck and dive their way to the lee of the doorway, and once they were safe, Vanka tore open the lapel of his jacket, extracted the picklock he had hidden there and began to work on the chains the Quizzies had fitted them with when they'd taken them from their cells. 'Product of a failed career in escapology,' he explained to Norma.

The chains fell free and, taking a firm hold on Norma's arm, Vanka led her down a dark corridor and away from the fighting. It was a nerve-shredding experience, tripping and stumbling along in the darkness, half-expecting to hear a stentorian voice bellowing at him to surrender, or the crack of a pistol firing the bullet that would send him to his maker. But they made it and fifteen minutes after escaping the hall they were standing at the back entrance of the prison.

The exit was guarded by a large oak door and by two large but fortunately very dead GrandHarms. Cautiously Vanka eased open the door and then stepped warily out into the alleyway beyond. It was pitch dark outside, and there was the smell of rain in the air.

'Good evening, Vanka Maykov, I am so pleased you could be persuaded to join me.'

Vanka glanced towards the speaker and his soul sank. Standing with a pistol pointed at his midriff, and surrounded by five very tough-looking confederates, was Godfrey de Bouillon.

For five long minutes de Sade scurried them through the maze of dark passageways, until he brought them to a halt alongside what appeared to be a featureless stretch of corridor. Giving the torch he was carrying to Machiavelli, he carefully examined the brickwork and then, with a grunt, scrabbled one of the bricks free. There must have been a catch hidden there, because immediately that part of the wall sank back to reveal a narrow staircase beyond. Blind and confused, Sister Florence allowed herself to be hustled and pushed through the doorway and up the stairs, at the top of which de Sade led the trio, blinking and bruised, into a small drawing room.

'That was a near-run thing,' gasped de Sade, 'but in the end we are all safe.' He bowed in greeting. 'I have the honour of welcoming you to my humble hidey-hole which occupies a little-used part of the Convent of Visual Virgins here in Paris. And, as we would in all the Convents in the Quartier Chaud, we now enjoy diplomatic immunity . . . for the moment. Perhaps I could offer you all a drink. I know I could use one myself.'

Sister Florence eyed de Sade suspiciously, noting he had a strange aura, one that flickered and faded, and was never still for a moment, never allowing her the opportunity to see precisely who – or what – the man was. All she knew was that there was something dangerously artificial about de Sade. He was hiding something. Somehow he'd camouflaged what he really was.

*Camouflaged?*

Yes, that was the word. And wasn't that what all dangerous animals did, use camouflage to help them stalk their prey, to get close to them until they were ready to make a final, killing strike?

The Sister shrugged those suspicions aside. She knew from her studies that it was impossible for anyone to alter their aura. De Sade was clearly just as she saw him: a disgusting, degenerate man, but harmless for all that. There was too much of the poltroon about de Sade for him ever to indulge in murder.

But there were other things about de Sade that needed explanation. She turned to Machiavelli. 'I am much befuddled, Your Grace. I know of this man, for he is the renegade exiled from Venice for the acts of gross indecency and bodily harm he did most venomously inflict upon the wench Rose Keller.'

As he poured four long flutes of Solution, de Sade gave an uncaring laugh. 'I don't suppose it would do any good to point out that she was paid for her trouble.'

'Thou art a foul beast who inflicted such pain and torment on a girl thou believest to be thy inferior, to be weaker than thee. Thou art a living stain on the purity of ImPuritanism.'

De Sade seemed totally indifferent to the Sister's criticism. He eased himself into a chair and sipped at his Solution. 'What can I say? I freely admit that I suffer from a deformity of spirit in that I derive pleasure from inflicting pain.'

As Machiavelli, struggling with his wounded arm, unlocked her fetters, the Lady IMmanual gave a wry laugh. 'You'll be pleased to know, Sister, that de Sade is as infamous in the Spirit World as he is in this. He is what we Daemons call a sadist.'

'A sadist? How intriguing,' said de Sade in a mocking tone. 'You Daemons have given me immortality.'

'Sadist or not,' observed Machiavelli, grimacing as he freed his wounded arm from his jacket, 'what is important is that de Sade has been working for the Inquisition at the order of the Doge. He was tasked with discovering the secrets of galvanicEnergy.'

'Which, by the by, I have done.' De Sade flicked a finger towards a slim file lying on a table. 'I have examined the thermopile brought to Paris by Mengele, and its secrets are now yours, Machiavelli. This, I believe, settles my account with the Doge.'

'Excellent. And if it does contain such secrets then I will ensure that you receive a full pardon.'

De Sade glanced at the Lady IMmanual and smiled. 'I must apologise for having cooperated in your torture by galvanicEnergy, my Lady, but the mission I was given by the Doge – in exchange for not having my head chopped off for my supposed crimes against Rose Keller – was of vital importance to the security of Venice. To accomplish this you had to be tortured. Happily you survived.'

'That you helped me escape from Torquemada makes us square, de Sade.'

'You are very generous, my Lady.'

*Too* generous, decided Sister Florence. The Lady IMmanual appeared to delight in de Sade's evil. Closer to the girl, now, Florence was able to study her more intently, and though her aura was as immaculate and as pure as ever, there was something about it that disturbed the Sister. It was almost *too* pure . . . *too* immaculate. It was more inhuman than divine: there was no emotion shown by the aura and no humanity, no charity and no holiness.

Sister Florence shook her head to try to free herself of these delinquent thoughts.

*Ridiculous.*

The Lady IMmanual *was* the Messiah and her aura, unusual though it was, proved that.

It was Machiavelli who interrupted her reverie. 'And now, Monsieur le Marquis, I have to order you to perform one further service. You must assist Sister Florence in escorting the Lady IMmanual safely to Venice. My wound has rendered my sword arm useless, so as an escort I would be more encumbrance than assistance. You, de Sade, will have to stand in my stead.'

For the briefest of instances de Sade's aura flared with the scarlet of excitement. For some peculiar reason that Sister Florence couldn't fathom he was *pleased* to have been given the chance to risk his life protecting the Lady IMmanual. This enthusiasm for danger sat oddly with the yellow of cowardice that flecked his aura.

'You're taking me to Venice?' enquired the Lady IMmanual.

Machiavelli nodded. 'Yes, my Lady, the Doge has charged me with the task of having you brought there as quickly as possible. Heydrich wants you dead, and Beria is bending all his might to achieve his master's wish. There are assassins loose in the Medi, and the bounty on your head is very large. Unfortunately, with you being a Shade, getting you out of Paris is going to be difficult; every ForthRight crypto in the Sector is going to be on the lookout for a girl of your colour.'

'Then it is best we hide a tree in a forest,' said de Sade quietly.

Machiavelli frowned. 'Tell me, de Sade, just where is this "forest" in which you would conceal the Lady?'

'The forest of painted people that is the Fleshtival des Quat'z Arts!'

Vanka hadn't seen Godfrey de Bouillon for over a year – not since he'd sold him that cargo of adulterated blood – and in that time the man had packed on a lot of weight and his fair hair had got decidedly greyer. What hadn't changed was his air of supercilious condescension and the disdainful twist to his mouth. Worse, he still had that vengeful gleam in his eye, which was bad news for Vanka, very bad news indeed.

Any hope he might have had that de Bouillon had forgotten how he had diddled him out of five thousand guineas – by switching a cargo of Class-A blood derived from those certified as Aryan stock for Class-D blood taken from nuJus and Shades – evaporated when the bastard pulled a copy of the contract out of his pocket.

'It seems that ABBA has smiled on me, Maykov. I had been summoned to the Bastille to take you for execution, but it appears that you are so eager to meet ABBA that you have come to me.' His smile hardened. 'You swindled me, Maykov,' he said quietly, 'and for that you must be punished.'

'A simple administrative mix-up, Your Grace,' Vanka said with a smile. 'And I am now in a position to fully recompense you for the financial losses you incurred.'

'Financial losses? Do you think a man of my rank is concerned with "financial losses"? Do you think noblemen trouble themselves with pecuniary matters of such a trivial nature? I have clerks and bookkeepers to do that. No, Maykov, I am here to extract payment for the assault you made on my honour. I actually *consumed* some of that vile nuJu blood you sent before I realised from the aftertaste what it was.'

*Oh, fuck.*

In the Demi-Monde the competition to be the most nuJu-loathing bastard was intense, but de Bouillon was certainly a front runner. For him to have drunk nuJu blood was a violation of all he stood for.

'You contaminated me, Maykov. By drinking blood taken from nuJus, my body – my soul – has been rendered unclean. For such an insult I must, of course, kill you.'

He flicked his head towards one of his toughs, who drew a long knife from his belt and advanced towards Vanka.

The man stopped in his tracks. From out of the darkness of the alleyway strolled three of the tallest men Vanka had ever seen. The way their leader had to duck to pass beneath a sign advertising a boulangerie indicated that he was a good six and a half feet in height.

And it wasn't just their height that made the three men so remarkable. Even though their broad-brimmed hats were pulled hard down over their heads, it was still possible to see how pale and chalk white their skin was. But most unsettling of all was the way their yellow eyes glistened in the lamplight, eyes that reminded Vanka of the wild animals he'd seen in London Zoo. They were eyes that had no place in the face of any man.

But then they weren't men, they were Grigori, or as they were better known, vampyres.

Certainly it was a somewhat melodramatic thought, but from what Vanka could see, an accurate one. The three men did look like the vampyres portrayed in penny dreadfuls.

The trio halted by the team of horses harnessed to an elegant carriage presumably belonging to de Bouillon. There one of them reached out to take hold of a bridle, to steady the team, though the horses still pawed the cobbles, as if they were as unnerved by the Grigori's sudden appearance as Vanka was.

'We will take the Russian man and the Anglo woman,' the first vampyre said, speaking with the precision of a non-native speaker. And as the vampyre spoke, Vanka saw in the lamplight that its teeth had been filed to points. He almost wet himself.

'Move aside,' shouted one of de Bouillon's toughs. 'This is His Grace, Senator Godfrey de Bouillon, Duke of Paris. His Grace takes instruction from no man. I am Captain Philippe Pétain of His Grace's personal bodyguard, and it is an offence to inter-fere with officers of the Senate or to delay them in the execution of their duty.'

As the attention of Captain Pétain and his men now seemed to be wholly concentrated on the three vampyres, Vanka took the opportunity to signal to Norma that she should get ready to run. If his bowels weren't deceiving him, in the next few moments they would need every bit of their sprinting abilities.

'Do not be foolish, Fragile, hand over the man and the woman or die.'

Captain Pétain nodded to his huge sergeant, who squared up to the newcomers. 'It'll be you doing the fucking dying, if you don't fuck off,' he advised.

The vampyre struck.

Now Vanka would have been the first to admit that, after ten days of being locked up in the Bastille and pretty comprehensively banged about to boot, his critical faculties might not have been at their best but there was no mistaking what he saw, unbelievable though it was. He watched as the vampyre retracted his arm, then stabbed his hand forward at quite astonishing speed, skewering two viciously taloned fingers deep into each of the sergeant's eye sockets. Then, without removing the fingers, he twisted his hand and threw – threw! – the eighteen stone or so of the sergeant's now lifeless body hard against the alley wall.

As all Hel broke loose, Vanka made a decision that the one place he wanted to be at that moment was called 'somewhere else'. And the opportunity to vacate the scene was given to him by the lunatic heroics of de Bouillon and his bodyguards. Vanka had very little time for Godfrey de Bouillon, but even he had to admit that the man was brave as a lion and his reputation as a soldier was second to none. So it came as no surprise to see de Bouillon unsheathe his sword and wade into the fight. His bodyguards were of a less chivalrous and more practical turn of mind, and in a twinkling they had flashed their sticks and were blasting away at the vampyres. And from what Vanka could see, as he edged quickly away from the fighting, they certainly knew how to use their pistols. As the vampyres leapt at them, Vanka saw the five men score at least three or four hits, but amazingly these hardly seemed to slow the attack of the vampyres at all.

This, he decided, was going to get nasty. He grabbed Norma

by the arm and dragged her down the alley, taking a moment to spare a look over his shoulder as he ran. Pistols now empty, two of de Bouillon's men had unsheathed their swords ready to defend themselves. It did them no good; the vampyres pounced on their opponents, ripping their throats out and hurling them aside. The stench of death and rended SAE was everywhere, mingling with the acrid smell of cordite.

Strangely enough, it was Godfrey de Bouillon who saved the lives of Vanka and Norma. Bellowing his war cry, de Bouillon slashed his huge sword at the leading vampyre. De Bouillon was a big man, taller than Vanka, and although no longer in his prime he was still enormously strong. His attack was so ferocious that even the vampyres were forced to take a step back, and for a moment de Bouillon's blade looked to have carried the fight. Then fate took a hand and de Bouillon tripped, barged into the horses, and the vampyres were on him in an instant, stabbing him to the ground. The spooked horses reared and bucked, smashing the carriage across the alleyway, in doing so putting a barrier between Vanka and Norma and the vampyres.

Never one to look a gift horse – or even a team of them – in the mouth, Vanka decided there was only one thing for it. 'Come on, Norma,' he screamed. 'Burn the ground! Run for it!'

# 16

## The apartment of
## Baron Giovanni Mangione: Paris
## The Demi-Monde: 13th Day of Spring, 1005

In an effort to ensure that MALEvolence was eradicated
from life in the Quartier Chaud, and recognising that
women by nature are more peace-loving than men, it was
agreed by the Senate that henceforward the Doge – the
spiritual guardian of the Sector – would always be a woman.
Doge Ninon de l'Enclos (also called 'the Great' or 'the
Enlightened') was the first female Doge, her coronation
taking place in 520. There are many sayings attributed to
Doge Ninon, but she will go down in history as the woman
who first coined the three words which so succinctly encapsulated ImPuritanism and became the Quartier Chaud's
famous motto: 'Liberté, Egalité, Fornication'.

**MALEvolence: Is that a Pistol in Your**
**Pocket or Are You Just Glad to See Me?:**
*Mary Jane West, Venetian Institute of Holistic Sociology*

'You sure it was this geezer Maurice Merriment you saw,
Burlesque?'

'Yeah, it wos 'im: I'd recognise that piece ov shit anywheres.'

'Then if he's a comic in the Rookeries, wot's he doing 'ere in
the Quartier?'

'Looking for me, that's wot. Old Beria must 'ave sent 'im 'ere spotting for the Checkya, which means they've got wun ov their assassins 'ere in Paris.' Burlesque gave a nervous look around the suite of rooms that Rivets had been calling home for the past few days. 'You sure no one knows you're living 'ere?'

'Course. Even the *owner* don't know I'm living 'ere. Wiv all this trouble wiv the ForthRight, he's upped sticks and decamped to Venice. I got in through a window in the kitchen.'

Although he'd never admit it, Burlesque was quite impressed by the hidey-hole Rivets had found for himself. The garden apartment belonged to an Eyetie banker, and was very well appointed, with a formidably well-stocked wine cellar just off the kitchen from which Burlesque had selected a very fine blood-merlot to help settle his jangling nerves. Seeing Maurice Merriment had really rattled him: he had known that Beria would come looking for him one day, he just hadn't expected it to be quite so soon.

What he did know was that there was no way Maurice Merriment could find where he and Rivets were hiding. They had doubled back so many times after leaving the bar that even Rivets, who knew where he was going, had ended up lost. But Burlesque still couldn't throw off the idea that Beria's jackals were gathering somewhere outside. He must have checked that his Webley revolver was loaded three or four times already.

In the end, desperately trying to take his mind off Beria and his thugs, he had challenged Rivets to a game of billiards, with a pot of five guineas a game. But Rivets was such an inveterate cheat – every time Burlesque turned his back to post the scores, Rivets shifted the position of the balls on the table – that around midnight Burlesque gave it up as an exercise in futility.

'I'm off to bed, Rivets. I'll just go round to check all the windows and doors, and then call it a day.' Rivets, annoyed that Burlesque had spotted his cheating and refused to pay up, decided to turn in too. Still grizzling, he'd disappeared, accompanied by a bottle of the banker's finest cognac, down the corridor to the room he had commandeered for himself at the rear of the apartment. With Rivets gone, Burlesque set about making sure that all the doors were locked and the windows tightly shuttered. Everything seemed secure, though the lock on the kitchen window, where Rivets had forced entry, was still knackered. The frame was rotten, too.

With a deep sigh, he selected a book from the library shelves – he was too worried to sleep – and then headed back to attend to his final task, the extinguishing of the sitting-room oil lamps.

''Ello, Burlesque, me ol' mate. 'Ow's you diddlin'?'

Burlesque very nearly dropped the lamp he was carrying. There, sprawled in an armchair, was Maurice Merriment, who looked to have grown even fatter since the last time Burlesque had seen him perform at the Prancing Pig.

*Shit!*

'Maurice Merriment, as I live and breathe,' Burlesque replied in what he hoped was a fair facsimile of a welcoming voice. 'Wot the fuck you doin' 'ere?'

Absent-mindedly, Maurice wiped a lump of wax he had extracted from his ear onto the cream velveteen of the chair he was sitting on. This done, he looked up at Burlesque and gave a disingenuous smile, displaying a mouthful of rotten teeth as he did so. 'Now that's not a very pleasant way to greet yer ol' pal, now is it? Not when you led me such a song an' dance through the backstreets ov gay Paree.'

''Ow the fuck d'you get in?'

Maurice held up a set of keys and jangled them. 'Best set ov twirls in the 'ole of the Rookeries. I 'ad to take up 'ouse-breaking when me career as a comic went tits-up. An' that wos all 'cos ov you.'

Burlesque cursed himself for leaving the front door unbolted.

'Weren't nuffink to do wiv me, Maurice. Yous always wos a shit comic. Yous couldn't tell a joke iffn your life depended on it.'

'I wos a fuckin' good comic, I wos,' protested Maurice Merriment.

'Bollocks.'

Maurice shrugged, his shoulders moving powerfully under his lime-green gabardine jacket. Fat and funny-looking he might be, but there was no denying that he was a strong bugger. Burlesque eyed him carefully: if it came to a tussle, the outcome would be a close-run thing. He made to snake his hand around his back to his Webley and then cursed himself when he remembered he'd left it in the billiard room. It had dug into his arse every time he'd gone down for his shots.

'Well, that wos then, an' this is now.' Maurice looked about the place, assessing it. 'Nice gaff this. You've fell on your feet 'ere, Burlesque, an' no mistake. You must be really comfy, tucked up 'ere wiv Rivets.'

'Wot you want?'

'My employer would like to know where the Lady IMmanual is.' The soft voice came from behind Burlesque and his flesh ran cold at the sound of it: there was a certainty about the tone that told him that whoever was speaking was a killer. He turned and smiled, trying to exude a confidence he most certainly wasn't feeling. 'And 'oo might you be?'

A tall, elegant man oozed out of the darkness. 'I am Count Andrei Sergeivich Zolotov and I have the honour of being in the service of the Vice-Leader of the ForthRight, Lavrentii Pavlovich Beria.'

Burlesque's scrotum tightened. Zolotov looked a chilling cocktail of cool politeness, vaunting arrogance and crystal-cold cruelty. Trying to push his fear to one side, Burlesque did what he had always been best at, talking his way out of trouble. 'So wot can I do for you, Mr Count?'

With a chuckle, Zolotov sauntered into the penumbra cast by the lamp Burlesque was holding. For a bloke Zolotov looked almost beautiful, but his Aryan perfection was marred by the sabre scar that decorated his right cheek. He was the most exquisitely dressed man Burlesque had ever seen: his steel-grey suit was made from a wonderful, shimmering silk and his matching top hat was worn at a jaunty angle. His boots were nice too, but the gun in his hand wasn't.

'The Lady IMmanual escaped from the Bastille less than an hour ago, and naturally Comrade Vice-Leader Beria is eager to recapture her. It occurs to me that you will have intelligence which might aid me in that endeavour, being, as you are, one of the girl's confederates.' Zolotov took a long drag of his cigarette. 'Your Checkya file says that, despite your boorish behaviour and penchant for gutter-snap, you possess a mind of some rare intelligence. Therefore you will have realised by now that I am not a man given to dalliance, so tell me, where is the Lady IMmanual?'

For a second Burlesque wondered whether to make a dash for it, but the click of the Russian's pistol being cocked dissuaded him. 'Don't even consider it, Bandstand,' Zolotov purred, as though reading his mind. 'I am an excellent shot.' He used his pistol to gesture Burlesque towards a seat on the couch. As he sat down, Burlesque placed the oil lamp on the low table next to him.

'I don't know where the Lady IMmanual is,' answered Burlesque truthfully. 'I didn't know she'd even escaped from the Bastille until yous told me.'

'I think you are lying, Bandstand. I will ask you just once more, and please appreciate that your ability to retain possession of various parts of your body will depend on the veracity of your answer. Do you understand?'

From the moment Zolotov materialised, Burlesque had

known his one chance would be if he could rile Maurice Merriment into doing something stupid. If he remembered correctly, Maurice had a very short fuse.

'Yus, I understand yous, Mr Count, but I'll translate for the brainless tosser on my left. Wot Mr Count is saying, Maurice, is that iffn I tell porkies—'

Maurice Merriment's temper erupted. 'I know wot he's a-saying, Burlesque-bleedin'-Bandstand. I don't need some fat fuck like you tellin' me wot's wot.'

'Just trying to 'elp, that's all, Maurice,' Burlesque crooned, in his most oleaginous tone. 'It's just that I remember 'ow fuckin' stoopid you were.'

Maurice Merriment leapt to his feet. 'Say that again, you fucker.'

'Sit down,' Zolotov snapped with real venom in his voice and, with studied reluctance, Maurice Merriment did as he was told. 'Enough, Bandstand, no more nonsense. I want to know where the Lady IMmanual would have run to. You are her friend, so you must know where she is heading.'

Burlesque gave a shrug. 'Dunno. Soon as I saw her taken by the Quizzies, I thought she wos dog meat.' He turned to Maurice Merriment and smiled. 'Talkin' ov dog meat, 'ow is Mrs Merriment? She still workin' the Lane?'

Maurice Merriment was out of his chair like a shot, to tower over the seated Burlesque. 'Wot you's sayin'? You sayin' that my Bessie is a prossie or somethink?'

'Sit down, Merriment,' snarled Zolotov, but such was the man's chagrin that he refused to be deterred.

'I ain't 'aving this bastard bad-mouthin' my Bessie.'

'Back off, you fool. Can't you see he's doing it deliberately? He's trying to provoke you.'

As a scowling Maurice Merriment very reluctantly did as he was told, Zolotov turned to smile at Burlesque. 'Very well, it would seem that you can be of no use to me, and therefore your life is forfeit. Comrade Vice-Leader Beria has asked that I make your death as protracted and as painful as possible.' He glanced towards Maurice Merriment. 'You may kill him now but, as we agreed, you are to proceed at a leisurely pace. I would begin by cutting out his eyes.'

Burlesque wiggled his arse. 'Nah, you won't wanna do that, will ya, Maurice? You'll probably want to arse-fuck me first, won'tcha?'

Maurice Merriment's face darkened. 'You saying that I'm a zadnik or sumfink?'

'Well, ain't that wot you and Bessie have in common? You both like taking it up the jacksie.'

Face flushed with anger, Maurice Merriment advanced towards Burlesque, razor-knife in hand. In truth, Burlesque didn't really have a plan, all he had been intent on was causing a kerfuffle. But the sight of the knife and the vengeful look in Maurice Merriment's eye informed him that somehow he'd miscalculated.

Suddenly – amazingly – Maurice Merriment stopped in his tracks and stared towards the room's entrance. When Burlesque turned to see what had surprised him, he saw Rivets standing gawping in the doorway, resplendent in an oversized striped nightshirt.

'Gor blimey, Burlesque, wot the fuck—?'

They were the only words Rivets had a chance to utter, but they were enough. Zolotov raised his pistol, but Burlesque was faster: quick as a flash, he grabbed the oil lamp from the side table and hurled it at the Russian. Zolotov ducked, the lamp shattered against a wall where it exploded in a 'whoomph', flames leaping up towards the ceiling, forcing Zolotov back. But the flames didn't prevent the Russian firing his pistol in the general direction of Rivets. As a bullet whined past his ear,

Rivets yelped in fright and leapt for safety behind the cover of the door jamb.

Knowing that he had to act whilst he had the advantage of surprise, Burlesque hurled himself at Maurice Merriment, employing all the dirty tactics he had learnt on the streets of the Rookeries. He gouged and scratched, spat and swore. He bit down savagely on an unprotected neck and pummelled his knee into Maurice Merriment's groin. But it was no good: Maurice Merriment was heavier and stronger than him, and as the seconds passed the man's extra weight and strength began to tell.

As he struggled, he caught a glimpse of Zolotov taking careful aim with his pistol. In that instant, Burlesque knew his number was up, but he gave one last desperate heave and, as the pistol cracked, shoved the squirming Maurice Merriment between himself and the bullet. He felt the impact through the man's body, smelt his rancid breath as he gasped out his agony, and tasted Astral Ether as a second bullet tore off the side of the fat man's head. Frantically, Burlesque rolled the flaccid body off him and leapt towards the doorway. As he scuttled out of the lounge and into the welcoming darkness of the hallway, he felt the door jamb shudder as a bullet smacked into the woodwork, showering him with splinters.

'This way,' he screamed as he grabbed the bemused Rivets by the shoulder and hauled him along after him. Desperately he twisted them this way and that, searching for an exit from the burning apartment and the murderous Zolotov. It was then he remembered the rotten window in the kitchen. Dragging Rivets behind him, he pounded down the service corridor, sobbing with fear that at any moment a bullet would blow his head off.

It was pitch black in the kitchen, and he tripped painfully over a bucket that sent him sprawling and cursing across the stone floor. But, energised by desperation, he was up in an instant, ignoring the protests of his skinned knees and palms, and like a blind man, with arms outstretched and whimpering in panic, he frantically searched the room. His fingers eventually touched the soft, rotten window frame and, with an acrobatic ability he never realised he possessed, he hoisted himself up onto the sill. As he shoved with his shoulder, the decayed wood gave easily under his weight.

'Quick,' he yelled at Rivets, 'back-slang it!' Grabbing Rivets by his hair, he pulled him up onto the sill and then shoved and kicked him, screaming and protesting, through the ruined window, thanking his stars that Rivets was so very small. As Rivets disappeared into the darkness of the garden beyond, Burlesque jumped after him, tumbling out into the cold, damp night.

A shot rang out behind him, and he felt searing pain as a bullet ripped into his body.

As he landed on the rain-sodden lawn, Burlesque's mind was spinning. It was a racing certainty that Zolotov would have more confederates nearby, and with that in mind, he had to find somewhere to hide, pronto.

'You's all right, Burlesque?' he heard Rivets whispering in the darkness, somewhere off to his left. 'I'm over 'ere.'

Burlesque scuttled across the grass in the direction of the voice, and found Rivets cowering behind the protection of a privet bush. 'Who the fuck was that?' the boy asked, his voice reduced to a panicked croak.

'That was Count Zolotov, assassin extraordinary in the empty of my friend Beria,' murmured Burlesque, as his fingers tentatively examined the wound to his backside. 'A real bastard, full of spite an' spittle, who's come lookin' for me on account ov me playing Beria for a fool.' There was shouting from inside the burning apartment and when Burlesque looked, he could see that the flames from the smashed oil lamp had really taken hold. Soon the entire block would be an inferno. They had to move and move quickly.

The trouble was, he was in a Sector where he barely spoke the lingo, was dressed in just his shirt, trousers and boots, had no money and, as best he could establish after some painful probing, had a bullet lodged in his arse. And to make matters worse, he had Rivets in tow, a Rivets dressed in just his night-shirt. The boy's teeth were already chattering with cold. These harsh facts, coupled with the knowledge that he had a deranged and murderous bastard on his trail, meant that unless he could find a bolthole sharpish he had a life expectancy measured in minutes rather than in years. But then, as the pair of them were sneaking through the shrub-bery bordering the garden, Burlesque had a moment of inspiration. Careful of his wounded arse, he pulled the bit of paper the Frog tart had given him out of his pocket and exam-ined it by the light of the burning apartment. *That* was where they would go.

They exited the garden via a hole Burlesque booted through the fence, sneaked out onto the dirt road running at the back of the apartment block, then terrorised a pedestrian they met into giving them directions. Cursing Rivets's continual complaining, he had them dipping in and out of the shadows for a mile or so, until they came to a cluster of small cottages crowded along a narrow alley. Odette's place was the smallest house of the lot, the one with the white door.

Tired but exhilarated, Odette had got back to her uncle's little house just before midnight, after following a convoluted route home from the Bastille in order to avoid prowling GrandHarms. And there had been a *lot* of the buggers about. Robespierre, taking fright that the storming of the Bastille was the precursor to a general rising against the Gang of Three, had called out the GrandHarms, the army *and* the Quizzies, and had immediately declared a curfew.

Fortunately for Odette, with the Fleshtival des Quat'z Arts scheduled for tomorrow, the art students were out in force, and they didn't give a fig for the Quizzies or their attempts to curtail their fun. So despite Robespierre's curfew, the streets of Paris had been crowded, and Odette had been able to slip through the back alleys without being noticed.

But she knew it would be a different kettle of fish tomorrow. Then, no matter how tight-lipped everyone was, inevitably the Quizzies would hear the name Odette Aroca being bandied about and would come looking for her with a vengeance. Maybe now was a good time for her to head for the Coven: they were always pleased to welcome women refugees there. But, being an ImPuritan, Odette couldn't really see herself being happy spending the rest of her life in a Sector where her only male company would be a NoN. Better to make for Venice.

After making sure that her Ordnance and her shotgun were loaded and ready to hand, she decided to get a couple of hours' sleep and then hightail it to Venice, an hour or so before dawn. By then, with any luck, the Quizzies would be so fed up and tired that they wouldn't be looking too hard for fugitive UnScreweds.

Burlesque sneaked up to the door and knocked quietly. He seemed to have been tapping for an age before he saw a light flicker behind the shuttered window, and heard the suspicious voice of Odette.

'*Qui est là?*'

'Odette, it's me, Burlesque,' he whispered, as loudly as he dared.

'*Burlesque? L'Anglo? Qu'est-ce que tu veux? Il fait très tard!*' ('Burlesque? What do you want? It is very late.')

Flummoxed by the girl's French, and stimulated by the throbbing pain in his right buttock, Burlesque's whispering became a little louder and more urgent. 'Odette, let me in. I need help!'

He heard giggling from behind the door. *'Oh, mon cher Burlesque, tu es un coquin!'* ('Oh, my dear Burlesque: you are a wicked man!')

'Oh, bugger, just let me in, you daft Frog bint.'

There was more giggling. *'Tu es venu ici pour coucher avec moi?'* ('Have you come here to sleep with me?')

'Oh, fuck knows, Odette. Just stop playing silly sods and open the fucking door.'

It must have been the word 'fuck' that persuaded Odette to let him in. He heard bolts being shot, and a key being turned in the ancient lock. The door creaked open and there stood a beaming Odette, resplendent in a biliously yellow nightgown that enveloped her from her neck to her ankles. Not that he was given much opportunity to study this apparition of French womanhood; she reached out, grabbed Burlesque by the collar, and yanked him into a passionate embrace. Burlesque might have objected, but he found his protests muted by the substantial bosom his face was pressed into. When he did try to mouth his objections, it seemed that Odette – now murmuring entreaties about her *grand Anglais* – took the movement of his mouth as an attempt at amorous nuzzling, and simply squeezed him even harder. Desperate to get Rivets into the house, and the front door shut, before they were either spotted by the forces of Count Zolotov or he was suffocated by an excess of Frog breast, Burlesque twisted so that he could reach out a leg to slam the door shut behind him. He succeeded in getting the door closed, but the exertion aggravated the wound to his nether regions, and he let out a plaintive shriek.

Hearing the yelp, Odette's maternal instincts seemed to come to the fore, and she released her death grip on Burlesque's neck. Gasping for air, he staggered back a step.

*'Tu es blessé?'* ('You are hurt?') she asked with genuine concern

and, reluctantly, Burlesque turned around and pointed to his backside. He wasn't overpleased the silly girl started giggling again.

'*Un mari jaloux t'a tiré dessus, Burlesque? Tu n'as pas été sage, coquin anglais?*' ('Have you been shot by a jealous husband, Burlesque? Have you been a naughty Englishman?')

Although he didn't have a clue what Odette was rabbiting on about, Burlesque could tell that she wasn't taking his predicament at all seriously. It was then that Odette noticed Rivets standing sheepishly by the door, clad only in a nightshirt and blowing on his frozen hands. From the look on Odette's face it was obvious that she was uncertain what Rivets was doing here, and what exactly his role might be with regards to her tryst with Burlesque.

'Bad people shootez moi et Rivets,' Burlesque tried to explain. He looked to Rivets. 'What the fuck's the Frog for "shoot"?' he asked.

'Fuck knows, Burlesque,' shrugged Rivets unhelpfully, 'but ask the tart wevver she's got any blokes' togs. I feel a proper muffin standin' 'ere in just me undies.'

Burlesque made another attempt. 'Mal homs visitez l'apartement de mon ami, Rivets. Ils . . .' He stopped, brow furrowed, and then put the first two fingers of his right hand together and, as he had done as a child when he played soldiers, mimicked the sound of gunfire. 'Bang, bang,' he said, pointing his fingers at Odette.

Odette frowned in concentration and her ruddy face tightened as she tried to understand what Burlesque was attempting to communicate. '*Des scélérats? Lesquels?*' ('Bad men? Which bad men?')

'Oh, I dunno, les UnFunDaMentalists . . . les hommes dans l'armée de Reinhard Heydrich. Any'ows, avez vous some clobber pour mon ami, Rivets?'

Amazingly, Odette seemed to understand. She disappeared off into her bedroom at the back of the house and returned with an armful of clothes which she handed to Rivets. '*Voici quelques vieux vêtements de mon oncle. Lui aussi est nain, donc ils seront probablement à votre taille.*' ('Here are some of my uncle's old clothes. He is a midget too, so they'll probably fit you.') Rivets grabbed the clothes and ducked into a corner to get dressed.

Odette turned her attention back to Burlesque. '*Et maintenant, Burlesque, occupons-nous de toi. J'ai l'impression que tu es blessé.*' ('And now let me attend to you, Burlesque. I understand that you are hurt.')

Before Burlesque could protest, Odette had grabbed him by the arm – by ABBA, the woman was strong! – and manoeuvred him over to the table and nearer to the lamp. With a firm shove, she pushed him down so that he was now leaning over the table with his damaged arse up in the air. 'Non, non,' he protested. 'Give over, Odette, c'est bon. It's just a wound de SAE . . .'

Odette ignored his shouts, whipped his braces off his shoulders and yanked his trousers down to his knees. It took a lot to nonplus Burlesque Bandstand but having his strides pulled off by a besotted French tart almost did for him. The one blessing was that today was Sunday, the day he put on his clean linen. If all this had been happening on a Saturday, he would have died of shame.

He felt Odette easing his drawers down over his arse, and crouching forward to get a better look at the damage inflicted by Zolotov's shooting. After a moment, she straightened up. '*Ce n'est qu'une égratignure*' ('Oh, it's nothing, just a scratch') she announced and then gave Burlesque a quite unnecessary pat on the bottom. '*Oh! Quelles jolies fesses tu as!*' ('Oh! What a nice bum you have!') She giggled again, breathed an '*Un moment*' into Burlesque's ear, and disappeared back into her bedroom.

'I fink you're made up here, Burlesque, me ole cock,' commented Rivets as he stuffed some old newspaper into the boots Odette had given him to make them fit better.

'That Odette bird couldn't get yer pants down fast enuff.'

The pain infecting his arse and the ridiculously vulnerable position he was in provoked a stream of abuse from Burlesque. He had just paused in his haranguing of Rivets when he discovered just how vulnerable he really was. The front door suddenly flew open and a gust of cold air whisked around Burlesque's exposed SAE.

He looked over his shoulder and, for the second time that evening, he knew he was a dead man. Standing in the doorway were two of Maurice Merriment's associates from the Rookeries, the larger of the two being a truly evil bastard who went by the name of Stan Shoreham. He sauntered into the room and pointed a large revolver at Burlesque's arse.

'Hello, Burlesque, 'ow you diddlin'? Count Zolotov sends 'is compliments an' wonders wevver you would like to join 'im for a scraggin'. Your scraggin', that is.' Shoreham laughed. 'After you've given that table wot for, ov course. Gor, Burlesque, fings must be rough iffn you've been reduced to fucking furniture. Wot you an' your lady-love 'opin' for as a result ov your couplin'? A nice set ov side tables, perhaps?'

It was a very happy Odette who rifled through the medicine cabinet hanging on the wall of the bedroom, hoping that would be where her uncle kept his bottle of tincture of iodine, which she judged would be just the thing to clean poor Burlesque's wound.

And she was happy because all of a sudden her life had become so very exciting. Running a meat stall in Les Halles was all well and good, but it wasn't terribly romantic, and Odette was, under her somewhat forbidding exterior, a true romantic. What she most certainly did not want to do was spend the rest of her life standing knee-deep in offal, gutting chickens and skinning cows. No, she wanted to go on adventures, to right wrongs and defend the weak, to vanquish dragons and to be swept off her feet by handsome princes and all the rest of the good stuff that proper heroines did.

Of course, Burlesque wasn't quite as dashing as she'd imagined her Prince Charming would be, but she liked the idea of having a man who was something of an outlaw, forever fighting the bad guys and saving damsels in distress.

Not that Odette had ever been in distress. No one fucked with Odette Aroca unless they had a deep desire to be hospitalised. But she knew that men preferred women who were a bit fluttery and in need of rescuing, rather than those, like Odette, who were a dab hand with a blackjack and had been known to lay a GrandHarm out with one forearm smash.

So, determined to emphasise her more feminine aspects – notably her cleavage – she had just decided to change into the floral frock her mother had bought her the previous summer, the one her father always said made her look like an armoured steamer disguised as a rose garden, when she heard voices coming from the next room.

Angry voices.

It took very little intellectual effort on Odette's part to realise that the 'bad men' Burlesque had been so worried about had made a surprise visit. This made her cross. She had been waiting a long time for Prince Charming to come into her life and now that he had, she was buggered if anyone was going to take him away from her.

She decided to play out the role of one of the heroines in her favourite penny dreadfuls: she'd fight for her man, and then afterwards, when he was impassioned with gratitude, she would allow him to give her a really good seeing to. As she reached for her shotgun, Odette smiled. Life just kept right on getting better and better.

*

The two men's laughter stopped abruptly as Odette pushed her way back into the room with a large double-barrelled shotgun in her hands, the muzzles pointing squarely at Shoreham.

Shoreham wasn't impressed. 'Fuck me from 'ere to Fenchurch, Burlesque, is this your Froggy bit on the side? Bit 'ard-lookin', ain't she? I fink I'd sooner fuck that table than give 'er one. Still, I bet yor just doin' your best for the old intense cordial, right?'

For such a big bloke, Shoreham moved fast, but not quite fast enough. As he whirled his revolver around to shoot her, Odette pulled the trigger and the right-hand barrel of the shotgun flamed. The shot took Shoreham plumb in the centre of the chest and sent his lifeless body flying hard against the front wall, his head cracking a windowpane as it snapped back.

Shoreham's partner was slower to react. Maybe it was being sprayed with offalised SAE that slowed him down but he hadn't even begun to drag the pistol out of his jacket pocket before Odette let loose with the second barrel. The shot blew a chunk off the left side of his face, leaving him a gasping wreck.

Burlesque was up off the table, and had his trousers back on in an instant, knowing that it was a penny to a pound that the sound of the firing would bring more of Zolotov's gang running. He shouted for Rivets to help and together they quickly rifled Shoreham's pockets, extracting his passport, his billfold full of guineas and francs – Zolotov obviously paid well – and a box of spare cartridges for his pistol. Satisfied that there was nothing else worth nicking, they turned their attention to the man with the ruined face. Here, what Burlesque wanted was the man's jacket and coat. They might be a bit small but they were serviceable, and would make him a damned sight less conspicuous than if he went wandering around Paris in his shirtsleeves. That the coat was spotted with the remnants of the man's face, he'd just have to live with.

It was a little difficult pulling the coat and jacket from the dying man but, fuelled by a desperate energy and with a callous disregard for the man's groaning, Burlesque finally managed it. As he buttoned himself up, he saw that Rivets had commandeered the coat from the back of Stan Shoreham's body: it hung down to the boy's boots and looked faintly comical, but as Rivets explained it was 'better to look like a twat than 'ave yer nuts freeze orf'.

After taking a quick look to check that the Bulldog pistol he'd lifted was loaded, Burlesque turned to say thank you and goodbye to Odette.

But Odette was obviously not of a mind to be said goodbye to. While Burlesque and Rivets had been frisking the two bodies and removing the coats, Odette had been busy putting on her own coat and stuffing various bits and pieces into a voluminous carpet bag. The message was very clear: as far as Odette was concerned, wherever Burlesque was going, she was going too.

Burlesque looked at her and shook his head: 'Non, non, Odette, vous can't comez. Il est très dangereux. Beaucoup de bad men. Lots of killing. Much bang, bang, fucking banging.' He put his two fingers together and again mimed shooting with a pistol.

Odette smiled, nodded enthusiastically and then pulled a very businesslike revolver out of her pocket and brandished it with a really quite remarkable flourish. She pointed it at the two bodies. 'Bang, bang,' she said, laughing.

Burlesque didn't have the energy or the vocabulary to argue. As he stepped around the bits of liquidised body puddling Odette's living-room floor, he wondered who he should be more afraid of: Zolotov and his gang of rippers or this murderous French sort he would be traipsing around the Quartier with.

# 17
## The Moulin Rouge: Paris
## The Demi-Monde: 13th Day of Spring, 1005

```
TO DOCTEUR NIKOLAI KONDRATIEFF FUTURE HISTORY
INSTITUTE VENICE PO BOX 27/54 + + + SALUTATIONS
+ + + ACKNOWLEDGE SAFE RECEIPT OF CONFIDENTIAL
PAPERS + + +  WORK UNBABELISING FLAGELLUM HOMINUM
UNDER WAY + + +  HAVE EXAMINED EDDIC OF LOCI AND YR
NOTES RE SAME   + + + CONCUR WITH YR IDENTIFICATION
OF THE MESSIAH AND WITH THAT OF THE <<ONE WITH NO
SHADOW>> + + +  IMPERATIVE REPEAT IMPERATIVE LATTER
IS KEPT SAFE AND IS DELIVERED 2 JAD ASAP + + + USE
EVERY EFFORT 2 SECURE THIS OUTCOME + + + ETHOBAAL
```

**PAR OISEAU**

*Copy of PigeonGram message sent by Doctor Jezebel Ethobaal
on 14th day of Spring, 1005*

*Here we go again*, thought Norma, as she ran through the darkened streets of Paris. It had been only a few weeks ago that she'd been running from Archie Clement, and her capture then had precipitated all the misery she had endured since. But she was determined about one thing, that whatever those creatures were – and she was still coming to terms with Vanka calling them *vampyres* – that had attacked them outside the Bastille, she wasn't going to let them take her. Her sole comfort now was that she had Vanka with her. She might not like him – there was too much of the sharp about him for that – but he was one hell of a guy for getting out of tight spots.

As they raced along, Norma tried to get focused. Survival needed a clear head. But as she scuttled down the dark alley-ways leading away from the Bastille, it was difficult to remain calm: she'd seen what that tall, skinny vampyre bastard had done to Godfrey de Bouillon, and it hadn't been pretty.

Thinking about that broke her concentration and as she hurdled the body of a drunk lying across the pavement, the hobnails decorating the soles of her boots skidded on the rain-slick cobbles and her leg buckled awkwardly, the knee the Witchfinder had smashed with his cane cracking ominously.

*Fuck!*

She was back on her feet in an instant, trying to hobble on, trying to ignore the leg, trying to stifle her sobbing. Vanka grabbed her by the elbow to support her, all the while urging her forward. 'We're close now. As best I can tell, the Moulin Rouge is only a few streets away.' He tapped a finger on a poster pasted on a wall. 'An old friend of mine is performing there.'

*The Moulin Rouge?*

Norma didn't have a chance to think on this any further as a stabbing pain tramlined up her leg, radiating out from her wrecked knee. 'I think my leg's gone, Vanka,' she gasped.

There was the sound of a shot behind them and a brick just above Norma's head shattered under the impact of a bullet, spraying fragments into her face as it disintegrated. Galvanised by the near miss, Vanka hauled her down a side alley, the pair of them bouncing off the walls of the narrow passage as they ran. Ignoring as best she could the pain in her knee, Norma lengthened her stride, trying desperately to put distance between herself and the gunman.

*This is ridiculous. Why is it me who always ends up running from the badniks?*

Just as she decided that her leg was a goner, Vanka ducked them into a darkened doorway and placed his finger to his lips, signalling that she should be quiet. Norma didn't need telling: she stood silent in the darkness, coated in sweat and feeling like shit, waiting for a vampyre to come and kill her.

*Déjà vu times two.*

Even by the fucked-up standards of the Demi-Monde, it had been a weird day. Whilst she knew the Demi-Monde was a very trippy place, she had never expected to meet *vampyres* wandering around the ville! Vampyres didn't exist in the Real World, so how could ABBA have modelled them? It didn't make sense. And then there was all that screwball stuff with Ella Thomas announcing that she was the Messiah. The Demi-Monde was fast becoming not only weird but downright spooky.

From somewhere out in the darkness there came the sound of boots scraping on cobbles. Norma froze, trying to still her panting breath. There were shouts in a strange language, the voices angry. The vampyres were searching for them . . . kicking over dustbins . . . rattling doors. Norma looked around for a weapon: a stone, a stick, a bottle – anything to even up the odds. It was then that she noticed the fog seeping around her ankles.

Fog? No wonder Bela Lugosi and his buddies were so desperate to find them; give it another couple of minutes and she and Vanka would be lost under the swirling fog. All they had to do was stay hidden, stay quiet and let the pea-souper save them from their would-be assassins. Norma gritted her teeth against the fire burning in her knee and waited. Long, torturous minutes slumped by. Then . . .

'Okay,' whispered Vanka, 'I think they've gone.' He pushed himself out of their hiding place, took a quick look round, announced that the fog was now so thick that he couldn't see his hand in front of his face and then the pair of them took off at a crouching, loping canter. A few hundred yards later they rounded a corner and there, shimmering in a blaze of gaslight that cut through the thick fog, stood the Moulin Rouge.

'Gee whiz, Vanka, I gotta say, your dress sense has sorta nose-dived since the last time I saw you. Looks like you've just taken a runaway powder from the Bastille,' pronounced Josephine Baker, as she sat, flawlessly elegant as always, watching her two guests drink their coffee.

'That's because we *have* just escaped from the Bastille.'

'Yeah, I know, I got a message telling me about it a little while ago.'

Vanka frowned. For anyone to know the details of their escape so quickly meant that they were plugged into a really efficient intelligence system. Vanka wondered just *who* Josephine Baker really was, because she certainly wasn't just the dancer she pretended to be.

'So who's the nouvelle frail?' asked Josephine, nodding towards Norma. 'Hot dog, Vanka, you sure ain't big on monogamy; you change your squeeze with the breeze.'

'This is Miss Norma Williams, and she's not so much a friend as an encumbrance.' Immediately the words were out of his mouth Vanka regretted them. It was a cheap shot which was rewarded by Norma's cheeks colouring.

'That's right, Vanka, I don't have any friends do I? But then, neither do you, so maybe we deserve each other.' She gave Josephine a wan smile. 'Ignore Vanka, Miss Baker, and may I thank you for taking us in.'

'Any time, honey. Any opportunity to take in the famous Vanka Maykov.' Josephine gave Norma a wink. 'But like always, Vanka baby, your coming has, like, precipitated my going.' She waved a hand towards the men and women busily packing crates and trunks, hauling down props and pushing rails hung with costumes around. The Moulin Rouge looked like it was being dismantled.

'End of the season?' suggested Vanka.

'A big no to, Vanka. It's endsville for the Quartier Chaud, more like. Word is, the ForthRight Army will be coming through the gates of Paris early tomorrow, and as they come in yours truly will be exiting stage left. Thanks to you, Vanka, I had a taste of what those Checkya cats are like a couple of weeks back, and I only got them off my black ass because of my diplomatic passport – and because the Mayor of Berlin didn't want his wife to dig that he'd been mixing and mingling with a frail of the Shade persuasion. And talking of Shades, I've got some good news for you, Vanka baby: Ella made it outta the Bastille okay.'

Vanka let out a sigh of relief. All he'd been thinking about since he and Norma had escaped the prison was whether Ella was safe.

'I don't know what sorta shape she's in, they worked her over real good when she was in there. Got some bad guy in from the ForthRight called Mengele who hooked her up to a galvanicEnergy engine and turned it up to the max.'

'They tortured her?' Now that was something Vanka hadn't realised. Maybe that was why she'd been acting so strangely.

'Yeah. She's really pissed off Heydrich, who put the word out that Torquemada should get hot and heavy on her ass. Man, that cat is all white and spite.'

'But she *is* okay.'

'Don't sweat, Vanka, your girl's fine as wine.'

'Yeah.'

'You laying a line on me?'

'Would I do that?'

Vanka sat for a moment struggling with conflicting emotions: anxiety that the girl he loved had been tortured and relief that she hadn't been permanently harmed. It took a long swig of Solution to calm him down. Obviously worried that he was sipping more Solution than was good for him Josephine waved to a waiter, and had their coffees refreshed.

Vanka thought this a a good sign: if Josephine was going to boot them out, she'd hardly be worried about more coffee.

Is it right what they say Ella did, that she opened the Boundary Layer and saved all those items trapped in the Ghetto?'

'S'right, she let two, maybe three million people escape into the Great Beyond.'

'Hot diggity-dog. Heydrich must be really pissed off about the Lady IMmanual vacating the Bastille. That'll be why everyone and their brother's out looking for Ella.'

'But she's okay?'

'Chill, Vanka baby. Some goodniks have got her holed up in the Convent of the Sacred and All-Seeing Order of Visual Virgins here in Paris. They're gonna be sneaking her out to Venice real soon.'

'Then I've got to get to her—'

Josephine shook her head. 'Not a good idea, Vanka. You gotta keep a real low profile. Man, you're hotter than a two-dollar pistol. There's a real big reward on your head.'

Vanka lapsed into a worried silence, anxious about Ella being able to keep out of the clutches of the Checkya and wishing he was there to protect her. With an effort he tried to pull himself together; worrying wouldn't do Ella any good. To do that he needed Josie's help to get to Venice and that meant turning on the charm. 'So, Miss Baker . . . Josephine . . . Josie . . .'

'You can moniker me as "Miss Baker", Vanka baby, until I diggeth exactly what you want.'

'As we're such old friends and business partners, is there any chance that you would let us hide out here until the heat has died down, and then help us cadge a ride to Venice?'

'You gotta real fucking nerve, Vanka Maykov. You waltz in here pouring on the oil, after you got me kicked outta the ForthRight . . .'

'You were leaving anyway.'

'. . . and then ask me to help you rip and run to Venice.'

'Ah c'mon, Josie, don't be such a grouch.'

'A grouch!'

'Yeah. Look, Josie, I've got to get to Venice. If that's where Ella's going, then I'm going there too, to make sure she's okay. Somebody's got to look after the Lady IMmanual. I've got to get to Venice to protect her.' Vanka adopted his very best puppy-dog look, the one that had been so effective in luring so many rich widows into his bed. 'C'mon, Miss Baker . . . Josephine . . . Josie . . . you've gotta help us.'

'You know, Vanka, I wouldn't trust you as far as I could throw you, but I gotta admit, that was a real neat stunt the Lady IMmanual pulled in Warsaw.'

'You'll never forgive yourself if you don't help her.'

'Some of the nuJu cats are making a lot of noise that the Lady IMmanual is the Messiah.' Josephine made the statement in an offhand sort of way, but there was something – just something – in her tone that indicated to Vanka that it wasn't a statement she'd made idly.

'Yeah,' said a suddenly very cagey Vanka, giving Norma a surreptitious kick under the table. The last thing he wanted was her spilling the beans about what Ella had told Torquemada. 'People got a little overexcited about her opening the Boundary, and they started calling her the Messiah. But it's all moonshine.'

'That's not what I hear, Vanka. Word is that she's the real deal, the One and Only sent by ABBA to lead us all onwards to Revelation. That's real dangerous jive . . . real dangerous. Lotta badniks will be out and about trying to murderalise that little lady.'

'Like I say, Josie: it's all smoke and mirrors.'

'Maybe, maybe not, but I've got a mind to see for myself.

Okay, I'll take you and Norma to Venice, but we've gotta make our move tonight. A little bird's been whispering in my ear that the Quizzies are gonna be making a house call on yours truly and when they do, I wanna be residing on the Rialto. You dig?'

Vanka didn't dig. 'Why would they be trying to arrest you, Josie? The way you dance, I'd have thought you were the epitome of ImPuritanism.'

'That's the whole point, ain't it, Vanka? ImPuritanism ain't flavour of the month in the Medi no more, not after the Rapprochement with the ForthRight. Anyhows, there's more to it than Robespierre's nose being dejointed by my doing a hoochie-coochie number with a bunch of bananas. Seems Heydrich's got real excited about the lobbying I did in Venice on behalf of those Warsaw cats. Thanks to *moi*, the Venetians ended any ForthRight trading on the Bourse and forced the devaluation of the ForthRight guinea. Right now money's too tight to mention in the ForthRight.'

Vanka gave her a sideways look: he knew when he was being blown smoke. 'What else?'

Josephine laughed. 'Well, I suppose there's no harm in telling you now, Vanka. I think that after tonight my cover's blown.' The girl held out her tiny, elegant hand. 'Vanka Maykov, may I introduce you to Josephine Baker, agent of the Code Noir.'

That explained how Josephine knew so much about what was going on in Paris: the Code Noir – the secret organisation operating out of the JAD which aimed to protect WoeMen from the worst excesses of HimPerialism – was reputed to have one of the best intelligence networks in the whole of the Demi-Monde.

'. . . and mambo extrordinaire.'

Now *that* was a straightener. 'You're a WhoDooist!'

'Sure am, Vanka, and now we've been pronounced Enemies of the Revolution by Robespierre, it's time I headed for the tall timber. That cat's too keen on using his guillotine for my liking.'

'Mambo? What's a mambo?' interrupted Norma.

'A woman who practises WhoDoo magick in the JAD,' Vanka answered reluctantly.

The truth was, he wasn't feeling comfortable with the idea that Josephine Baker was mixed up in WhoDoo. WhoDoo had a bad rep. But for Norma's sake he tried to sound as matter-of-fact about it as he could; the last thing he wanted to do was alarm the girl, she'd had a bad day. But sounding matter-of-fact about what Josie Baker had announced was one thing and *being* matter-of-fact was quite another. All that business about WhoDoo dolls and zombis was enough to give anybody sleepless nights.

'You dig WhoDoo magick, Vanka?' asked Josephine Baker.

'Yeah. Ella played a WhoDoo mambo when we freed Norma from Crowley. I learnt a lot about it from her.'

'Ella played a mambo?'

'Sure, and she was bloody good at it too.'

'And did she give herself a handle when she performed as a mambo?'

'Yeah, she called herself Marie Laveau.'

Josephine Baker started, as though she'd just been stuck with a pin. 'You certain?'

'Sure. Why, is it important?'

'No, not really . . .'

*Bullshit.*

'. . . it's just that the tag Marie Laveau is real famous in WhoDoo circles. She was a powerful mambo in the olden days.'

Now Vanka was *sure* Josephine Baker was blowing him smoke. Since he'd mentioned the name Marie Laveau, her whole attitude had changed. She'd become a lot more serious. The trouble was that Vanka didn't understand why. He had thought that this Laveau character had just been dreamt up by Ella, but the way Josie was talking he had the worrying suspicion that she had been very real . . . and real unpopular.

Suddenly Josephine stood up from the table. 'Okay, cats and kittens, it's time to hit the cobbles. I got a steamer puffing and panting outside and a gondolier with real big *cojones* ready to take us across the Grand Canal. Yeah, I'm looking forward to getting to Venice.' She gave Vanka a smirk. 'And I'd like to meet and greet with Miss Ella Thomas when I'm there too, and get to talk over old times . . . *very* old times.'

# 18

## The Convent of the Sacred and All-Seeing Order of Visual Virgins: Paris The Demi-Monde: 14th Day of Spring, 1005

This newspaper is delighted to report that Hero of the ForthRight, Comrade Colonel Archie Clement, has been released from hospital where he had been undergoing treatment for gunshot wounds. As our readers will know, the Colonel was the victim of an attempted assassination whilst on a diplomatic mission to the Coven. The perpetrator, the renegade Royalist Trixie Dashwood, was arrested by the Coven's authorities but efforts to have her extradited to the ForthRight have been rebuffed. It is hoped she will languish in Rangoon's Insane Prison for many years to come. It is understood that Comrade Colonel Clement, after a period of recuperation, will return to active service in the Summer.

*Extract from* The Stormer, *23rd day of Spring, 1005*

'A brilliant idea, de Sade,' chortled Machiavelli. 'Tomorrow is the fourteenth day of Spring and even someone as remarkable as the Lady IMmanual will be lost in the mayhem that is the Fleshtival des Quat'z Arts.'

'You must forgive me, Abbé Niccolò,' said the Lady IMmanual, 'but I'm not familiar with Fleshtivals.'

'Fleshtivals are the means by which all good ImPuritans celebrate the joys of the body and search for communion with ABBA through the rapture of the ultimate orgasm, JuiceSense. By indulging in such pleasures, we in the Quartier Chaud praise ABBA and demonstrate our belief in HisHer reincarnation in the form of the Messiah.' Machiavelli laughed. 'And with you being the Messiah, my Lady, what could be more appropriate than you escape the Medi by losing yourself in a Fleshtival?'

'But what *is* the Fleshtival des Quat'z Arts?'

'It's the art students' ball and, even by the unrestrained standards of the Quartier Chaud, it's a wild and untrammelled saturnalia. The Fleshtival takes place in the open streets surrounding the École des Beaux-Arts and celebrates the coming of Spring. For two days and nights the hedonistic inclinations and the artistic talents of thousands of excitable art students are put on public display.'

'Artistic talents?'

'Each Fleshtival has a theme which is open to artistic interpretation by the students, and for this year's celebration the one chosen is "Daemons and all their Works".' Machiavelli gave a wry chuckle. 'In your case, my Lady, it is a most appropriate motif, is it not? Especially as amidst all this lunacy and debauchery we will be able to slip you out of Paris, through Rome and Barcelona and then on to Venice.'

'There is still the problem of my being a Shade,' the Lady IMmanual protested. 'Even in a crowd as large as the one you suggest I'll still be very noticeable.'

'Then you will need a disguise. Tomorrow we'll provide you with a costume to conceal your ethnicity and which will allow you to blend into the crowds celebrating the Fleshtival. Don't worry about a thing, my Lady, we'll make sure everything is ready, and anyway, remember that you won't be alone when you make your escape, both Sister Florence and the Marquis de Sade will be acting as your escorts.'

The Lady laughed. 'And I guess there's no one better qualified to accompany me to an orgy than the Marquis de Sade.'

The dresser – a vision in checks and velveteen – arrived at the Convent on the stroke of noon on the following day. The boy – and he *was* a boy, being perhaps less than twenty years of age – performed a bow of greeting so deep and so extreme that de Sade feared for his back. Straightening up with a rather over-elaborate flourish, the boy handed the Lady his pasteboard. 'I am Jules, senior dresser at the House of Monsieur Worth,' he announced. 'I have been instructed to create a costume to be worn when you, the beauteous Lady IMmanual, attend the Fleshtival des Quat'z Arts.'

Once pleasantries had been exchanged, Jules was all business. 'Could I ask you to pose for me, my Lady?' Jules asked.

It was an odd request, and one which de Sade thought might embarrass the Lady. But he was wrong: the girl stood up and did just as she had been asked.

Jules nodded his appreciation of both her beauty and her willingness to pose. 'You are fortunate, my Lady, for you are both wonderfully tall and possessed of a figure which is remarkable in its perfection. It is unfortunate that I am instructed by the Abbé Niccolò to disguise the colour of your skin, as I have never seen such a wonderful *mélange* of hue and texture. You are blessed by ABBA, my Lady, and hence I am confident that we will be able to create a costume of the required devilishness.'

Jules took a scrapbook out of his portmanteau and placed it on the table. 'I have brought with me a number of pictures of the costumes that I might create for you. Perhaps you would do me the honour of selecting one?'

For several minutes the Lady IMmanual flicked through the book, until she finally alighted on a picture that took her fancy. 'This one,' she declared.

De Sade couldn't resist; he rose from his chair to peek over Jules's shoulder. The picture the Lady had selected showed a young woman, her head and face concealed behind a cowl made from filigree gold, wearing a floor-length, diaphanous skirt and a tight leather gilet that barely contained her breasts. But perhaps the most disturbing aspect of the image was that her skin appeared to be painted a blood-red colour, with tattoos of snakes covering her body. 'That looks a little extreme,' he observed.

Both the Lady and Jules ignored him.

'Oh, bravo, my Lady,' chortled Jules. 'This is a picture of the Dark Temptress herself, Lilith. It is the perfect choice for the Fleshtival, especially as your skin, my Lady, will be so effectively concealed by red dye and by snake tattoos, these created by the use of *décalqueurs*. It will, undoubtedly, be a daring . . . a risqué costume, but one perfect to display your glorious body and all its wonders.'

For some reason he couldn't really understand, de Sade found himself quite disturbed by the selection of Lilith as the Lady's muse. But then Lilith was the mortal enemy of his kind, so the thought of her once more loose in the Demi-Monde was an unsettling one. 'A little *too* perfect?' he queried. 'Students are not famous for the sophistication of their costume and the last thing we wish to do is draw attention to the Lady.'

Jules gave a sniff in de Sade's direction. 'If, my Lady, you favour the advice given by the Marquis, I will, of course, provide a more respectable costume. But I warn you, the Fleshtival des Quat'z Arts is no place for either subtlety or modesty.'

The Lady IMmanual gave an imperious toss of her head. 'No, Jules, I will attend the Fleshtival as Lilith,' she said firmly, and the look on her face made de Sade understand that any further objections would be worthless.

'Then to work,' announced Jules. 'And have no doubt, my Lady, when Jules has completed his work, Lilith will once more walk the Demi-Monde!'

And for some peculiar reason the Lady IMmanual found this remark incredibly amusing.

Andrei Zolotov enjoyed the hour or so he whiled away in the café situated across the road from the Convent. His window seat afforded him an excellent view of the comings and goings of the Convent's visitors; the gateau he had just enjoyed was of a very passable standard; and the pretty little waitress who had been so attentive to his needs seemed very amenably disposed to a late-night assignation.

Yes, Zolotov was in excellent spirits. That Beria had been as good as his word and extinguished his troublesome debts, and thus called off his equally troublesome creditors, had had a marked effect on his mood. Being debt-free meant he was in an excellent position to acquire new and larger *Medi* debts – Medi debts that he would adroitly renege on when he returned to St Petersburg. And with this return in mind he'd invested several hours that afternoon in the important task of ordering five new suits and two pairs of boots – these latter items urgently needed to replace the troublesomely tight ones he was now enduring. Once he had his new boots, life for Andrei Zolotov would be almost perfect.

Almost . . .

Perfection was marred by the unfortunate incident the previous evening when that ruffian Burlesque Bandstand had refused Zolotov's invitation to die. This failure rankled, but as he was determined that Beria would never learn of this faux pas – least said, soonest mended, was Zolotov's motto – then there was little harm done. He would just have to be more careful of Bandstand in the future. The man was obviously more intelligent and resourceful than he looked.

Fortunately, though, events had connived to make this imbroglio with Bandstand seem like very small beer. The PigeonGram he had received from Beria had been very clear.

Everything had to be abandoned in favour of assassinating the Lady IMmanual, who since she'd escaped from the Bastille had been elevated to number one on Beria's People I Would Most Like Dead list. And that was why Zolotov found himself enjoying a pleasant afternoon spying on the Convent of the Visual Virgins.

Beria's informant had indicated that the girl would try to escape to Venice while disguised as a participant in that evening's Fleshtival. This was very good news since during the chaos of a Fleshtival assassinating her would be a very simple undertaking, and once he had killed her and dealt with that oaf Bandstand, Zolotov would be free to meander his way slowly and expensively – Beria's expense, of course – back to St Petersburg to resume his place in society and between the ever-open legs of the Lady Irma Dolgorukov. There was nothing in this mission that troubled either Zolotov's conscience – what little there was of it – or the supreme confidence he had in his ability to execute it.

As he brought the coffee cup to his lips Zolotov's hand paused in mid-air: the Lady IMmanual, if he was not sorely in error, had just exited the Convent. Even enveloped in a wonderful scarlet cloak, even with her face covered by a mist of filigree gold, she was unmistakable: there couldn't be more than a handful of women in the whole of Paris as tall or as beautiful as she was. She matched Beria's description perfectly, but while Beria had catalogued her features accurately, he had failed to convey just how breathtakingly lovely the woman was. Beria, Zolotov decided, must be devoid of even the smallest vestige of a poetical soul if he couldn't better communicate the Lady's physical perfection.

There was a gust of wind and just for an instant the woman's cloak was blown back, allowing Zolotov to witness how delightfully her body rippled as she stepped into a steamer, and to admire those long, long legs, which seemed to have been coloured a very ImPure red and embellished with what appeared to be tattoos of snakes.

How intriguing.

Andrei made a little pact with himself that, one way or another, this was a woman he would possess. Achieving this ambition would, he realised, necessitate having to combine murder with a little gentle pre-assassination seduction, but that, with a woman of the Lady IMmanual's beauty, would be no hardship. And if she resisted his charms, then maybe he'd have to indulge in a little less than gentle rape. It was all one to Zolotov.

As he stood up from the table, Zolotov raised his glass in a final salute to the rather crestfallen waitress. 'To tight cunts and easy boots, my dear,' he crooned. It was a toast which Zolotov thought pretty much encapsulated his philosophy regarding life.

Bole, as he sat toying with his croissant, directed all his formidable concentration towards the side door of the Convent, the one where, so his agent had informed him, Ella Thomas would make her appearance.

Pushing the plate away – Bole refused to eat stale foodstuffs even when they were a product of ABBA's digital magic – he shuffled impatiently in his seat. He *hated* having to enter the Demi-Monde, as each manifestation left him feeling weak and dyspeptic on his return to the Real World. But to ensure that matters proceeded satisfactorily it was sometimes necessary for him to get hands-on and give his cyber-experiment a little nudge in the right direction. And as nudges went, they didn't come any bigger than organising the assassination of Ella Thomas.

She had to be killed and killed quickly. That she was a Lilithi was troubling enough, but now that she had proclaimed herself to be the Messiah, her capacity for mischief had grown alarmingly. The girl had the potential to undo the work of a lifetime . . . of several lifetimes. She had to be disposed of.

It was a disposal made all the more difficult by the destruction of the girl's PINC. Now ABBA was unable to track her, obliging Bole to rely on informers to find out where she was in the Demi-Monde. But, he supposed, there *were* advantages even in this setback, the chief of which was that she would no longer be able to distinguish friend from foe.

Bole sat back in his chair and closed his eyes, concentrating on the task ahead. He had underestimated Ella Thomas and that was not a mistake he would repeat. He would make *doubly* sure that she was eliminated. He had instructed his most trusted crypto to give Beria's man, Zolotov, every assistance in finding and killing the girl, but should Zolotov fail, then the Grigori most certainly would not. It was unthinkable that the formidable Semiazaz, who was standing in a shadowy corner of the café waiting for the last rays of sun to disappear, would allow himself to be bested by a Fragile for a second time.

At the moment, though, Bole was ignoring Semiazaz, letting him contemplate his master's displeasure regarding his failure to kill Vanka Maykov. Bole could smell Semiazaz's embarrassment; the Grigori were not accustomed to having to report a defeat, and by allowing Maykov to escape they had most certainly experienced one. Not a *major* defeat, of course – after all, Maykov was only a bit-part player in the drama unfolding in the Demi-Monde – but a defeat nevertheless.

Bole took a sip of his honeyed water and sighed.

*So many problems.*

He was given no time to ponder this further: he saw the door of the Convent open and Ella Thomas and Sister Florence scuttle out and into a waiting steamer. Behind them came a man Bole recognised as the Marquis de Sade. He almost laughed: Machiavelli couldn't have selected a more ineffectual bodyguard.

*Excellent!*

Now the game was truly afoot. 'There is your prey, Semiazaz,' he said, pointing to Ella Thomas, 'and I beg you, no more mistakes.'

# 19

## Paris
## The Demi-Monde: 14th Day of Spring, 1005

The wearing of masks in the Quartier Chaud is a custom that began shortly after ImPuritanism was adopted as the philosophy governing life in that Sector. Understandably, many CitiZens were uncomfortable and embarrassed by the sexual responsibilities placed on them by ImPuritanism, and took to wearing masks in order to be better able to assume a new and more sexually enfranchised personality. Over time it became de rigueur for all CitiZens, when in public, to wear a mask, as this allowed them to project *any* personality they chose towards the outside world, even personalities diametrically opposite those inculcated by Nature. Hence the famous saying: 'Masks are dangerous things, as behind a mask I am anonymous and there is nothing more dangerous than anonymity.'

A Life of Masks and Masques:
*Giacomo Casanova, Fleshtival Books*

With the Lady IMmanual swathed from head to toe in a hooded, cloak, the Marquis de Sade ushered her and Sister Florence out of the Convent and bustled them towards the waiting steamer. As soon as the three of them were safely aboard, he rapped his knuckles on the panel which separated the passenger compartment from the driver. 'The École Nationale Supérieure des Beaux-Arts,' he ordered, 'and don't stop for anyone or anything.'

As the steamer puffed and panted its way out into the traffic, de Sade pulled down the blinds so that now they were hidden from the outside world. This done, he turned to the Lady. 'When we come to the École, my Lady, we must abandon this steamer. In all probability the Convent is being watched by Beria's cryptos and undoubtedly they will be following us. But do not be alarmed: once we have disembarked, the confusion of the Fleshtival will make it impossible for anyone to pursue us and, hidden by the crowds, we will make our way through Paris to the Basilica in Rome, where agents of the Abbé Niccolò are waiting to escort us to Venice.'

'Mark what the Marquis de Sade says full well, my Lady,' urged Sister Florence. 'But more, it is imperative that thou think and act as a true ImPuritan this night, lest thou draw unwelcome attention to thyself.'

'And how should I act?'

'With sexual abandon. It is the way of ImPuritanism that each CitiZen has a responsibility to aid his brother and sister CitiZens in their quest for sexual satisfaction and for enlightenment through orgasm. During Fleshtivals, all those who participate must make free with their bodies. Mark me well, my Lady, for thou wilt be much accosted and propositioned this night.'

*Now that*, decided de Sade, *is a truism.* No man seeing the Lady in her guise as Lilith would be able to resist her . . . unless he was blind, that is.

'And it is important that by thy reaction thou dost not cause scandal or raise alarums.'

'But if I find these propositions unwelcome?'

'A reckless smile and a butterflied kiss are oft enough to

satisfy all but the most ardent of would-be lovers.' Sister Florence paused for a moment to collect her thoughts. 'For those more determined, or for enemies who may wish thee dead, I will be on hand to protect both thy honour and thy life most forcibly.' Here the Sister conjured a nickel-plated derringer from her cloak. 'There is but one shot in this barker, yet trust thee that I am most accurate and resolute in its use, my Lady.'

Their journey was brought to a premature conclusion a hundred yards or so from the art school, the mass of people swarming through the streets obliging the steamer driver to drop Sister Florence and her two companions at the bottom of Rue de Torquemada. But there was no likelihood of them becoming lost in the strange streets of Saint-Germain-des-Prés: all they had to do was follow the mob. Hundreds upon hundreds of young people, dressed in the most minimal of costumes and displaying a superfluity of flesh, were swarming noisily through the narrow alleys, the local residents leaning out of their windows and doorways yelling encouragement as the revellers passed by. Sister Florence took the Lady's right arm whilst de Sade took her left, and together they steered her into the throng, the three of them being instantly swept away by the mass of dancing, singing and cavorting students, all of whom were dressed in costumes that made those the Sister and the Lady were wearing look the epitome of decorum.

Even Sister Florence, who was used to the ways of ImPuritanism, had never seen so much bare flesh on display. If she had been in any way anxious regarding how openly the Lady's charms were presented, then the number of young women who were clad in nothing more than a loincloth and a smile quickly thrust these concerns to the back of her mind.

There was obviously a huge discrepancy between how Jules had interpreted the theme of 'Daemons and all their Works' and the interpretation given to it by the art students. As far as the students were concerned, the image of Daemons could best be conjured by smearing themselves in red and blue paint and wearing next to nothing . . . and by getting very drunk on cheap Solution. Her worry now was that the Lady IMmanual might have taken too *much* care over how she was dressed. The couturier-contrived costume and body art she sported were considerably more stylish than the rather déclassé outfits of the students, and this inevitably marked the Lady out as being 'different'. Not that the Lady seemed inclined to let this 'difference' prevent her enjoying herself. Tossed around in this shouting, cheering swirl of merrymakers, Sister Florence watched as a student thrust a Solution bottle into the Lady IMmanual's hand. Amazingly, the girl took a deep swig, the price she paid being a very profound kiss and the pleasure of having her right breast fondled. Absent-mindedly, the Sister wondered if the real Lilith ever permitted such familiarity from her disciples.

Zolotov was aghast at the mayhem that greeted him when he stepped out of his steamer. Although he had alighted only seconds after the Lady IMmanual, it was enough time for his quarry to have become lost in the swarm of people that packed the streets.

As he stood there, jostled and pummelled by the crowd, he was at a loss as to what to do next. The Lady IMmanual and the Sister Florence, tall though they were, had vanished from sight. What he needed was a vantage point . . .

Quick as a flash, he clambered up onto the steamer's roof – ignoring the cabbie's protests – and stood there for a moment, peering out over the sea of people.

He saw her!

Leaping down from the steamer, he plunged into the crowd, fighting and wrestling his way towards the girl. It wasn't easy:

the streets were blocked by very drunk and very boisterous students, who obviously thought it a great game to tease and torment a respectable-looking man like Zolotov. His top hat was the first to go, and it was only by the very adept use of his boots and fists that Zolotov was able to ward off several impassioned attacks on his manhood. His bright red codpiece made a very tempting target.

The five minutes he spent struggling in that frenzied mêlée, pushing and shoving his way towards the Lady, were enough to reduce the wonderfully coiffed and costumed man of fashion that was Andrei Zolotov to a howling, deafened vagabond, his jacket torn at the pockets, his trousers soaked in wine and his long hair swishing in disarray about his shoulders. Ever the *élégant*, Zolotov was not pleased, and he determined that he would make this witch pay dearly for his discomfort. Her death, he decided, would be very slow, very painful, and all the more enjoyable for it.

As de Sade quickly discovered after leaving the sanctuary of the steamer, the Fleshtival des Quat'z Arts was a very noisy event. Several makeshift bands were playing – only occasionally in tune – for the encouragement of the crowd, and quite a few of the celebrants had equipped themselves with drums and tambourines, which meant that the crowd moved to a noisy rhythm, every eighth beat being echoed by loud shouts of *vive les artistes* or *vive les sculpteurs*. And to accompany the music and the singing there were jugglers and fire-eaters, acrobats and contortionists, and all of these were mixed up in the confusion of laughter and lovemaking that was the Fleshtival des Quat'z Arts. In the end de Sade simply yielded to fate, allowing himself to be swept along by the tide of people, but after ten minutes of being jostled, pawed and manhandled, deafened by raucous music and drenched in spilt Solution and sprayed champagne, de Sade found it was all becoming just a little overpowering and somewhat unpleasant. He began to feel like an adult who had strayed into a children's party.

Unfortunately, the Lady IMmanual seemed far from bored, that is if the way she was so enthusiastically throwing herself into the spirit of the Fleshtival was any indication. In all the excitement, she seemed to have forgotten that the objective was to use the Fleshtival to cover her escape to Venice. Indeed, the fervent way she was responding to the overtures of the art students suggested that this was the last thing on her mind.

Suddenly the crowd seemed to thin, probably a result of a line of naked girls being borne past atop floats pulled by equally naked male students loudly proclaiming the praises of their particular 'Daemon'. Whatever the reason, it gave de Sade a chance to pull his two companions out of the press. But as they stood in the shelter of a doorway catching their breath, he felt Sister Florence stiffen.

'There . . . over the road,' she gasped, 'dost thou see them? Dost thou see those two tall men masked as Bauta?'

De Sade *did* see them, indeed it was almost impossible *not* to see them, they were so very tall, each man standing a good head taller than any around them. And even by the uncertain glow of the gaslight cast by the lamp standard to their right, it was possible to see that there was something feral about them. De Sade shivered.

'Their auras are inhuman,' stammered Sister Florence, 'like none I have ever encountered. Could they be . . . Grigori?'

*Grigori?*

Grigori were mythological devils who had supposedly haunted a pre-Confinement Demi-Monde. Well, de Sade *hoped* they were mythological; if they were real, then someone was in real trouble. Grigori were reputed to have been evil bastards, with superhuman abilities to boot. But more to the point, their appearance told him that he'd been double-crossed, and that if he didn't move quickly then the rewards he'd been promised would have all the substance of smoke.

And then one of the Grigori did something *very* strange: he inclined his head back, testing the air. De Sade had seen Blood Hounders do the selfsame thing when they searched for the spoor of their prey, and he had no doubt that the Grigori's prey was the Lady IMmanual.

Sister Florence had obviously come to the same conclusion. 'Thou knowest Paris and its districts better than any, de Sade. So I beg thee most earnestly: take the Lady IMmanual to a safe haven.'

Hardly able to believe how generous ABBA was being, de Sade gabbled out an answer. 'Yes, I know a place . . . the Maison d'Illusion. It's a bal-musette – a public dance hall on Rue de Simeon.'

'Good. If I am not with thee in an hour, go from thence to the Basilica and seek Machiavelli.'

'What about you?' asked the Lady IMmanual.

'I am of no consequence. Exchange thy cloak with mine, my Lady, and I will serve as a decoy, leading these most malignant Grigori away from thee.'

Quickly the Lady did as she was bade, the Sister taking her scarlet cloak in exchange for her more anonymous brown one. This done, Sister Florence gave de Sade a fierce look. 'The fate of the Demi-Monde is in thy hands, de Sade. The Lady IMmanual must be preservèd at all cost.' And with that she raised the cloak's hood and disappeared into the crowd.

With the Lady IMmanual at his side, de Sade scurried through the backstreets of Paris, streets which suddenly seemed very dark and very foreboding. Even without the pursuing Grigori, this was a very dangerous arrondissement to be walking around at night. It was not a neighbourhood where respectable people ventured after dark . . . even less than respectable people thought twice about it.

But that was why de Sade had chosen it. The district's clutter of alleyways provided a perfect escape route. No one could follow them here; to do that they'd have to know exactly where they were heading.

Not that de Sade was overly sure where *he* was going. In all the excitement his usually infallible sense of direction had become addled and, as the pair of them twisted and turned through the backstreets, he'd lost his bearings. But thankfully, just as he was about to succumb to panic, he spotted, perhaps fifty metres ahead of him, the glowing lantern that signalled their destination. Its flickering red light illuminated a sign that read 'Maison d'Illusion'.

He and the Lady IMmanual were now standing on the Rue de Simeon, an infamous Parisian thoroughfare favoured by pimps, prostitutes and wayward intellectuals of a particular – even peculiar – bent. It was a place to be careful of, so, taking a firm grip on the butt of his Cloverleaf, he marched the Lady IMmanual along the pavement, the clip-clopping of his boot heels echoing off the scarred walls of the buildings they passed.

The Maison d'Illusion wasn't so much a bar as an open-air dance hall, so even at a distance of fifty metres he could hear the strange music come drifting out of the place. It was located in a courtyard bounded on three sides by the walls of decrepit tenement buildings, the remaining side closed off by a red-painted wooden wall, in the centre of which was an entrance fashioned in the style of a Covenite pagoda. The entrance was guarded by a couple of startlingly young toughs in tattered, baggy suits, who had propped themselves up against the wall on either side of a narrow doorway. It was one of these, a dark-skinned youth sporting an ugly scar on his cheek, who raised his hand to halt the pair of them as they approached.

The boy looked the Lady IMmanual over carefully, winked at her and then asked, '*Combien?*' In reply, de Sade tossed him a franc and a dismissive '*Trop cher,*' which provoked a laugh as the boy stood aside to let them in.

The Maison was crowded with drinkers and dancers, all of them swaying to the music provided by a quartet playing on a low stage set at the rear of the courtyard. Anxious that the Lady IMmanual should understand that bals-musettes also functioned as brothels, de Sade made a whispered entreaty to her that she should not return any looks or stares she might receive from the Maison's customers. In a place like this, misunderstandings were often settled with a knife and the last thing de Sade wanted was to die protecting the Lady IMmanual.

With the dance hall being so crowded, and the moon obscured by clouds, it was almost impossible for de Sade to see where he was going, and what little he could make out in the gloom reminded him of how cheap and down-at-heel the Maison was, the tatty decor made even more vulgar by the efforts of art students to embellish it. Everywhere de Sade looked there were painted images of demons and devils, elves and imps, ghosts and Grigori, which, together with the decadent and diabolical costumes adopted by the students who were capering around the place, gave the Maison a thoroughly sinister ambience.

There was a similarly sinister mixture of patrons. Apart from the boisterous and scantily clad art students, there were customers of a better class who were presumably intent on sampling the primitive and dangerous pleasures of one of Paris's famous bals-musettes. There were women dressed as men, wearing dinner suits and with their hair oiled flat, and men dressed as women, with only their broad shoulders and blue chins betraying their masculinity. Nothing was off-limits in the Maison d'Illusion.

As always, it was the women who caught de Sade's attention, women resplendent in unambiguously and unashamedly provocative costumes created from leather, satin, lace . . . and lots and lots of bare flesh. Certainly their clothes were cheap and brash, and their make-up heavy and obvious, but they wore both with a coquettish exuberance. Steeped as they were in the teachings of ImPuritanism, the women of the Maison were confident in their sexuality.

Indeed, they were so blatant that the Lady IMmanual was emboldened to flaunt her body, too. She pushed her cloak back over her shoulders, allowing it to fall open, making her red-dyed body flex and ripple as she did so, obviously pleased by the way the tops of her black-tinted nipples peeped so cheekily above the leather gilet she was wearing, and that, as she walked, her naked legs glided in and out of view under her transparent skirt.

*Not a wise move*, decided de Sade, especially when he noticed how the tough-looking, hard-faced men were watching her, peering hungrily at her from under their caps. Trying to ignore them, de Sade urged the Lady towards the sanctuary of the dance floor.

There were about thirty couples dancing in front of the stage, moving with passionate abandon in some kind of pastiche of the tango, the men and women locked in a tight embrace as they swayed and snaked around to the sound of the accordion and the rhythm of the guitar. The strange music was a disturbing amalgam of jad and gypsy, syncopated to a rhythm that seemed wrong but also oddly correct.

'Java,' explained de Sade, in answer to the Lady's unvoiced question. 'It's the bastard music of the streets, spawned by the bals-musettes of the Parisian underworld.'

Further attempts to explain were interrupted by a loud shout from across the floor. 'I know you, you bastard!' yelled a tall and well-set man. 'Mask or no, I know you as that bastard the Marquis de Sade.'

De Sade looked up and, to his great relief, found his dissolute past pointing at him from the other side of the smoke-filled dance hall. He knew who the man was: Paul Keller, the father of the girl whose accusations had led to him being exiled from Venice. It was obvious that Rose Keller had got her looks from her father . . . they even wore their moustaches in the same style.

'My Lady, an old acquaintance is beckoning me, one who is less than enamoured of my presence here in the Maison. It would be safer if you were to distance yourself from me for a moment.'

Watching de Sade slink his way into the crowd, the Lady IMmanual couldn't resist smiling: he made a ridiculous guardian. But being such a duplicitous and venal individual, he might have other uses. Yes, de Sade had potential. Further consideration of de Sade's limitations as a bodyguard was cut short when she felt her arm being taken, the hand doing the taking belonging to a lean and very elegantly dressed – if considerably mussed – young man clad in a well-tailored cream suit that showed off his fine figure to perfection. She suspected he was also very handsome, though a mask of red leather concealed his face rather effectively. What the mask couldn't hide was the mischievous twinkle in his eye.

'Mademoiselle,' he yelled to her in heavily accented French, 'would you permit me the honour of introducing myself to the most beautiful and provocative woman in the whole of Paris?'

She had to laugh at the man's impertinence. 'Of course,' she answered with an encouraging smile. She had a soft spot for rascals.

The man clicked his heels military-style, and bowed. 'I am Count Andrei Sergeivich Zolotov, and I have been sent by the Abbé Niccolò Machiavelli to escort you to safety.'

'And the Sister Florence?'

'Quite safe,' announced Zolotov, then he cocked an ear towards the band. 'We have to wait here, Mademoiselle, until more of Machiavelli's agents arrive, so might I be so bold as to suggest a dance? They are, after all, playing our tune.'

*Why not? She was in the mood . . . for many things.*

With a nod she held out her hand.

Zolotov led her out to the centre of the dance floor, clasped her tight in his powerful arms, and then began to sway in a most distracting way to the pulse of the music. She soon felt herself falling under the spell of the strange, hypnotic rhythm, and began moving as sensuously as the other women crowding the floor.

Zolotov danced well, holding her hard against him. He made an excellent partner; he didn't so much dance as ripple across the floor, the joints in his limbs seemingly made of rubber rather than bone and tendon. And the way he used his hands was interesting, especially when they began to make a very intimate exploration of her body.

It was all very . . . stimulating.

For two numbers, Zolotov spun and whirled her around the dance floor, which streamed past in a dizzy blur of colour. It was intoxicating stuff, and as they moved around the floor, sliding their bodies against one another with increasing passion, she realised just how much she was enjoying herself.

But then she had thousands of years of practice in the art of mesmerising men with her charms.

As she twirled about the dance floor, held fast in Zolotov's arms, the Lady was emboldened to ask him a question. 'Tell me,

Monsieur le Comte, are you always so familiar with girls you barely know?'

Zolotov's lips brushed her neck, the fleeting touch making her tremble. 'Of course,' he breathed. 'And, if I might be so bold, your costume this evening does indeed warrant the description "barely".'

She laughed and thrust her body harder against his, encouraging his advances. Flirting, she decided, was an amusing pastime.

'Over here,' he whispered. 'Let us take a moment to get to know each other a little better.' With that he led her off the dance floor to a shadowy alcove. There Zolotov clasped her to him, manoeuvring her so that her back was pushed hard against the wall. She gasped as his hands began to fondle her, delving under her flimsy skirt, and as she arched back in delight she caught sight of herself reflected in the mirror set on the wall of the alcove. The girl that stared back at her looked the embodiment of dissolute sexuality, a disconcerting *mésalliance* of the knowing courtesan and the transcendent naïf.

Duality made flesh.

Delighted by her wantonness, she watched herself as a voyeur might, watched as her arms clasped themselves around Zolotov's neck, as her left leg snaked around him, dragging him harder to her. The juxtaposition of what she was seeing and what she was feeling was so very arousing: she was simultaneously the voyeur, the lover and the loved.

It was the sight of the knife in Andrei Zolotov's hand that drove all thoughts of passion from her mind.

# 20

## Paris
## The Demi-Monde: 14th Day of Spring, 1005

To my mind the most intriguing – and controversial – aspect of all the myths and legends attributable to Lilith are those which involve the Living. The work of Professor Heinrich Schliemann, regarding the deciphering of the Mantle-ite pictograms etched on the Great Wall, has revealed that the Living were imagined by the Pre-Folk to be invisible spirals which were present in all living things. It was Lilith's ability to alter and influence the Living which gave her the power to interfere with the evolution of HumanKind and to create the Lilithi, the Grigori and the Kohanim. It was her hubris in usurping HisHer power over the evolution of HumanKind that moved ABBA to send the Flood that destroyed the Empire of the Lilithi.

**Progressing Backwards: the Curious Case of Pre-Folk Pictograms:** *Professeur Michel de Nostredame, a paper presented to the Pre-Confinement Society of Venice, Fall 1001*

The blade wielded by Zolotov would have gutted her if it hadn't been for the intervention of Sister Florence. Materialising out of the crowd, the Sister grabbed at the knife, taking the thrust through the palm of her outstretched hand.

With a curse Zolotov yanked the knife free, but the moment was gone. There was a sharp and deafening *crack*, the familiar smell of cordite, and then all hell broke loose. The bullet fired from the revolver held in de Sade's shaking hand smashed into Zolotov's shoulder just as he moved in for a second strike, but the hit didn't prevent him dragging out his own pistol and blasting back. What it *had* done was give the Lady the chance to duck behind an overturned table which offered at least a modicum of protection from the flying lead.

The gunfire had a dramatic effect on the crowd. Obviously experienced enough to realise that a gunfight wasn't part of the scheduled entertainments, the crowd had made a mad dash for the exit, an exit which, unfortunately, was too narrow to accommodate the mob of people struggling to put as much distance as possible between themselves and any stray bullets. In a instant, disorder deteriorated into panic: fighting broke out, glasses were thrown, a lamp was smashed and exploded into flames, people screamed and the Maison d'Illusion was reduced to pandemonium.

'Run, my Lady, run!' yelled Sister Florence as she struggled to her feet, cradling her ruined hand. 'This is one of Beria's agents and there may be more of his confederates nearby. Run!'

It was sound advice but, determined not to succumb to the mood of panic, the Lady took a moment to get her bearings, then decided that the best line of retreat wasn't out through the jam-packed entrance, but over the bar, behind which, she hoped, would be the Maison's rear entrance. And as it was better to be armed than not, she grabbed a cane abandoned by one of the fleeing patrons, and, suitably equipped, vaulted the counter, dodged between wooden cases packed with Solution bottles, then raced along a dingy corridor in the hopeful direction of 'Out'. She was in luck. At the end of the corridor she saw a door that led to the streets beyond the dance hall and with one firm shove of her shoulder she had it open.

*

Soaked by a burst of rain, the Lady IMmanual strode along the narrow streets leading away from the chaos and violence that had engulfed the Maison d'Illusion. As she marched through the darkness, her eyes flicked hither and thither, peering into the gloom of the night trying to see if she was being pursued by cryptos of Lavrentii Beria.

And, of course, it would not do for her to forget that the Grigori were also abroad. Oh, she had recognised them immediately, even before they had been pointed out by Sister Florence; she, after all, had been the one who had created them, the most perfect killers the Nine Worlds had ever seen.

It was this somewhat disturbing thought that persuaded her to lengthen her stride, walking until the noise of the fracas engulfing the Maison had faded behind her. Now the only sound accompanying her was the slap of her sandals on the cobbles. Finally, when she was sure that there was no one following her, she paused for a moment under a gas lamp to take stock of her situation and to decide what to do next. But try as she might, she found it difficult to compose herself: her heart was beating like a steam hammer with excitement, and she was almost vibrating with unsated lust.

*Lust?* Now that was a feeling she hadn't experienced for a good many centuries.

Her tryst with Zolotov had rekindled remembrance of what it was to be the master of men, and having them dance to her will. And it was lust seasoned by an undercurrent of danger – even Goddesses could be assassinated – and danger was one of the most potent of all aphrodisiacs. She shivered in the cold night air and tried to calm herself, pleased that she'd kept the cloak with her in the Maison and even more pleased when she found Sister Florence's derringer in one of its pockets.

The question now was, in which direction should she go? It was a difficult thing to answer as her PINC was no longer functioning. Fortunately, from where she was standing she could see the top of the Awful Tower away in the distance and this allowed her to orientate herself. Rome was to the south.

Hefting the comforting weight of the cane in her hand and with a quick glance up and down the street to check it was still empty – the rain and the late hour having ensured that even the most tenacious of Fleshtival revellers had given up for the night – she began to head in what she hoped was the direction of safety.

By her calculations, she was only half a mile or so from Rome when she heard the click of heels reverberating along the deserted streets behind her. The night was crisp and clear, so the sharp snap of steel-capped boots striking on cobbles carried easily through the darkness.

The Lady picked up her pace, and immediately her followers matched it. She dodged right and left down the maze of alleyways, and her followers imitated her, turn for turn. They were moving faster too, closing in on her. She tried to estimate how many were in pursuit, and decided there were three of them – and now they were only a minute or so behind her.

She gave an experimental swish of the cane and that was when she had a moment of inspiration. As she strode along, she tested the cane, twisting the silver pommel, searching for a catch. There was a sharp click and the pommel turned in her hand. The cane was, as she had suspected it might be, a swordstick, and triumphantly she pulled the thin but savagely sharp blade from its scabbard. As a sword, it was a little light for her taste, but in a mêlée it would be a hugely serviceable weapon. But even while she was celebrating this piece of good fortune, Lady Luck turned against her. She glanced up to see that the alleyway she had turned into was a cul-de-sac, blocked at the far end by a huge pair of wooden gates. She was trapped.

As she stood looking about her, searching for an escape route, she heard the pursuing footsteps turn into the alley. Pirouetting, she saw, silhouetted by a gas lamp, two Grigori advancing towards her. They were immensely tall and moved with a dancer's fluency, but from the look of the long blade that each of them held, the dance they were intent on performing was not one that would ever be popular in the more fashionable salons of Paris.

*Grigori* . . .

The Lady IMmanual knew them well. They were old friends . . . and old adversaries. For three thousand years she had bred the Grigori, and generation by generation they had become stronger, faster, more implacable and more fearsome. They had become a race of supreme warriors, the most terrifying breed of humans – or neo-humans – ever to stride the Nine Worlds. She had bred them to be the fastest and the strongest, without peer in battle. She had bred them so they could fight at night, when stealth and surprise gave them advantage over their enemy. She had bred them so they were utterly ferocious and without mercy. And then she had fed them blood.

The Lady IMmanual shook her head in rueful remembrance. As the years had passed and as she trained them and fed them, so they became less and less human. They had hungered for darkness, they had hungered for violence, and they had hungered for blood. And now, once again, they were loosed on the world, the world which had come to know them as vampyres. But formidable though the Grigori were, it would not do to forget that she had once been their Mistress.

Readying herself for their attack, she palmed the derringer into her hand and then shucked off her cloak. If she was to fight for her life, then she would do so unimpeded. This done, she raised her sword to the *en garde* position, and waited as the two Grigori sidled towards her.

It was difficult to make out details of their appearance: the alley was very dark and what light there was was behind the Grigori. All she could see was that they were dressed in tight-fitting black suits, giving them the look of unusually athletic undertakers.

*And that is exactly what they are*, she mused, *and I am destined to provide their next cadaver.*

The Grigori stopped ten feet in front of her and studied her in silence for several long seconds. Finally . . .

'You are Mademoiselle Ella Thomas?' the one on the right asked.

'I do not recognise that name. The girl who once was Ella Thomas is gone, and in her place stands the Lady IMmanual.' She raised her hand and slid the gold cowl from her head, revealing herself to the Grigori. 'By what right do you interrogate me?' she demanded. If she was going to return to the Living, then she would do so resolutely and with honour.

'I am an emissary of Septimus Bole. He requests that you accompany us.'

*Septimus Bole? So the Dark Charismatic finally breaks cover.*

'I fear Professor Bole overreaches himself, regarding the rights of others. I have no inclination to go anywhere with you two . . . gentlemen.'

'Be advised, my Lady, that Professor Bole is unaccustomed to his invitations being refused. If you decline to come with us voluntarily, then unhappily we must . . . persuade you to accompany us.'

She laughed, the sound of her laughter echoing off the walls of the tenements that huddled in onto the alley. 'Be advised, sir, that I take no orders from Septimus Bole or any of his ilk. I am a woman who is ready to fight to protect both her honour and her freedom.' And, for emphasis, she rotated her blade so that it flashed and flickered in the gaslight.

The two men chuckled and the one to the left turned to his colleague. *'Gospodin skazal shto ved'ma dolzhna sdohnut.'*

Thankfully Russian had been spawned by the Old Tongue, and effortlessly she interpreted the words the Grigori had spoken: *The Master has told us this witch must die.* Now, at least, she knew that Bole had ordered her assassination; now she knew this would be a fight to the death. As surreptitiously as she was able, she drew back the hammer on the derringer concealed in her left hand. She suspected that such a tiny pistol would be very arbitrary in its aim and useless at a distance of anything more than a couple of feet. Best, then, to lure one of the Grigori close in before using it.

The Grigori separated, advancing towards her, one on either side of the alley, coming at her from two directions at once. Instinctively, she retreated until her back was firmly against the gates at the end of the cul-de-sac, and then pressed herself as hard into a corner as possible. Positioned in this way, she restricted the options of her attackers, and limited the exposure of her flanks. She shuffled her feet on the cobbles, ensuring as firm a stance on the rain-slick stones as possible, then flexed her knees and the elbow of her sword arm, preparing herself for the onslaught.

From one of the windows above the alley there was a sudden shaft of light as a sleeper disturbed by the voices peeked out, then, seeing the swords brandished, just as quickly re-shuttered the window. But that instant of illumination allowed the Lady to see her adversaries. The Grigori were just as she remembered them: slim and sinewy with almost transparent skin possessing a blue tinge produced by the veins and arteries throbbing beneath it. But, as always with the Grigori, it was their eyes that singled them out as something different, something inhuman. Their eyes were coloured a feline yellow, like the eyes of a ravenous beast.

But if the light had illuminated the Grigori, it had also illuminated her and this prompted a comment from one of her adversaries.

'*Smotri, ona odieta kak Lilit. U neio znak zmei. Na nei simvol Lilit. Ty dumaesh . . . ?*'

*Look, she is dressed as Lilith*, the Lady translated in her head. *She sports the sign of the snakes. She wears the symbol of Lilith. Do you think . . . ?*

'Be quiet,' the other Grigori snapped and immediately his partner was silent. 'It would be better that you surrender to the inevitable, my Lady,' he suggested in an ingratiating tone. 'Your ruse to deceive us by the use of a decoy wearing your red cloak only delayed us, we saw through the deception quickly enough. And any attempt to resist us will be similarly futile: your abilities with that little pig-sticker are undoubtedly inferior to those of myself and my companion with our blades. Surrender or die.'

She said nothing. The die was cast, the time for discussion over, the time for blood was at hand.

The two men took her reticence as the throwing down of the gauntlet. They drew closer, brandishing their long swords more threateningly. 'My Lady, I beg you, do not oppose us. You have no understanding who it is you face.'

*And neither do you!*

They struck simultaneously, and it was their overconfidence that undid them. As she had assumed they would, they had taken her for just a woman, a Fragile, who would, as a consequence, be incompetent in her defence and irresolute in attack. They found themselves disappointed in both respects.

The Grigori on the right made a feint, pretending to lunge, intent upon distracting her attention away from his colleague who made his own attack with astonishing speed. But whilst she was surprised by how quickly the Grigori lunged at her – time had dulled her memory of how fast these creatures of the night moved – it was nothing to the surprise appearing on his face when, in a twinkling, she flicked her blade and turned her defence into attack, flashing the tip of the sword towards the Grigori's eyes, and forceing him into a cursing riposte.

The Grigori retreated a step but in that instant his partner darted towards her, moving so fast that he had grabbed her by the arm before she could pull away. Unfortunately for him, all he succeeded in doing was to wrench the hand holding the derringer hard against his stomach. As soon as she felt the muzzle dig into his guts, she pulled the trigger. There was a muffled *bang*, the Grigori buckled and then staggered back, holding his stomach, his coat scorched from the heat of the bullet.

'*U etoi suki pistolet!*' he gasped.

*Yes, this bitch does have a gun.*

Now the second Grigori attacked with even greater fury, and the speed with which he used his blade incredible. He was far, far faster and far, far stronger than any man had the right to be – but then he wasn't a man.

As their blades clashed, a shudder of pain stabbed through her wrist, as she struggled to hold the Grigori's sword away from her eyes. It took all of her strength and power to hold him and for a second their faces were just inches away from each other's, so close that she could smell his foul breath and could see the fear in the creature's eyes.

Yes, he was frightened of her, frightened of her ability with a blade.

With a surge of strength he pushed her back, then came at her again, his blade a blur of flickering steel, darting this way and that in a maniacal flurry of cuts and sweeps, the blade controlled with almost unimaginable speed, dexterity and power. She retreated, desperately parrying his sword strokes, her arm and wrist aching damnably from the effort needed to withstand the attack and to match the fury of his assault.

But she *was* matching it!

Suddenly she realised that, superhumanly fast though the Grigori was, she was his equal. And as this realisation dawned, a clarity descended upon her. Her sight was suddenly sharper and her speed of thought faster. Now, when the man's blade lunged at her out of the darkness, she saw it clearly and knew instantaneously how to make her riposte. Her movements were faster too, ensuring an effortless ease in the way in which she dealt with the attack, so effortless that, though she still recognised the danger she was in, she exalted in the fight. Now she began to take the fight to her adversary. Now it was *her* blade driving the Grigori back, forcing him to retreat from her sword point. She saw a look of bemused desperation appear on the creature's thin, feral face: a disbelief that someone was matching him . . . and was bettering him.

He made a feint and reeled out of the reach of the Lady's sword, and for a moment the two of them stood considering each other, their panted breath billowing like white steam in the cold night air.

'What are you?' snarled the man. 'What manner of devil are you?'

She said nothing, waiting silently for the next attack, her sword held high, its point aimed directly at the Grigori's face.

From far away, they heard the sound of a police whistle shrilling through the cold night air. The Grigori she had shot with the derringer staggered to his feet. '*Semiazaz, suda idet policya i uzhe svetaet. Poshli!*' he yelled at his comrade.

*Yes, Semiazaz, the police are coming and it is near dawn. You must go.*

For a moment it seemed Semiazaz would fight on, but then, step by reluctant step, he edged back along the alley, though never for one moment did he allow his eyes to leave those of the Lady. 'Know this, day-hag,' he called out to her, 'one day we will meet again and then I will know you for what you are. And on that day I will kill you. On this you have the word of Semiazaz of the Moon.'

With that he turned and, dragging his wounded companion along behind him, hurried out of the alley.

Exhausted by the fight, the Lady slumped back against the wall of the alleyway. She was astonished by her ability with a sword, by the way she had tapped into long-forgotten memories, memories of a time when she had been the finest of all the Lilithi in the use of a blade.

She trembled in the cold night air, which prompted her to pick up her cloak and draw it tightly around her. There was much to think about, but now there were more prosaic problems to solve. She had to get to Venice and, with both Zolotov *and* the Grigori trying to kill her, the sooner she vacated Paris the better. To survive, she had to find a safe haven, but how to get there? It was very late and the streets were empty of cabs and steamers, and for all she knew there were gangs of killers still on her heels.

'You fought amazingly well.' The cultured voice drifted towards her from the open end of the alleyway.

Automatically, if a little wearily, the Lady IMmanual brought her sword back to the *en garde* position, a move that was rewarded with a derisive laugh. 'Somehow, my Lady, I don't think you will find me as big a threat as your previous assailants,' and out of the shadows sauntered the Marquis de Sade. 'Yes, my Lady, I thought you dealt with those . . . things very ably.'

'And you just stood by and watched?'

'Of course! You couldn't possibly expect me to risk life and limb for you *twice* in one evening, now could you? Anyway, I expended all my ammunition trying to blow your would-be assassin's head off and, as I am no master with the sword, I decided that this was one tussle I should sit out.'

She almost laughed. The sheer impudence of the man! His bare-faced, unashamed hypocrisy was breath-taking . . . and potentially, very useful.

'And what of Sister Florence?'

'Wounded and in pain, but otherwise still in one piece.'

The Lady nodded and then smiled an off-kilter smile. This was the moment to entice de Sade into her web. 'And now I suppose you want thanking for intervening on my behalf back in the Maison?'

'Thanking?'

'I have had my appetites piqued this evening, de Sade: piqued but unsatisfied.' With that, the Lady drew back the folds of her skirt to reveal her nakedness. 'I make it a point of rewarding all my disciples who serve me well.'

'It would be an honour, my Lady,' said de Sade, as he unclasped his codpiece.

# Part Three
# Venice

In Lilith I I was reborn.
And reborn I Lilith scorned
ABBA's chaos. I And through Lilith's
Sorcery I the Chaos
Became Perfection.

Perfection she said I is the Iced Touch
Of the Idea. I The Dead Hand that guides.
The Frozen Soul. I The Unvoiced Idea.
The Unfurling I of the Flower
That never Blossoms.

So, to Build I anew
Lilith I in her quiet fury
Reised I This is the first truth.
To build I you must first destroy.
The Vanir vanquished.

Aye, Lilith I destroyed to create.
And by destroying I became the One
Who is Four I Mother
Maiden I Whore
Gaia.

She who would be ABBA I climbed Yggdrasil
The Tree of Knowledge I and in its branches and roots
Found hidden I Knowledge
Became mistress I of the Nine Worlds.
And usurped blind Skuld.

Yes, to Yggdrasil's roots I Lilith delved.
Deep. I Deeper than the deepest
Thought. I Deeper than the deepest
Sorrow. I And there she drank
At the spring of Mimir.

Where bubbles I all knowledge
Of the Living I and of Seidr.
Here Freyas salt tears I flow.
Here Lilith came to know I the truth
Of the Living.

Lilith I drank greedily.
Became I the Mistress of Time
The Mistress of Darkness I the Mistress of Death
The Mistress of Thought. I Became
The Dark Mistress of the Living.

Then Lilith I Trickster that she was
Caused the Lilithi I to rise
Caused the Grigori I to rise
Caused the Kohanim I to rise
Trickster and Fool.

*Diagram and translation reproduced by kind permission of Snore Igholinn, Cartographer-General to the Court of Her Most Reverend Excellency, Doge Catherine-Sophia*

# THE EDDIC OF LOCI 3: LILITH
PLATE 3

# 21

## The White House: Washington DC
## The Real World: 15 September 2018

By any measure the vaccine distribution network established by Frank Kenton to combat the Plague that swept
across the US in the spring of 1947 was responsible for
saving millions of American lives. Hailed as 'America's
Saviour' and with impeccable Evangelical credentials, it
was a given that Kenton would be wooed by the Republican
Party to stand as its Presidential candidate in the elections
of 1949. Kenton accepted the nomination and in the
campaign that followed, showed that he, more than
anyone in the political establishment, had grasped that
the mood and the make-up of America had fundamentally
changed. Americans believed the Plague had been sent by
God to punish them for their sinfulness and that was why
only the faithful had been spared. Kenton's policies
reflected this: his election platform was that he would
change the First Amendment to the effect that henceforward the US would be an exclusively Protestant country
where religious freedom was robustly curtailed.

iSuccess in GCSE-Dip: A Revision Guide to Modern
History, *ParaDigm Publications*

There was a noticeable spring in Aaliz Heydrich's step as she
walked along the White House corridor to the room where she

would be meeting with Jim Kenton and his wife. That she had just imbibed a full one hundred millilitres of prime-stock Italian blood had something to do with it – her spirits and her mental acuity always soared after partaking – but there was more to it than that.

That she'd managed to rid herself of most of the stupid affectations of her host body certainly helped. She'd had her hair cut to a more sensible length and dyed back to an approximation of her natural blonde colour. She'd completely overhauled her wardrobe, with all those rather infantile goth outfits consigned to one of Washington's numerous charity shops. And she'd finally persuaded her 'mother' to stop trailing around after her, watching every move she made.

But the main reason for Aaliz Heydrich's excellent mood was that today she would finally begin the journey that would see the fulfilment of her destiny, and would hasten the moment when she would be reunited with her father – her *real* father. Soon they would stand shoulder to shoulder as master and mistress of this, the Real World.

Waiting for her in the conference room were Jim Kenton and his wife Marsha – aka God's Couple – the most famous and influential evangelists in America. But after having spent several hours studying Polly footage of the pair and watching edited highlights of their tele-missionary work, in the flesh Aaliz found them something of a disappointment. They were certainly older than Aaliz had expected. A Polly scan had told her that Jim Kenton was in his mid-fifties, the exact year of his birth somewhat mutable, and his wife a couple of years younger, but by the look of them Aaliz suspected they'd shaved a good ten years off their true ages. Oh, the lines and the wrinkles were skilfully concealed by tucks and Botox injections but all this did was give them that peculiarly doll-like appearance typical of those trying to conceal the ravages of time.

And then, of course, there was their use of the wonder of PollyMorphing; but nobody ever talked about *that*.

Kenton stepped forward as Aaliz entered the room. 'Good morning, Miss Williams. I'm the Reverend Jim Kenton, and this here's ma wife Marsha.' His Southern drawl was so thick that Aaliz had trouble understanding him. 'May I say what an honour it is to be invited to the White House.'

The codicil 'at last' was left unvoiced.

As Aaliz took the man's soft, plump hand, she sensed from the look in his eyes how aggrieved he was that the President had never allowed him anywhere near this, the ultimate seat of power. Not that he should have been surprised: President Sam Williams hated Jim Kenton and all the religious nonsense spouted by Believers' Broadcasting.

But Jim Kenton's chagrin was understandable. Ever since the First Prophet, Frank Kenton, had been elected President in 1949, the Kenton clan had ruled America. Indeed it had only been the humiliation following the 12/12 Outrage that had given a platform for Sam Williams's nuDemocrats to squeak – by the narrowest of electoral margins – into the White House. The defeat obviously still rankled: as far as Jim Kenton saw it, Samuel Williams had deprived him of his birthright. The two men loathed one another.

The hatred was so intense that it had taken Aaliz a great deal of effort – and crying – before her father had reluctantly given her permission to meet with Kenton. That Professor Bole had had a quiet word with him had helped: since Bole had so miraculously restored his daughter's memory, the Professor, in the President's eyes, could do no wrong.

Aaliz waved her guests into seats, and settled herself on the chair opposite. 'May I thank you for taking the time to visit with me today,' she began. 'As you may have read, I have been ill recently but now I am quite recovered.'

A 'God be praised' from Jim Kenton, and an indulgent smile from his wife. 'Perhaps we should pray?' he suggested. 'Remember what Jesus told us, my child: "Whatever you ask for in prayer, believe that you will receive it, and it will be yours."'

'Amen,' said Marsha Kenton.

'Mark 11:22,' observed Aaliz sweetly, after a prompt from PINC, though inwardly she did object to Kenton's patronising tone. *Child, indeed!* 'As I was saying, the illness I suffered was quite traumatic, leaving me helpless in a coma. But on waking from unconsciousness, it would seem that I have undergone a radical transformation of spirit. My illness, Mr and Mrs Kenton—'

'Jim and Marsha, please.'

'My illness, Jim and Marsha, provoked a revelation. Just as Paul experienced his epiphany on the road to Damascus, so I had mine in a hospital bed in the Walter Reed Hospital. In short, Jim and Marsha, I have found God.'

'Hallelujah,' the Kentons responded in unison.

'I have been called by God to do a great work, and to lead the children of America back to His Grace.'

'To lead?' queried Marsha Kenton, who Aaliz suspected was uncomfortable with anyone other than her husband being called upon by God to *lead*.

'Yes, God has told me how Satan has been undermining the spiritual and moral health of our beloved country by corrupting America's youth. Young people today are addicted: they are addicted to drugs, they are addicted to the demon drink, and they are addicted to sex and other pleasures of the flesh. This is Satan's handiwork, and God has set me the task of freeing young people from these addictions and guiding them back to the path of righteousness.'

Such was Aaliz's blind certainty that Jim Kenton was stunned into silence. He simply sat on the couch with his mouth hanging open in a most unappealing manner. It was left to his wife to try to take control of the situation. 'You've *spoken* to God?'

The look on the woman's face was a picture of incredulity. It was one thing for the Kentons to claim to be in regular and intimate communion with God, but it was quite another for them to meet with someone else who believed they were doing the same thing. It seemed, as far as Marsha Kenton was concerned, that when Jim spoke with God it demonstrated his divinity, but when someone like Norma Williams spoke to Him, it demonstrated that they were out to lunch.

'Yes,' confirmed Aaliz with a breezy smile, 'I have spoken to God, and His message is very clear. I am to form a youth league to be called the Fun/Funs.'

'The Fun/Funs?' From the expression on Marsha Kenton's face, this conversation was progressing rapidly from the rather odd to the downright lunatic.

'It's short for the Fun-Loving Fundamentalists. It's God's name for the movement that will put the joy and the certainty back into young people's lives.'

'But we've already got several youth groups,' spluttered Marsha. 'We've our own League of Young Believers.'

Aaliz paused to pour some coffee for her bemused guests. 'The fact is, Marsha, God was quite disparaging to me about the existing Christian youth movements: He called them "Mickey Mouse".'

'God said that?'

'His very words. He said that these youth movements would never be successful because they lack two important elements.'

'And these are?' asked Jim Kenton cautiously.

'Well, the first is obvious. They lack a charismatic leader.'

The Kentons glanced at one another, presumably thinking they already had a charismatic leader in Jim Kenton. 'And who would be the "charismatic leader" of these Fun/Funs of yours?'

'Why, *me*, of course. God says I must dedicate my life to the saving of America's youth. For many years we Americans have betrayed the sacred trust God placed in us. We allowed Satan to infiltrate our lives and to corrupt our great country. In the years since the Founding Fathers inaugurated the bastion of faith that is the USA, this blessed land has been diminished in stature: it has gone from being the most powerful country in the world to being one that is reviled and humiliated. We have been weakened and distracted by the specious, devilish, nuJu . . . Jew-inspired philosophy of humanism. We have been confused and rudderless. The First Punishment God imposed for this dereliction of our divine duty was, of course, the Great Plague of '47, but even after such a profound cleansing of the ungodly the United States has never been able to fulfil its manifest destiny. God believes this is because American leadership has been weak and ineffective. He is *very* annoyed.'

Jim Kenton's eyes widened. He obviously took God's criticism personally, especially as the majority of the presidents since the Great Plague had been Kentons.

'Yes,' Aaliz went on, 'America has betrayed its Protestant legacy, and by doing so has betrayed God. The unjust terms imposed by those hateful British in reprisal for the 12/12 destruction of Edinburgh were God's way of punishing Americans because their faith faltered. This was the Second Punishment, suffered when we allowed ourselves to be led astray by presidents who were nothing more than false prophets, claiming they were God's messengers when in reality they were nothing more than charlatans.'

Jim Kenton twitched, which was hardly surprising given that Aaliz had just dismissed the work and the divinity of all of the Kenton clan for the past sixty years. He began to object, but Aaliz would have none of it. Before Kenton could get another word out, she had moved on. 'God has told me that we must now plan for the future and to do this we must expunge doubt and addiction from America's youth. In this way we will forge a nation which is united by one blood, one nationality, one language, one religion, and by a government blessed by God.'

There was an awkward silence, and Aaliz took the opportunity to pour herself a fresh cup of coffee. Neither Jim nor Marsha seemed to have touched theirs.

Jim Kenton shuffled nervously on his chair. 'Miss Williams . . . Norma, whilst I am always reluctant to dampen anyone's enthusiasm for doing God's work, I don't think you quite understand the enormity of the task facing you. Sure you are an attractive, intelligent young woman. Sure you have a certain celebrity. But it will take more than that to establish these Fun/Funs of yours. That your father is one of the most liberal presidents in living memory *and* an avowed atheist will make people suspicious of your motives. They'll think this is just a madcap scheme to make him more popular in the Bible Belt . . . after all, there's an election due in two years. And then there's the more prosaic problem of money. To set up and promote an effective youth league, you'll need a minimum of a hundred million dollars of seed money—'

'Two hundred million,' interjected Marsha Kenton helpfully.

'Two hundred million.' Jim Kenton shook his head. 'No, Norma, better that you take on something a mite less ambitious. Fund-raising for the poor and the destitute, perhaps? That sort of thing.'

Aaliz gave a dismissive wave of her hand. 'Oh, God's got much bigger plans for me than just being involved in charity work. He's content to leave that in the hands of less able people like you, Marsha.' Marsha Kenton went bright red but, to give her credit, she did manage to bite her tongue. 'This brings me to the second thing that God's been telling me,' continued Aaliz. 'In His opinion, the other problem with existing youth movements is their lack of miracles.'

'Miracles?' prompted Jim Kenton, a baffled look on his face.

'That's right, miracles. The reason why Christian youth movements have been so uniformly unsuccessful – apart from having poor leadership, that is – is that they have not been able to convince their target audience that they are truly backed by God. What they palpably lack is the ability to perform miracles.'

'Miracles?' murmured Jim Kenton again. He was obviously having difficulty in assimilating what Aaliz was saying. She decided to make it simpler.

'Miracles are important, Jim, because they prove that you've been endorsed by God. It's a little perplexing for Christians when they are obliged to stop to ask why God isn't a little more hands-on, isn't more out-and-about, so to speak, raising the dead, curing the infirm or feeding the hungry. It's all very well moving in mysterious ways, but if there is a distinct lack of divine involvement, then the people in the cheap seats tend to get a trifle restless. God has recognised this and has asked me to take up the slack.'

'You're going to perform miracles?'

'Yes.'

'What sort of miracles?'

'I will dispel addiction.'

'Addiction?'

'Addiction is the root cause of all the corruption in the world, Jim, and I will dispel it.'

'How?'

'By using a Get-Me-Straighter Meter.'

'A *what?*'

'A Get-Me-Straighter Meter,' Aaliz repeated. 'It's a device which allows me to realign a soul. God has told me how the soul residing within a human being flows through spiritual pathways that criss-cross the body and unify all its parts. It is akin to the Japanese concept of Qi, the life essence that permeates our bodies and maintains our mind and our soul. When a boy or a girl is caught in the grip of an addiction, these pathways become twisted and blocked. God has shown me how to straighten them out using my GMS Meter.'

'Does it work?'

'Of course it works!' said Aaliz indignantly. 'It's God-inspired, after all.' She gave her guests an innocent smile. 'Shall I demonstrate it on you, Jim and Marsha? Shall I show how it can eradicate *your* addictions?'

'I don't have any addictions,' objected Jim Kenton.

'Oh, I think we both know that's a lie,' said Aaliz quietly. 'ABBA, I would be grateful if you would show the footage taken by moteBot in the bedroom of Jim Kenton yesterday evening.' The screen covering the side wall of the conference room ignited into a swirl of colours, and then settled down to show a high-quality eyeVid of Jim Kenton leaning over the glass top of his wife's dressing table snorting two very long lines of cocaine.

'How?'

'How did I get a moteBot past your Sentinels? God only knows, Jim.'

'But . . . but . . . but that's a violation of the privacy assurances contained in the Patriot Protection Act,' spluttered Jim Kenton. 'It's illegal to use moteBots to violate an individual's Domestic Curtilage.'

'Absolutely correct, Jim, and absolutely fucking irrelevant. If I was to have ABBA post this on the Polly, the violation of your human rights would be the least of your concerns, you'd be too busy defending yourself against charges of rampant hypocrisy. It's one thing to fulminate against drugs, Jim, and it's quite another to be caught using them – especially when I have footage of you undergoing surgery in Brazil to repair a rather large oro-nasal perforation caused by your excessive snorting.'

Jim Kenton slumped back in his chair, all colour drained from his face.

'And, of course, Marsha, you have your *own* demons to wrestle with, don't you? What does the Christian Women's Forum, of which you are chairperson, say about lesbianism? That it's an abomination and a vile affectation, I believe.'

The next footage ABBA ran was remarkable both for its clarity and its graphic content. Indeed, it was so clear and so graphic that for a moment Aaliz worried that Marsha Kenton might be about to suffer a coronary. 'You're right to be worried, Marsha,' Aaliz oozed. 'This could be an *enormous* Polly hit! I especially like the tuxedo you're wearing, very Dietrichesque. It demonstrates a certain equivocality in your sexuality which explains what Congresswoman Samples is doing to you with that . . . object.'

'What do you want?' asked Jim Kenton, in a whisper.

'I want to save you.' Aaliz stood up and walked across to the table standing in the centre of the room. With a theatrical flourish, she drew back a sheet from a black and very purposeful-looking machine. 'This is a GMS Meter, and I'm going to use it to rid you of your addictions. After all, Jim and Marsha, it won't do for my new partners-in-God to be flawed.'

'Your partners?'

'Yes, tomorrow you will announce that I have been appointed as the new leader of your Young Believers movement, which we'll then rechristen the Fun-Loving Fundamentalists. There's a PollyPress release already being prepared, so you won't have to worry about any of the nasty little administrative details. Then you'll make the two hundred million dollars you have stashed away in that oh-so-private bank account in the Grand Caymans over to the Fun/Funs to pay for its launch.' She smiled. 'God tells me the Fun/Funs will be a great success. He's already given me the eyeMail addresses of thirty million new members.'

# 22

## Paris
## The Demi-Monde: 25th Day of Spring, 1005

Consider individuals as you would the stones and the rocks that constitute the detritus of our temporal avalanche. These stones and rocks – Nature's quantum elements – move and tumble in a seemingly haphazard and chaotic fashion, and hence could be said to possess Quantum-InDeterminism, which is akin to free will. However, an overly bright young philosopher named Nikolai Lobachevsky working in the Coven has shown us that the quantum world is *not* random, it is merely so complex that we had been unable to discern the patterns underpinning its behaviour. By discovering that pattern, Lobachevsky demonstrated that there is order within all chaos and gave support to Laplace's notion that we live in a Clockwork Universe.

A LayPerson's Guide to preScience: *Nikolai Kondratieff, Future History Institute Press*

Beria hated to be away from the ForthRight, but since the debacle in the Bastille, Heydrich had been very insistent that he take a more hands-on approach to the pacification of the Quartier Chaud.

Being away from the centre of power, Beria felt cut off, out of touch and very vulnerable. Although he had a myriad of cryptos and informants squirrelled away within the White House, none of them was able to communicate to him the feel of the place; none of them could sense, as he could, the mood of the Great Leader or the way the political wind was blowing. Who knew what schemes and betrayals his enemies – and Beria had *so* many enemies – were plotting behind his back? And since that little shit Archie Clement had returned from the Coven – wounded but unfortunately still breathing – Beria's most formidable rival had the Leader's ear. How that cow Trixiebell Dashwood could have missed from such close range was astonishing.

But he had needed to come to Paris. Whilst Comrade General Skobelev, the Commander of the ForthRight army, was quite capable of blasting down the city's gates and marching the army around to terrify the population, the more subtle arts of diplomacy and realpolitik were beyond him. And anyway, since the Lady IMmanual's escape from the Bastille, the Leader had become somewhat agitated, so agitated, in fact, that Beria thought it wise to keep certain intelligence hidden from him. He saw no reason why the Great Leader should be burdened with the news of Zolotov's failure to kill the bitch. This was something that he would deal with personally and quietly: it didn't do to admit to failure in the ForthRight.

Absent-mindedly, Beria gazed out at the streets of Paris streaming past the window of his armoured steamer and was pleased to note that it had the appropriately hushed and fearful feel of an occupied city. And the Parisians had every right to be fearful because after the outrage of the Bastille, Beria's Checkya – aided and abetted by the Inquisition – had gone to work with a vengeance, weeding out the counter-revolutionaries and the rest of the reactionary scum that polluted the Medi. Weeding them out and then hanging them by piano wire from the lamp-posts that lined the Champs-Élysées. Beria was a great believer in advertising.

But whilst he was relatively satisfied with the security situation in the Medi, he was less sanguine about the progress made in achieving the secondary objective of the occupation, to wit, stripping the Sector of all its wealth. These economic adjustments were fast becoming *urgent* economic adjustments, otherwise by the Summer the ForthRight would be bloodrupt. War was an expensive business.

On the very day the ForthRight Army had entered the Quartier Chaud, Doge Catherine-Sophia had decreed that all trades handled by the Rialto Bourse with respect to the ForthRight be summarily suspended. Immediately the Bourse had frozen all ForthRight assets, including a sizeable proportion of its out-of-Sector blood reserves. Overnight the guinea had come off the Blood Standard and been hit by intense nuJu-inspired speculation. The ForthRight had been reduced to having to pay for its imports blood-on-the-nail.

And of course, the misery hadn't stopped there. Ever eager to kick a man – especially a *man* – when he was down, those bastard LessBiens in the Coven had demanded an ever higher blood-price for their coal. The ForthRight had, reluctantly – *very* reluctantly – been obliged to accede to this bloodmail as without coal its steamers would stop, its engines would grind to a halt, and its people would go cold. The ForthRight had paid up, and the consequence was that its blood reserves were being fast depleted.

So, to keep the ForthRight's war machine running, the order had gone out to confiscate every last drop of blood from the Blood Banks of Paris, Rome and Barcelona.

Lost in these unhappy thoughts, Beria hardly noticed that his steamer had arrived at the Élysée Palace where he was to have his audience with Senior CitiZen Robespierre. Robespierre, as was right and proper, was standing on the palace steps, waiting to greet his distinguished visitor. It was the first time Beria had met the man, and for someone with such a formidable reputation as a dispenser of firm government he was a disappointment. Beria – a sometime student of physiognomy – studied Robespierre's face carefully as he climbed the steps, and silently declared himself less than impressed. The man's eyes were set too far apart – denoting stupidity; his nose and mouth were small – denoting pettiness and a love of detail; and his skin and hair colour were almost albino-pale – denoting that his mother hadn't been too picky about who she slept with.

'Three sectors Forged as One,' declared Beria as he made the party salute.

In reply Robespierre made a grandiloquent bow, sweeping the polished marble floor with his top hat as he did so. 'Comrade Vice-Leader, may I welcome you to Paris and assure you that my city stands ready to embrace both the liberating forces of the ForthRight and the True Religion, UnFunDaMentalism.'

Beria smiled and decided not to begin this encounter by quibbling over Robespierre's claim that Paris was *his* city. With five divisions of the ForthRight's RedCoats currently marching through its streets, there was only one person who could be said to be in control of Paris . . . him. 'I bring fraternal greetings from Comrade Leader Heydrich, who congratulates you on your success in leading the people of the Quartier Chaud out of the shadows of ImPuritanism and into the uplands lit by the light of UnFunDaMentalism.' Beria hated all this diplomatic shit, but he knew it went down well with the peasants.

Then followed an interminable ten minutes posing for daguerreotypists from the press, after which Robespierre led Beria to his private offices.

As was his wont, Beria got straight down to business. 'I understand that the decrees regarding the pacification of the Medi made after the unfortunate events at the Bastille have been successfully promulgated.'

There was silence from Robespierre.

Perhaps the fool needed prompting. 'These included a dusk-
to-dawn curfew, the banning of gatherings of more than four
people, the reduction of the blood ration, the closure of all
ImPuritan temples, and the prohibition of Fleshtivals and of
the wearing of masks.'

'I am familiar with the content of the decrees, Comrade Vice-
Leader . . .'

Beria took a self-satisfied sip of his Solution. If there was one
thing he was skilled in, it was cowing a recalcitrant population.

'. . . but . . .' continued Robespierre.

Beria looked up: he wasn't a great lover of 'but's.

'. . . but, unfortunately, these measures have caused a great
deal of unrest.'

'Unrest?' queried Beria.

'It is the edict regarding the wearing of masks that the people
have found most irksome, Comrade Vice-Leader.'

'Masks?' asked a decidedly baffled Beria.

'Yes, Comrade Vice-Leader, there is a feeling that the removal
of masks will stifle the amatory pursuits of the Medis.'

Beria began to feel a little confused. He had been expecting
a discussion regarding how best to deal with rebels and malcontents, yet here they were discussing trivia. 'Amatory pursuits?'
he ventured.

'You should understand, Comrade Vice-Leader, that the
wearing of masks in the Quartier Chaud is a tradition of many
hundreds of years' standing. It is something of an *idée fixe* with
the hoi polloi. They believe masks to be an indispensable aspect
of recreational lovemaking, which in turn is seen as vital in
sustaining a CitiZen's sexual animus. Without his or her mask,
a Medi feels somewhat neutered.'

Beria sensed that his grip on the conversation was starting
to slip. *What is this idiot talking about?*

'But casual sex is anathema to UnFunDaMentalism,' protested

Beria, who for the first time in his life wished that clown Crowley was with him to debate this sort of theological claptrap. 'The creed of Living&More teaches us that sexual relations with a woman who is not your wife lead to a diminishing of the bodily humors and a depletion of potency.'

'Of course, of course,' agreed Robespierre hurriedly. 'To intellectuals such as you and me, Comrade Vice-Leader, the denial of the urges of the body is recognised as being essential in the quest to attain oneness with the Supreme Being . . .'

Robespierre *was* a fool, decided Beria: he actually *believed* all this Living&More twaddle. *Real* politicians saw it for the nonsense it was, merely a means by which the masses could be controlled and their animal urges directed to more constructive ends.

'. . . but for the man and woman in the street, accustomed to being guided by their loins rather than their logic, it is a matter of some moment. Medis *like* wearing masks.'

Beria sighed. He could not believe, with the thousand and one urgent issues he had confronting him, that he was squandering time discussing *masks*. 'Comrade Senior CitiZen, please, we are trying to pacify a Sector. We are trying to eradicate all the numerous malcontents and seditionists that oppose our great work. To do this we have to be able to identify those who are our enemy, and then shoot them. Now, I may be being a little obtuse, but I think this process is not helped by everyone in the Sector wandering around wearing a fucking – and I use this adjective deliberately – mask.'

'I understand, Comrade Vice-Leader, but—'

Beria's fist slammed down on the table, and Robespierre jumped back in shock. 'With all due respect, Comrade Senior CitiZen, no more fucking "but"s. Nothing – *nothing* – must be allowed to stand in the way of the Rapprochement. So are we agreed that anybody seen wearing a mask on the streets of the Medi is to be shot on sight?'

Robespierre whispered a quavering 'Yes' in reply.

Beria took a long slurping gulp of Solution in an effort to calm himself. 'Shall we move on? So tell me, Comrade Senior CitiZen, how goes the rounding up of the Shades?'

Robespierre had turned quite pale, which, given his lack of skin colour, was quite an achievement. 'Not well, Comrade Vice-Leader. There is a high level of Shadophilia in the Quartier Chaud based on the belief – a *mistaken* belief – that Shade men are better endowed than other races. Shade men are very popular in the Medi, especially with Medi women.'

A groan from Beria. 'Does everything in the Quartier Chaud revolve around sex?'

'Pretty much, Comrade Vice-Leader. The Medi people *like* Shades, and this is an attitude reinforced by the rumour that you mean to execute them all.'

Beria was astonished by Robespierre's naïveté. '*Of course* I'm going to execute them all. I am searching for the ForthRight's most deadly and intractable enemy, the Shade girl named variously Marie Laveau, Ella Thomas and the Lady IMmanual. The same girl, lest we forget, that *you* had captive in the Bastille but allowed to escape.'

Robespierre at least had the good grace to blush.

'And the simplest way of eliminating her is to shoot *all* the Shades in the Medi.'

'Male Shades as well?'

Another longer sigh from Beria. 'When you have been in the business of maintaining the peace and tranquillity of a Sector for as long as I have, Comrade Senior CitiZen, you will come to realise that the instructions given to your security forces – who are, of necessity, intellectually challenged – must be as simple as possible. Now, the instruction "shoot all Shade women" necessitates them having to make *two* intellectual judgements: they have to decide whether the person in front of them is a Shade and then to decide whether that person is female. As this can lead to confusion, better therefore to reduce the instruction to its most basic. The instruction thus becomes "shoot all Shades". Do you understand?'

'Yes, but the NoirVillian Ambassador has made strenuous objections.'

'Is he a Shade?'

'Why, yes.'

'Then just shoot the fucker.'

This advice was so implacable that Robespierre was rendered speechless for several seconds. He spent that time rearranging his already immaculately arranged desk furniture into an even more immaculate disposition. Finally he roused himself from his trance, and spoke. 'I understand you also wish to discuss the visit of Comrade Great Leader Heydrich to Paris, in order that he might sign the Declaration of Unification ratifying the Rapprochement of our two great Sectors.'

'Indeed, Comrade Senior CitiZen, and it is, of course, essential that I satisfy myself of the Great Leader's safety whilst he is in Paris for this ceremony. Recent events have somewhat undermined confidence in the efficiency of your security forces. That a mob of *women* should be able to storm the Bastille . . .'

Robespierre wrung his hands. 'Yes, it *was* a humiliation. *More* than a humiliation, since the Medi lost a great leader in the disturbances. His Excellency, Senator Godfrey de Bouillon will be sorely missed.'

*So now it's the Gang of Two.*

'And we must not forget that Grand Inquisitor Torquemada was severely wounded by these harridans from Hel.'

*Correction: the Gang of One and a Half.*

'But you should have no concerns regarding security, Comrade Vice-Leader. There will be no repetition of those deplorable events. Even as we speak, the Inquisition is moving to root out malcontents and troublemakers from within the Medi.'

*Fuck the Inquisition. It's the Checkya who will be sorting out the Medi.*

'Of course,' Beria replied in his most conciliatory voice, 'and I am sure, with the help of the Checkya, that the Medi will soon be tranquil. And this brings me on to my next point: the Awful Tower.'

'The Awful Tower?' All the bounce had gone out of Robespierre's voice: he now sounded like a whipped dog.

'Yes, I believe that the refurbishment of the Tower is nearing completion.'

A suspicious nod from Robespierre. 'Indeed. We are refurbishing the Tower to commemorate the embracing of UnFunDaMentalism by the Medi. Our plan is that it will be reopened on Spring Eve, on Walpurgisnacht.'

'Could the reopening be brought forward?'

A frown. 'I suppose so. The engineers report that only minor cosmetic works are outstanding.'

'Good. I have been looking, Comrade Senior CitiZen, for a symbol of the unity of our two Sectors; for something that embodies the Quartier Chaud's embracing of UnFunDaMentalism. UnFunDaMentalism has at its heart the concept of Biological Essentialism, that men are superior to women, and the phallus is the symbol of that natural superiority, is it not?'

'Yes . . .'

'And the Tower *is* a very phallic structure.'

'Yes . . .'

'I think it would be symbolic of the union of the Forthright and the Medi if Great Leader Heydrich was to be invited to Paris to officially open the refurbished Tower, and for the Tower to be renamed the Reinhard Heydrich Tower in his honour.'

Robespierre looked decidedly unhappy about this suggestion.

'The Senate was rather leaning towards calling it the "Maximilien Robespierre Tower",' he said a little testily.

'Oh no, we can't have any "leanings" where towers are concerned.' Robespierre seemed to be less than amused by Beria's quip. 'No. I really must insist: let it be the Reinhard Heydrich Tower.'

The look Beria gave Robespierre was enough to convince the man that any further objections would be both futile *and* dangerous.

'Very well.'

'Good, then let us plan to have the opening on the sixtieth day of Spring. Thirty-five days should be enough for you to organise a spontaneous outpouring of the joy of the Medi population, should it not? It must be a grand affair, with fireworks . . . lots and lots of fireworks. The Great Leader likes fireworks.'

All Robespierre could do was nod.

# 23

## Venice
## The Demi-Monde: 25th Day of Spring, 1005

```
TO DOCTEUR NIKOLAI KONDRATIEFF FUTURE HISTORY
INSTITUTE VENICE PO BOX 27/54 + + + UNBABELISING OF
FLAGELLUM HOMINUM COMPLETE + + + WAR IN QUARTIER CHAUD
PRECLUDES FRWDING COPY 2 U + + + B AWARE REVELATIONS
ASTONISHING + + + RAGNAROK UPON US + + + IMPERATIVE
REPEAT IMPERATIVE COLUMN DOES NOT FALL UNDER CONTROL
OF THE BEAST + + + PLS CONFIRM SOONEST <<ONE WITH
NO SHADOW>> SAFE/UNTHREATENED + + + CODE NOIR AGENT
DESPATCHED 2 VENICE 2 ASSIST + + + ETHOBAAL
```

**PAR OISEAU**

*Copy of PigeonGram message sent by Doctor Jezebel Ethobaal*
*on 23rd day of Spring, 1005*

Burlesque Bandstand sat sipping his glass of Solution on the veranda of the Café de Rialto, enjoying both the afternoon sunshine and the hustle and bustle of the area around the Bridge of Thighs. He liked Venice. It was by repute the wealthiest city in the whole of the Demi-Monde, and it wore its wealth on its sleeve. The buildings were fine and richly decorated, and Burlesque especially liked the way they were painted bright colours. It made a change from the dour and monochromatic Rookeries where everything was coloured a shade of off-turd.

And Venice was such a *clean* city. The streets were regularly swept and were, amazingly, free of the shit and refuse that befouled the streets of London. This he put down to the Venetians having all these funny canals running through the place: anything swept into them was eaten by exCreatures. Bloody convenient.

The Venetians seemed a well-made people too – there were no blood-starved indigents begging on the streets of Venice – and remarkably well dressed. Of course, the style of their clothes had taken Burlesque a little getting used to. The colours were a little too sharp for his taste, but he liked the masks and he most certainly approved of how provocatively the women dressed . . . or rather undressed. Venetian women were inclined to show a lot of flesh.

All in all, Burlesque had decided that Venice was his sort of town. It was busy and vibrant and full of chattering crowds of people. Indeed the muddle of people swarming around the café was as fair a cross-section of the peoples of the Demi-Monde as he could imagine. There were NoirVillian sailors with monkeys on their shoulders, Chink NoNs mincing their way to the Bourse, gondoliers in their striped shirts taking a shot of Solution and eyeing the crowd for customers, and even the occasional red-robed Visual Virgin en route to the Convent.

Yeah, Burlesque liked Venice, and most of all he liked that he'd managed to get there with his SAE intact. Well, almost intact. The bullet wound in his arse was still giving him gyp.

After the set-to with Stan Shoreham, the three of them – Rivets, Odette and himself – had escaped under cover of night, making their getaway from Paris via steam charabanc. It had been a miserable journey, Burlesque having to endure the four hours that the steamer had taken to meander its way from Paris through Rome and Barcelona, while seated on a hard wooden bench surrounded by squabbling children, wicker cages packed with squawking chickens, and by the very large women who were taking said chickens to market.

But these discomforts and the throbbing of his wounded arse were as nothing to the suffering inflicted on him by Odette. The girl seemed never to tire, and she had talked to him non-stop in her indefatigably chirpy manner – and in her heathen French – from the moment the charabanc had left the station. The other irritant was that she'd developed a passion for patting him: she patted him on his knees, on his head, on his cheeks, and once – but only once, as the pain of his wound made him squeak in outraged agony – on his bottom. Her affection for Burlesque, and her sheer joy of sitting next to him, increased with every mile the charabanc puffed and wheezed towards Venice, so much so that Burlesque had the very disconcerting impression that Odette was a woman in love.

Burlesque had been so nonplussed by the girl's ardour that he decided that, immediately upon their arrival in Venice, he would use the crowds to slip away from the mooning Odette and make his escape. He'd even thought about using the same tactics on a sullen Rivets, who was *still* moaning about his boots. In the end, the thought of the damage a deranged and unsupervised Rivets might inflict on Venice had decided him against such an underhand manoeuvre.

But, as the NoN poet Burns noted, the best-laid plans of marmots and men often go awry: Burlesque hadn't anticipated how protective Odette would be of the new man in her life. No sooner had they descended onto the platform in Venice – theirs, by the grace of ABBA, being the last Medi charabanc allowed into the city – than she had taken both him and Rivets by an arm and hustled them through the crowds. And with the girl being a good stone heavier than him, whither she went he perforce went too. He decided he'd have to sneak away from her later.

Unfortunately, in the ten days they'd been in Venice, Odette had stuck to him like glue, so despite his best efforts he found himself sitting with her and Rivets in the aforesaid café, waiting for something to turn up. And today that something was Vanka Maykov.

Although, back in the Real World, Norma had seen pictures of Venice, she had never been there – her father having refused to take a 'goth' along with him when he'd gone to the city for the summit meeting with the hateful British – so she was excited to find herself arriving in one of the most romantic and exotic cities in the whole world . . . *both* of the whole worlds. And Venice – even a digitally contrived Venice – was as wonderful as she had ever imagined it would be.

'So what do we do now?' she'd asked, once they had disembarked from the gondola Josephine Baker had hired to bring them across the Grand Canal and were safe in the city. 'Go sightseeing?'

As it turned out, she was almost right. The plan they agreed upon was that Josephine would disappear off to use her contacts to find out what she could about the whereabouts of Ella, whilst Norma and Vanka would repair to a hotel to . . . repair. And for this Norma was enormously grateful.

The adventures they had endured since their arrival in the Quartier Chaud had left both her and Vanka looking more than a little worse for wear, and although Venetians had a tolerance for idiosyncrasy, this tolerance didn't extend to those whose costumes appeared to have been concocted from rags. So over the next week, Norma invested time attending to her toilette, her coiffeur, her ensemble and her poise. More, she spent a great deal of Vanka's money purchasing a new wardrobe, which she determined would include some of the most shocking gowns that Venice's boutiques could offer. Norma had seen the fashions the ImPure girls in Venice sported, and she was determined not to be outdone.

It was a busy and interesting week, and one during which she transformed herself from careworn fugitive into society beauty: anyone who had seen the bedraggled traveller entering the wonderfully sumptuous Hotel Baglioni on her arrival in Venice would have had difficulty in recognising her as the elegant young woman who now stood before her dressing mirror. Rested and recovered, bathed and perfumed, she felt totally rejuvenated and ready to face anything this strange world could throw at her. It was amazing what a week without being shot at, chased, threatened or having to sleep on a prison cot could do to both her spirits and her appearance. Norma was re-energised.

And her buoyant mood was assisted by the gown she was wearing. Vanka had decided that, as nothing untoward had happened since their arrival in Venice, it was now safe for them to venture forth in search of Burlesque. And for this promenade, Norma opted for a gown that was, in her opinion, a marvel, a marvel which showed off her slim figure and her splendid bust to perfection . . . especially her bust. The dress was cut so dangerously low that Norma's marvellously full bosom was displayed in a manner that flouted both propriety and gravity, and hence would gain her the instant admiration of every man whose gaze was fortunate enough to alight on her – or, rather, on them.

A mask made of deep blue satin, a string of pearls around her neck, a matching bracelet on her right wrist and a sequinned bag to hold her Cloverleaf pistol completed the ensemble.

When Norma sashayed down the hotel's grand staircase to meet Vanka that lunchtime, she knew she had been correct to delay her assault on Venetian society. As she glided across the marble floor of the hotel's vast and very opulent reception area, every eye in the place turned towards her in rapt appreciation.

Even Vanka – himself resplendent in a new and eye-poppingly bright suit complete with a formidably large codpiece – was impressed.

'I never realised . . .' he spluttered, and then got a grip on himself. 'You look wonderful, Norma.' Vanka shuffled his feet. 'Norma . . . I said something back in Paris which I regret. I said you weren't my friend and that was stupid of me. I would be proud to call a girl as strong and resilient as you my friend.'

Norma smiled and then leant forward to kiss him on the cheek. 'Vanka, you have no idea how happy that makes me feel. I'm honoured to be able to count you as my friend.'

Vanka offered her his arm. 'And I am honoured to prome- nade with such a beautiful and elegant young lady. The Bridge of Thighs is only a short gondola ride away, so why don't we go there and see if Burlesque has managed to make his way to Venice?'

'Bloody hell, Wanker, you look made up and no mistake,' admitted Burlesque, when Vanka and Norma arrived at the rendezvous. 'An' you ain't looking too scruffy neither, Miss Norma. Nice tits.'

Norma was in so good a mood that she interpreted Burlesque's observation as a compliment. She had had to do a double take herself, never having seen either Burlesque or Rivets in a mask before. In her opinion, Burlesque actually suited being masked. 'Aren't you going to introduce me to your young lady, Burlesque?' she asked.

'Yeah, this is Odette, a friend ov mine.' Burlesque nodded in an offhand way towards the substantial girl clinging very posses- sively to his arm.

Burlesque Bandstand's 'friend' was a big woman – not fat but with muscles bigger than any woman's had a right to be – so it was with some trepidation that Norma held out her hand.

Odette would have none of it. Instead of shaking Norma's hand, she leapt to her feet and engulfed Norma in a huge bearhug, crooning as she did so that *'Je suis très heureuse de rencontrer une amie de mon chéri, Burlesque.'* ('I am so very pleased to meet with a friend of my darling, Burlesque.')

When Odette had deposited a breathless Norma back on her seat, it was Vanka's turn to be greeted.

As he always did when confronted with anyone even vaguely feminine, Vanka Maykov bowed and smiled. *'Enchanté, Mademoiselle,'* he crooned, as he doffed his top hat. His gallantry did not prevent him from being hugged with an enthusiasm which left him red-faced and panting.

'So when did you arrive?' Vanka asked, when he had recovered his composure.

''Bout ten days ago. We 'ad a bit ov bovver wiv Beria's lot in Paree an' 'ad to lie low for a while, ovverwise we would 'ave bin 'ere sooner.' He leant conspiratorially close to Vanka – taking the opportunity, as he did so, to have a good look down the front of Norma's dress. 'So wot's to do, Wanker? You 'eard anyfink about Miss Ella?'

'I understand she's been brought safely to Venice, but other than that, not a word. I have a friend here who has contacts within the government. She's making enquiries on my behalf, and has agreed to meet me . . .' His coffee cup paused in midsip. 'And here she comes now.'

Josephine Baker was unmissable. Sure her bright yellow and incredibly tight gown helped, as did her breathtaking beauty, but there was more to her entrance than that. Josephine Baker, Norma decided, possessed so much sexual charisma that even if she had been wearing sackcloth and ashes, she would still have turned the head of every man and woman she passed. She had that certain something that only a handful of women had: she had 'it'.

*Lucky cow.*

'Hiya, Vanka baby, that's one hard-cut suit you got there. Man, you're looking high, fly and too wet to dry, though I gotta say pink-and-blue Paisley don't really pump my pistons.' Josephine turned to Norma. 'And you, Norma, are a real shape in a drape. Jingo, honey, if you're ever looking for a gig, just give me the word. Jiggle those jangles around on a Saturday night, and the punters will bug out big time.'

'An' I'm Burlesque Bandstand, m'lady,' gasped Burlesque, as he shot to his feet. 'An' you, iffn I ain't mistaken, are the Sensual Shade, 'erself. I saw yous a couple ov years ago when you did that dance wiv the bananas.'

'Hiya, Burlesque. I'm always glad to meet one of my fans. So you dug my *danse sauvage*?'

'Yeah, yous wos great, though maybe you wos wearing a few *too* many bananas.'

Burlesque was interrupted by a tug on his sleeve from Odette, who obviously didn't like the way Burlesque was eyeing la Baker.

'Oh, yus – this is Odette, an' that there is Rivets.'

Once they were all seated and drinks had been served, Josephine became all business. 'Okay, first the good news. I met with a friend of mine from the Council of Ten – those are the big dukes who run this ville – and after a little billing and cooing he let slip a few things he shouldn't oughta. You'll be pleased to know, Vanka, that your pal Ella is fine as wine, and buttoned up safe and snug here in Venice. They've got her holed away in the Convent of the Visual Virgins, but Machiavelli's boys are watching her closer than a pimp watches his whores.'

'At least Ella's safe.'

'Yeah, she's safe but the thing you've gotta dig, Vanka, is that she ain't Ella no more. Now she's the Lady IMmanual, and she's a real big deal, the big barracuda. Now she's being officially billed as the Messiah which I guess is why Beria's men tried to deep-six her when she was en route to Venice.'

'Beria tried to kill her?'

'Sure, and it was a near-run thing. There were a lot of bad guys out and about trying to blow the Lady's lights out. Sister Florence got chewed up pretty bad helping defend the dame.'

'Sister Florence?' asked Vanka.

'The Visual Virgin the Doge sent to protect the Lady IMmanual. Josephine took a comforting swig of her Solution. 'But there's more. From what I can dig, there were even some Grigori trying to assassinate the Lady IMmanual.'

'Grigori? Them's vampyres ain't they?' snorted Burlesque. 'Nah . . . there ain't no such fings as vampyres. They're just bogeymen that movvers use to frighten their kids into being good.'

'You're wrong, Burlesque baby. The Grigori are real alright. I've seen the ancient WhoDoo manuscripts that tell of a time when these slimeballs strutted and strolled the Demi-Monde.'

'They're real right enough, Burlesque,' confirmed Vanka. 'Norma and I were attacked by three of them back in Paris.'

Now *that* shut Burlesque up, and a decidedly uneasy-looking Rivets started gnawing anxiously at his nails. He slid the book he'd been reading – *Gregory the Grigori* – back into his jacket pocket.

'It's a sign that Ragnarok is, like, approaching mucho de fast, when back issues like the Grigori start making an encore.'

'An' did these Grigori fingies get to Miss Ella?'

'Sure did, Burlesque. Not that that kitten needed much protection. Seems she sliced and diced said Grigori, and then made like Houdini to reappear here in Venice.'

Vanka took a long swig of his coffee. 'So that's the good news, Josie. What's the bad news?'

'There's a *lettre de cachet* out for your arrest, Vanka. Seems that you're *persona non grata* here in Venice.'

'Why? Why would they want to arrest me?'

'I ain't sure. It's all being kept *sotto voce*. My guy thought it was 'cos Machiavelli didn't want you raising dust with the Lady IMmanual, but I've got a feeling there's more to it than that.'

'Like what?' Vanka prompted.

'You in the mood for, like, a double helping of bad news?'

'Yeah.'

'Well, the lowdown is that it was the Lady IMmanual herself who put the finger on you, Vanka. Seems like you and she ain't jake no mores, like now she regards you as unflavour of the month.'

'Has Ella got that much clout in Venice?'

'Sure has, honey. Oh she's got to be *officially* verified as the Messiah by the Doge and then by the Grand Council but the fact is, Sister Florence has got a lot of pull in this ville and with her saying the Lady IMmanual is the Messiah then it's a done deal. And if the Messiah starts mouthing that Vanka Maykov is a badnik who would be better referred to only in the past tense, then that's what's gonna go down.'

Vanka shook his head, trying to clear it. 'I don't understand.'

'Lemme give it to you straight no chaser, Vanka baby. The Lady IMmanual wants you totalled. Seems she told Machiavelli you were out to assassinate her.'

'*What?!* She wants me killed? But why?'

'Who knows, daddy-o, maybe the Lady IMmanual is just cleaning house. Now she's the big Pooh-Bah, maybe she don't want her past coming crawling outta the woodwork.'

There was something in the way Josephine said this that gave Norma the strong suspicion that she knew perfectly well why Ella wanted Vanka dead, but just wasn't prepared to spill the beans. Most peculiar.

'But to want to have me killed . . .' Vanka was obviously having big trouble getting his head around what Josephine Baker was telling him.

Seemingly anxious not to be quizzed on the subject,

Josephine moved the conversation on. 'You better fall in and dig the happenings, Vanka. You gotta suss that the Lady IMmanual is now a political heavyweight . . . she's the Messiah! If the Doge can get her to endorse Venice in its fight against the ForthRight, then maybe the Coven and NoirVille will come in on the side of the Doge. So the last thing they want is a loose cannon like Vanka Maykov screwing things up.'

'I still don't believe it.'

Norma placed a hand on Vanka's. 'I'm sure there's a logical explanation,' she said in a comforting voice.

'I hope for your sake there is, Norma honey, 'cos there's a warrant out for your arrest too.'

Now it was Norma's turn to look shocked. 'Me? Why would Ella want me dead?'

'Dunno, honey, but you better believe this ain't no off-time jive I'm laying on you. Those Signori di Notte items of Machiavelli are out looking for you, and they're mean as catshit and twice as nasty. For you and Vanka, Venice is one ville it's best to live out of.'

Norma turned to Vanka for advice but all he did was sit there looking dazed. He'd gone pale, and his hand trembled when he raised his cup to his lips. Finally he spoke. 'This is madness. Ella and I . . . well, never mind. I've got to get to Ella. I've got to speak to her.'

'Only way to do that is to get into the Convent.'

'Then that's what I'm going to do.'

# 24

## Venice
## The Demi-Monde: 27th Day of Spring, 1005

The spelling of the name of the Trickster god of pre-Confinement mythology is endlessly mutable. Although the accepted, textbook spelling is *Loki*, there are many Confusionists who state emphatically that it should be rendered as *LoQi*, as this better denotes the Trickster's ability to disrupt the harmony of the spiritual essence, *Qi*, in the Kosmos. But following the unBabelisation of the Eddic inscribed on the column taken from the Venetian Lagoon it appears that the ancients preferred *Loci*, this presumably denoting the god's ability to be in more than one place at a time.

*Myths and Legends of the Demi-Monde:*
*Lucien Lévy-Brühl, Quartier Chaud Imprints*

It was now twelve days since he and the Lady IMmanual had arrived in Venice, and de Sade judged them to have been twelve very long and very boring days. On Machiavelli's orders he and the Lady had been held incommunicado in the Convent of Visual Virgins, with the Signori di Notte guarding the place to make sure that no one, but no one, came within stabbing distance of the Lady.

His incarceration had been made especially boring as – after how generous she had been with her body in Paris – the Lady IMmanuel had resisted his amorous overtures. All he could assume was that she didn't want to be observed during coitus by a Visual Virgin: as he understood it, at the point of climax the aura became especially bright and easy to read. But given that her aura had already been examined by Sister Florence, it was a peculiar reticence and one that de Sade found very frustrating. It was as though she was trying to hide something but even de Sade, who was a master of deception and double-dealing, couldn't for the life of him think what that secret might be. Everyone knew she was the Messiah.

It therefore came as something of a relief when de Sade was informed that they would at last be allowed to venture beyond the Convent's walls. True, a trip to a museum – albeit one as prestigious as the Galerie des Anciens – to attend the unveiling of some tedious artefact wasn't quite the debut into Venetian society he had hoped for the Lady, but he was still pleased to be given the opportunity to enjoy some fresh air.

By de Sade's estimation, they had the Doge herself to thank for their excursion. Presumably she had grown tired of simply having the Lady watched surreptitiously – like every other state building in Venice, the Convent was positively riddled with secret passages and peepholes – in the hope that she might be caught *in flagrante*. Now the Doge had decided that it was time to meet the girl face to face and to judge for herself if she was, indeed, the Messiah.

Such was the importance of the first appearance of the Lady IMmanual that the Doge had ordered she be accompanied by *all* of the Convent's Visual Virgins and *all* of the detachment of Signori di Notte set to guard her. It was therefore a very crowded gondola that slid alongside the mooring directly opposite the Galerie, where they were greeted by cheers from the large crowd gathered around the entrance to the museum. Obviously word had spread that the Lady IMmanual – the Messiah – would be visiting the place and the more religiously minded of Venetians had been moved to see this wonder for themselves.

And it was a wonder well worth seeing. Advised that this afternoon's soirée would be attended by the most fashionable and elegant personages in Venice, the Lady had determined that she would most certainly *not* be upstaged, and hence the outfit she'd selected was remarkable both for its elegance and its daring. Her shaven head was covered by a cowl of filigree silver which cascaded over her face, and her dress was a little – a *very* little – number sporting a quite outrageous bustle that jiggled most fetchingly with each step she took. It was an ensemble that announced her to be not only a woman of rank and importance but also one of rare beauty.

The crowd adored her, so much so that de Sade decided that from today the Galerie would no longer be remembered as a shrine dedicated to the worship of the artistry and genius of the Pre-Folk, but rather as the place where Venetians first bent their knee to the Lady IMmanual.

With de Sade on her arm the Lady swept imperiously through both the adoring throng and the Galerie's magnificent entrance doors. Once inside, she swirled off her magnificent velvet cloak, her rather theatrical unveiling ensuring that every eye in the Galerie turned in her direction.

But there was more to her performance than simply a beautiful woman delighting in the effect her appearance had on her audience. If there was ever a group of men who could appreciate the significance of the title 'Messiah', it was the preHistorians waiting to attend her in the Galerie. And as the Messiah was the one ordained by ABBA to lead the Demi-Monde through this Time of Tribulation, it was a very heavy mantle of greatness that was being readied to be draped over the slim shoulders of the Lady IMmanual. But before there could be any such draping, she needed to be *officially* ordained as Messiah by the powers that be in Venice. And for that she had to secure the imprimatur of the Doge, and to have her Messiahship rati-

fied by the Council of Ten. Venice had a mania for correct administrative procedure, a mania that extended even to Messiahs.
This selection process was to begin in the Galerie.

'My Lady IMmanual, *enchanté*,' gushed a small round man
who bounced up to greet her in a flurry of waving arms and
goggling eyes. 'I am Louis Molyneau, the curator of this
museum, to which I have the honour of welcoming you.'

'I am delighted to meet you, Monsieur Molyneau,' replied the
Lady with a smile, 'but I must ask, as we have never met before,
how did you know who I am?'

'*Facile*. The Lady IMmanual is by reputation of a beauty unsurpassed, and any endowed with eyes will see that you are indeed
that woman. Never has my museum been graced by such inef-
fable loveliness. You illuminate the afternoon with your presence.'

The Lady IMmanual rewarded the curator's compliments –
and his kiss on her hand – with another, even warmer, smile.
'May I, in turn, introduce my friend the Marquis de Sade.'

The two men exchanged bows and Molyneau signalled to a
passing waiter, who served his guests each with a flute of *champagne de sang*. De Sade eyed the Lady curiously as she took the
glass: legend had it that Daemons eschewed the delights of
blood, but not so the lady IMmanuel. All he could assume was
that Daemon Messiahs had atypical appetites.

Once he had refreshed himself, Molyneau recommenced his
gushing endearments: 'It is so rare, my Lady, that a woman of
such beauty and discrimination ornaments a gathering of anti-
quarians, as we are an almost exclusively male and invariably
dusty congregation. But of course, today is a meeting of the utmost
importance, as today Professeur Michel de Nostredame will reveal
a discovery of the greatest significance. As a consequence, here
in attendance are the foremost personages in Venice.'

'Among whom I believe that lady is the most important.'

De Sade looked across the room in the direction of the Lady's nod, it was obvious to him why she had noticed the Doge: the woman, who was currently holding an excessively animated conversation with a hugely powerful-looking Shade, was, after all, almost as tall as the Lady IMmanual and her outfit was similarly arresting. She was sporting a black dress and black veil, making her something of an oddity in a crowd that favoured the multicoloured fashions currently so en vogue, but then, as in everything, the Doge Catherine-Sophia was a law unto herself, which was no real surprise, given that she made the laws.

Still, de Sade did wonder when the woman would come out of mourning for Potemkin. Two years of very public grieving was, by any measure, excessive and the people were beginning to whisper that perhaps their Doge wasn't quite right in the head.

'You are correct, my Lady,' confirmed Molyneau, 'that is Her Most Reverend Excellency, Doge Catherine-Sophia, who has requested that you be introduced to her immediately upon your arrival.'

'It would be an honour.'

Without further ado, Molyneau escorted the Lady IMmanual and de Sade across the room to effect the introductions. 'Your Most Reverend Excellency,' he simpered, as he brought his guests to a halt at the Doge's side, 'may I have the pleasure of introducing the Lady IMmanual.'

The Doge stopped in mid-sentence, turned towards the Lady and extended a hand gloved in the softest black leather. The Lady IMmanual took the proffered hand and bobbed a curtsy.

'Zo, you are zhe Lady IMmanual. I have heard many disturbing reports about you, my Lady. I trust you have not come to Venice to create alarums or panic.'

De Sade breathed a sigh of relief. The Doge wasn't drunk.

'No, I came here simply to escape the ForthRight.'

'Gut, zhen I am pleased to offer you sanctuary. Unt I trust zhat you vill find zhis afternoon's revelations not mitout interest. Zhe find to be unveiled has, apparently, zome pertinence to your claim to be zhe Messiah.'

'Her Excellency is an expert in all things ancient,' interjected Molyneau helpfully.

'You are as inaccurate as alvays, Louis,' scolded the Doge, wagging a finger at the curator. 'My interest in things ancient extends only to zhe inanimate. In matters ImPure, I prefer zhe young unt zhe vigorous.'

Molyneau determinedly finished his introductions. 'And of course you know the Marquis de Sade, Your Excellency.'

The Doge gave an indifferent flick of her fan. 'I know zhe Marquis de Zade only too vell, as do most vomen in Venice. You are forgiven, de Sade, for your past indiscretions, but do not try my patience again.' She gestured towards the man standing beside her. 'Let me, in turn, introduce you to zhe Grand Vizier Selim, Master of the Court of His HimPerial Majesty Shaka Zulu.'

The tall Shade turned his black eyes towards the Lady and smiled. Despite himself, de Sade took an involuntary step back. The man was truly terrifying and looked, for all the world, with his turban, his cheek scars and his ridiculously ornate moustache, like some pantomime devil. Hardly surprising, de Sade supposed, given that the fellow was, by reputation, a monster. He looked every inch the skilled and vicious torturer he was rumoured to be.

But if de Sade was nonplussed by meeting such a fearsome individual, the Lady most certainly was not. She returned the man's smile and pushed out her hand. 'I am delighted to meet you, Your Highness, I am . . .'

'I know who you are, young lady, it is *what* you are that I have been debating with Her Excellency the Doge.'

'Jah, as zhe Grand Vizier is a major proponent of HimPerialism vhich believes zhat vomen vere created by ABBA merely to serve unt service men, he finds it most difficult to conceive ov a zituation vhen ABBA vould impose a *female* Messiah on zhe Demi-Monde.'

'Not difficult, Your Excellency,' corrected the Grand Vizier, '*impossible*. The HIM Book – the most sacred book in the NoirVillian religious corpus – states quite categorically that the Messiah will be a man.'

'I am not familiar with this work, Your Highness,' said the Lady quietly, 'and I would be most grateful for an opportunity to debate the eschatological aspects of HimPerialism in greater depth. Might I be so bold as to issue an invitation to the Grand Vizier to call on me at the Convent?'

De Sade felt a frown forming on his forehead. What was the girl playing at? If he wasn't mistaken, she was actually *flirting* with the man, which, as Selim was the head of the creed which venerated Man²naM sexual relations as being blessed in the sight of ABBA, was an exercise in futility. The man was an out-and-out zadnik and hence would be immune to even the Lady's undoubted charms.

The Grand Vizier glanced to the Doge for advice, obviously unsure as to the correct protocol when dealing with a putative Messiah. All the Doge did was shrug.

'It would be my honour, my Lady,' said the Grand Vizier, finally. 'I am ever willing to bring a woeMan to a fuller under-standing regarding the doctrine of subMISSiveness and to explain the repulsive and despicable nature of her gender.'

Not a terribly gracious acceptance, mused de Sade, but the Lady seemed in no way perturbed. 'Shall we say tomorrow, at noon?'

The Grand Vizier gave a nod, and then turned to the Doge and bowed. 'If you will excuse me, Your Excellency, but following our discussions it is important I consult with my staff.'

'Gut,' declared the Doge, as she watched the man stride off. 'I have little patience mit males from NoirVille. Zhey have a pre-pubescent attitude to matters zexual.' She gave the Lady IMmanual a very meaningful look. 'You did vell to charm him, my dear, as I am seeking an alliance mit NoirVille. Venice unt NoirVille are not natural bedfellows – zhe NoirVillians are reluctant to be seen taking aid unt assistance from a Sector governed by a voeMan – but zhe political situation in zhe Demi-Monde is zuch zhat needs must vhen Loki drives.' Another smile. 'Jah, you have quite enchanted him. Remarkable.'

The conversation faltered and the Lady IMmanual took the opportunity to look around at the men standing waiting on the Doge. 'I was led to believe by Monsieur Molyneau that some of the Demi-Monde's foremost academicians are gathered in this room. '

'Zhat is zo. All zhe best in zhe stuffy world of antiquity are met here today, desperate to be present vhen de Nostredame unveils his vonder unt, of course, to zee zhe famous Lady IMmanual. But zhey are still all just ninny-com-poopies, unt zhey are zuch because pre-Confinement History is predominantly a bastion ov zhe male ov zhe species, a discipline unleavened by zhe more spiritual unt intuitive insights offered by vomen. Zhere are few men capable ov original thought in zhe vorld, unt even fewer amongst zhose who delve like blind moles in zhe archives ov zhe Demi-Monde, lost in zheir study ov zhe Pre-Folk.'

'You are very censorious.'

'Merely accurate, my Lady,' retorted the Doge carelessly. 'Men are not equipped for intellectual pursuits, zheir minds are infused mit too much of zhe choleric humors of MALEvolence for zhem ever to be able to think logically. All zhey are gut for iz fucking unt fighting.'

This opinion was expressed in such an offhand manner that for a moment it seemed that the Lady wasn't sure if she had heard the Doge correctly. Even de Sade had to do a double take.

*Maybe she is drunk?*

Fortunately, the Doge was moved to eliminate any misunderstanding.

'Jah, as I say, men are only truly capable of outstanding performance in two fields of human endeavour: fucking unt fighting, unt mitout zhese two abilities zhey would be largely superfluous. Unfortunately, I zuzpect zhat mit regard to fucking, zhe men gathered here today are no more lively zhan zhe dusty tomes zhey investigate.' She gave a disconsolate shrug. 'Fifty men, unt not vun good fuck in zhe lot of zhem.'

The Doge turned to de Sade. 'I exclude you from zhis criticism, de Zade, zince your abilities in zhe realm of zhe prurient are vell documented. Unt az you, my Lady, come here today mit zhis pervert on your arm' – de Sade bowed in appreciation of the compliment – 'could it be zhat you, too, are in thrall to zhe darker aspects ov zhe erotic?'

Amazingly the Lady wasn't in the least perplexed by the Doge's rather impertinent question. 'I delight in all matters sexual, Your Excellency, whether they be darker or lighter.'

Nodding her understanding the Doge paused to extract a gold case from the folds of her dress and take out a cigarette. Raising her veil, she permitted an attentive waiter to light the cigarette for her and the light cast from the flaring match allowed de Sade to get a better look at her face. Hers was a sad beauty, he decided, a beauty marred by an over-indulgence in Solution . . . and by worry. The Doge was obviously more disconcerted by the Lady IMmanual than she cared to admit.

The Doge blew out a long stream of coiling smoke and then thrust the cigarette case towards the Lady. 'May I offer you a zigarette, younk lady?' The Lady shook her head. 'You are very vise. Although zhe medical profession vould have us believe zhat smoking iz beneficial to zhe constitution, I am ov zhe opinion zhat everything zhat a voman takes into her mouth, be it zigarette smoke, food, alcohol or zemen, shortens her life.

But zhen, a truncated life iz not always a bad thing. Life, especially a long vun, can be zo fucking boring.'

'I disagree, Your Excellency. My own experience is that a long life need be anything but boring.'

Now that, decided de Sade, was a very peculiar thing for such a young woman to say.

'Perhaps,' conceded the Doge and then she raised a finger to the Lady's cheek and ran it along her soft skin. 'Exquisite. Vould zhat I possessed an SAE as fine unt as zupple as yours.' She laughed in a most disconcerting manner. 'But zhen perhaps vun day I vill. Vot do you think, my Lady? Do you think zhat one day I might possess your body?'

Instinctively de Sade stepped closer. This was really quite remarkable: the Doge was clearly testing the Lady's sexual orientation. He took a quick look around and, as he had expected, there, almost invisible in the shadows shrouding the back of the room, stood the Auralist Sister Florence – her hand heavily bandaged – as she stared unblinkingly at the Lady, examining her aura. The Doge's overtures were obviously pre-planned, the woman desperate to have the Lady's aura examined whilst she was sexually excited.

But the question that troubled him was *why* they doubted her. If they had reservations regarding her Messiahship, then who did they think she was? There was one possibility, but that was a ridiculous notion . . . or, at least, he hoped it was.

The Lady didn't seem to be in the mood to be excited, rather, she was amused by the Doge's advances. 'I am your ever obedient subject, my Doge.'

All further discussion was interrupted by the sounding of a gong signalling that the attendees should take their seats for the presentation.

'Gut, I vill remember zhat. Unt now, my Lady, you must take my arm unt we will join zhe men to zee zhe vonder zhat de Nostredame has in store for us.'

# 25

## Venice
## The Demi-Monde: 27th Day of Spring, 1005

Of all the mythical creatures thought to have inhabited the pre-Confinement Demi-Monde, none were more fearsome (or more enigmatic) than the Grigori. Although references to them are meagre (most of the scant information having been gleaned from the inscriptions on the ExterSteine Column), it appears that they were a race of super-warriors in the service of Lilith. Their amazing strength, speed, vicious temperament and craving for blood have made them the inspiration for the vampyre characters popular in the more lurid of penny dreadfuls. Whether there is any truth behind the myth is the subject of much conjecture, though WhoDoo mambos are in no doubt: they revile the Grigori as the most hateful of all *loas*.

> Myths and Legends of the Demi-Monde:
> *Lucien Lévy-Brühl, Quartier Chaud Imprints*

Vanka was not a happy man. He had been too long in the conning business not to know when he was being fed bullshit, and as bullshit went, what he had been told by the butler who was guarding the entrance to the Convent of Visual Virgins was decidedly smelly. The butler had been lying through his back teeth when he'd declared that there was no such person as Ella Thomas, the Lady IMmanual or Marie Laveau staying in the

Convent. This suspicion had mutated into certainty when the man had turned down a hundred-guinea bribe – a hundred guineas! – to become less taciturn. In Vanka's experience, butlers were conditioned from birth to accept bribes, and for one to reject such a huge sum meant that he was either monumentally stupid or terrified of his employer. By the look of the man, Vanka thought it might be a combination of both.

It was a disconsolate Vanka who trudged back to the bar where Burlesque and his friends were waiting for him.

'You look a bit darn in the dumps, Wanker,' observed Burlesque, as he sat gnawing on an aged-looking apple.

'I've got a problem.'

'Oh, you don't wanna worry abart that none. There's this cream that does wonders—'

'It's not that sort of problem,' Vanka interrupted. 'I think Ella's been abducted.'

'Abducted? Wot's bin abducted?' asked Rivets, suddenly taking an interest in the conversation. 'Is it wun ov them Frog perversions they show on them funny cigarette cards?'

'It's *not* a fucking perversion,' insisted a suddenly very tetchy Vanka, as he tried not to let his worries about Ella overwhelm him. 'It means kidnapped.'

'Kidnapped? 'Oo by?' asked Burlesque, suddenly serious.

'My money's on that bastard Machiavelli, who's in charge of the Venetian secret police. I reckon the Venetians are holding Ella so that they can say that the Messiah is on their side. It's the only thing that makes sense. I don't buy Josie Baker's idea that she's changed; Ella isn't like that.'

'I dunno,' persisted Rivets. 'That Miss Baker is a really downy bird.'

Vanka ignored him. He *refused* to buy into Josie's claim that Ella's attitude towards him had altered to such an extent that she now saw him as an enemy.

'The trouble is that the bastard butler is so shit-scared of Machiavelli that he's playing Mr Stumm. I couldn't get a word out of him.'

'That's 'cos yous a gentleman, Wanker,' Burlesque observed, as he hauled himself to his feet and swilled down the last of his glass of Solution. 'Why don't you let me 'ave a word wiv 'im? I'm a dab 'and at interrogations.'

It was a little after five in the afternoon when Pascal Leroy, long-time butler to the Convent of Visual Virgins, opened the front door of the Convent in response to the persistent hammering. He was less than impressed by the three ruffians he found adorning his immaculately clean steps, a trio comprising two men and one very large woman. The two men – a man and a boy, rather – made an odd couple, since one was large and fat and the other small and thin. What they had in common, though, was that their clothes looked like they had been slept in. They made incongruous bookends to the some- what larger, florid-faced girl who stood between them. But what the men lacked in gravitas they certainly made up for in imper- tinence.

'Je church pour Mademoiselle Ella Thomas, silver plate,' said the fat one, his accent so appalling as to make the masticated sentence almost unintelligible.

'*Je ne connais aucune personne qui s'appelle Mademoiselle Ella Thomas,*' ('I do not know of anyone called Mademoiselle Ella Thomas') Pascal Leroy sneered, and made to shut the door, though his hand trembled as he did so. That the Lady IMmanual was lodged in the Convent was meant to be a secret, but this was the second time that afternoon that callers had come enquiring about her. He would, in normal circumstances, have sent an urgent message to the Abbé Niccolò, asking for instruc- tions, but that was impossible at the moment. He had only been able to smuggle Mademoiselle Armaros inside the Convent when the Signori di Notte platoon guarding the Lady and all the Sisters had left to accompany her to the Galerie des Anciens, and with the girl waiting to greet the Lady on her return the last thing he wanted was Machiavelli snooping about the place. Murder was a very private business.

The large hobnailed boot the small ruffian placed firmly across the threshold prevented him closing the door. 'Où is elle?' asked the boy, who was sporting a mask which gave him the appearance of a rabbit, and whose French accent was, remarkably, even worse than his colleague's. The boy compounded his insolence by spitting on Monsieur Leroy's freshly scrubbed steps.

Incandescent with rage at the violation of the sanctity of his Convent, Pascal Leroy wagged a warning finger at the truncated boy, refusing to be intimidated by such a small, insignificant individual. '*Va-t-en . . . vaurien . . . ou j'appelle les GrandHarms!*' ('Go away, you . . . nonentity you . . . or I will call the GrandHarms!')

'D'you want me to put wun on 'im, Burlesque?' Pascal Leroy heard the boy ask his friend. To Leroy, who prided himself in the fluency of his English, it seemed remarkable that he understood less of the boy's English than he did of his French.

The bearded man shook his head. 'Nah, Rivets, leave 'im be. There's more'n one way to skin a cat.' And with that, the malodorous trio turned around, marched back down the steps and, to Leroy's great relief, away from the Convent.

When they were safely around the corner, Burlesque attempted to explain his plan. 'Odette . . .' he began but was somewhat put off his stride by the beaming smile he received from her. The girl's burgeoning affection for him was becoming distinctly distracting. 'Je désire . . .'

He was stopped by the coquettish giggles he'd provoked from the silly girl. Desperately he searched his limited vocabulary to find what he'd said wrong.

'Odette,' he began again, 'je veux tu to climbez' – he mimed a walking motion with two fingers of his right hand, which he hoped would compensate for his rotten French – 'à la porte de la Convent et fait beaucoup de noise. Shoutez vous' – now he pantomimed shouting, which provoked even more laughter – 'et bangez sur la porte.'

Suddenly Odette's face became hard and resolute. She delved into the voluminous carpet bag she had slung over her arm, and drew out the huge pistol she'd brought with her from Paris. *'Je comprends, Burlesque. Je bang-bang,'* and she demonstrated how she intended to shoot the butler.

'Oh, for fuck's sake.' Burlesque shook his head desperately. 'Non, non, Odette, no fuckin' bang-bang avec le fuckin' pistol. Just fait beaucoup de racket. Makez-vous le tow-row.' Again he enacted what he was asking of the girl, and eventually understanding dawned in her eyes. She pushed the revolver back into her bag, sat down on the low wall that bordered the front garden of the Convent, and smiled at Burlesque, obviously awaiting his next instruction.

'I dunno, Burlesque,' observed Rivets. 'It might'n be a bad idea to top that Frog bastard. Why'n you let Odette just put a bullet frew 'is eye?'

'Oh, shut yer clack, Rivets. It's bad enough 'avin' to keep this bloodfirsty Frog tart from shootin' anywun wiv a beatin' body clock, wivout you encouragin' 'er.' He handed his watch to Odette. 'Dicks minutes,' he said, and Odette nodded in compliance. 'Right, Rivets, round the back.'

Burlesque had been advised by his old man – when his old man hadn't been corked by Solution or in clink, that is – that the bigger the house, the sloppier the security. And the sloppiest part of that security was always the servants. This being the case, his dad had told him, the best way to break into a house was through the servants' entrance. But when he tried all the basement doors at the back of the Convent, and found them securely locked and bolted, Burlesque was reminded once again of how his father had gone through life talking total bollocks.

'Fuck,' he commented, as he tried the last of the windows and found it firmly shut. He gave his arse a scratch, in search of inspiration and whatever it was that was gnawing at him down there, then in desperation looked over to Rivets. 'Waddya fink, Rivets, me old cock?'

Rivets shrugged. 'It ain't a problem, Burlesque. I'll get us in, easy as shellin' peas. Just wait until Odette's kickin' up a rumpus, an' I'm frew that door smoove as shit frew a goose. You's gotta remember that I'm a wonder at breakin' an' entry.'

So confident did Rivets sound that Burlesque was persuaded to follow his advice, taking the chance to pull out a fag and have a quick relaxing puff. But hardly had he got his cigarette lit than Odette began her assault on the Convent. He'd never have imagined that one girl could make so much noise; even though he was at the back of the building and Odette was attacking it from the front, the hammering, screaming, kicking and, he suspected, swearing were clearly audible.

'Gor, ole Odette's got a rare pair of bellows on 'er, ain't she?' commented Rivets admiringly. 'Gonna bust 'er stays, she goes on like that.'

Burlesque gave it a count of ten. 'Righto, Rivets, work yer magic.'

Rivets nodded and flicked the cigarette out of his hand, sending it spinning in a shower of sparks down the alleyway, then he stooped down to pick up a brick lying in the gutter and advanced on the half-windowed back door. With two savage and very noisy blows of the brick, he spanked the glaze, then reached through the shattered glass and unlocked the door from the inside. He pushed it open, and bowed Burlesque through with a triumphant wave of his hand.

'You daft prick!' gasped an astonished Burlesque. 'I thought you knew 'ow to crack an 'ouse proper.'

Rivets gave Burlesque a rather hurt look. 'Well, waddya fink I've just done? This gaff is proper broke into. It ain't called *breakin'* an' entry for nuffink, you know.'

'Everyone in the 'ole fucking street will 'ave 'eard yer 'ammerin'!'

Laughing, Rivets passed through the door and crunched his way over broken glass into the kitchen. 'I don't fink you should concern yerself abart that, Burlesque. The way ole 'Ollering Odette's givin' art wiv 'er vocals, I don't fink anybody's gonna be worried abart the sound ov a bit of breakin' glass. Anyway, careful as you go, Burlesque; wiv all these shutters shut it's black as midnight's arsehole in 'ere.'

It was difficult creeping through an unfamiliar house, especially one swathed in darkness and shadows, and most especially when Burlesque, who was leading the exploration, didn't have the faintest idea where he was going. He suspected though that Ella Thomas wouldn't be found in the kitchen, so when he bumped into the stairs leading from the basement, he climbed upwards. And every step he took, the noise that Odette was generating became louder. How one woman could make so much of a commotion was beyond him.

At the top of the stairs he stopped to get his bearings. He was starting to get more than a little unnerved by how deserted the Convent was, wondering that maybe Miss Ella wasn't in residence. He looked around and decided that the most promising direction in which to search was down the corridor to his left, the one which ran in the direction of the ruckus Odette was kicking up.

Edging along, he peeked into each dark room in turn, until he came to one which, from what he could make out in the gloom, seemed to be a library of some description. Maybe here, he thought, he might find a clue to Miss Ella's whereabouts. He looked around to check that Rivets was still behind him, and was aghast to see that the boy was now laden with various objets d'art he'd collected en route.

'Wot the fuck are you at?' he snarled, *sotto voce*.

'Pinchin',' said Rivets airily. 'Sum ov these movables is the business, Burlesque. I always fancied meself as a clanker-napper. Worth a small fortune wiv Jack the nuJu, these is. Specially this urn.' He thrust his chin towards a blue and white porcelain pot balanced precariously atop all of the other swag he had clasped in his arms.

With a despairing shake of his head, Burlesque turned up the gas lamp fixed on the wall of the library, and began a search. But look as he would, he could find nothing amongst the papers strewn so casually across the desk set in the middle of the room that gave any hint of where Ella Thomas might be. He was just about to give up and move his search to the upstairs rooms when he heard the merest of sounds from the doorway. Turning around, what he saw standing silhouetted at the entrance to the room chilled him to his core.

# 26

## Galerie des Anciens: Venice
## The Demi-Monde: 27th Day of Spring, 1005

Marring the Deterministic perfection of the Demi-Monde are two InDeterminate wild cards. The first is the periodic appearance of Dark Charismatics within the population of the Demi-Monde, but even here Kondratieff speculates that their manifestation is not entirely random. Although there is a paucity of Auralist evidence identifying exo-Chaudian Dark Charismatics, he is of the firm belief that each Sector has an ABBA-ordained quota of four such baleful individuals. This supposition, though unsubstantiated empirically, has enabled Kondratieff to compensate for the activities of Dark Charismatics in his 4Tellings.

> Dark Charismatics: The Invisible Enemy:
> *Professeur Michel de Nostredame,*
> *University of Venice Publications*

As the Doge and her party were ushered into the high-ceilinged presentation room, Nikolai Kondratieff saw that Molyneau – in anticipation of the Doge's visit – had been busy. A special reserved seat was standing to the very front of the chamber's tiered seating and Kondratieff had to smile when he saw the Doge insisting that another chair be brought in order that the Lady IMmanual could be seated next to her. That she had taken to the girl was very good news. Now all that remained was to give the Doge enough evidence to convince her that the Lady IMmanual was the Messiah. Only in that way could the *real* Messiah be protected.

It was a shame that the Doge had to be sacrificed on the altar of Temporal Intervention. Kondratieff admired the woman and was sad to be party to her demise, but really he had no alternative. Temporal Interventions were such delicate things that secrecy was vital to their success: the more people who were aware that attempts were being made to massage Future History, the greater the chance that one of them would be provoked into an action that would alter the desired Temporal OutCome. The Doge couldn't be warned of the threat posed by the Lady IMmanual because her death was necessary to secure the triumph of the Messiah.

Like a moth drawn to a flame, Kondratieff seated himself directly behind the Lady, so close that if he reached out his hand he could touch her – could touch a myth made SAE. It was a remarkable feeling. All those long hours he and de Nostredame had spent puzzling over the Future History of the Demi-Monde had led to this moment, when religious fancy became preScientific fact. And as he gazed at the girl, he decided that she didn't disappoint: she was very tall and very beautiful. Even with her shaven head and her face hidden behind a cowl of silver, Kondratieff could see that here was a woman born to steal men's hearts . . . and, of course, their souls.

A Goddess, indeed. A Goddess whose ambitions Kondratieff had dedicated his life to thwarting.

Once the Doge had settled in her seat, a hush fell as each member of the audience took a moment to study the large object shrouded under a dust sheet, standing just to the side of a lectern at the very front of the room. This, they realised, was the mysterious artefact they had come to see, and which was responsible for the almost palpable undercurrent of eager anticipation in the room.

De Nostredame, looking his usual dishevelled self, ambled across the floor to take his position behind the lectern. 'Good afternoon, Your Most Reverend Excellency, my lords, ladies and gentlemen. I am Michel de Nostredame, Professeur of pre-Confinement History at the University of metaPhysical Research here in Venice.'

Kondratieff could see de Nostredame's hands were trembling and he had, of course, every reason to be nervous. His was a daunting task, to fool the Doge, one of the sharpest minds in the Demi-Monde, and to persuade her that the message the Column contained said one thing, when in reality it said quite another. But only by doing this could they protect the Messiah.

As he always did when he was anxious, de Nostredame sucked on his pipe, billowing clouds of thick smoke towards the ceiling of the hall. He seemed too terrified to begin and it took a loud cough from Kondratieff to persuade him to stop procrastinating and get on with the presentation.

'The artefact we are to discuss this afternoon was discovered at the bottom of the Venetian Lagoon, at a point some ninety metres from the southern boundary of the city of Venice. Prior to its discovery and retrieval, the piece had been lying undisturbed, submerged in the Lagoon since time immemorial.'

He gazed up at the ceiling of the auditorium for a few moments, seemingly searching for inspiration. 'As you will all know, Mantle-ite, from which this artefact is hewn, is the hardest substance known to HumanKind, a substance that only the Pre-Folk knew how to work. Mantle-ite is invulnerable to attack by steel, by fire or by nanoBites, and it is this unyielding nature which has resulted in the artefact's immaculate state of preservation.' He leant forward and tugged hopefully on a cord hanging from the dust sheet. The sheet fell away. 'I give you Loci's Column.'

The piece didn't disappoint: it *was* magnificent. Standing on a hexagonal base – a base masked by a second dust sheet – the six-metre-high Column was simply breathtaking, the flawless Mantle-ite it had been constructed from glowing an eerie green under the room's lamplight. And Kondratieff's excitement was echoed by the rest of the audience: as soon as the Column was unveiled, there was a collective intake of breath and a shuffling forward in seats.

Kondratieff stole a glance at the Lady IMmanual, and he was amazed to see a tear meandering slowly down her cheek. Then he heard her mouth the words '*Exegi monumentum aere perennius.*'

He had suspected she would know the ancient languages of the Demi-Monde, and thus be familiar with the sayings of the Ancients – the poet Horace in this case – and now he had his proof. Automatically he translated what she had said: *I have erected a monument more lasting than bronze.*

He didn't have time to consider this remarkable occurrence further. When the hum of conversation had subsided, Professeur de Nostredame continued his presentation. 'As you will see,' and here a white-coated assistant rotated the Column on its plinth, 'five of the Column's faces have been inscribed with the lines of a poem – the Eddic of Loci – written in Pre-Folk A, the most ancient of all runic scripts. It is a script which, before the discovery of this Column, had defied all attempts to unBabelise it.'

There was another buzz of excited conversation. By suggesting that he had finally unlocked the secrets of the oh-so-enigmatic Pre-Folk A, de Nostredame threatened to set the preHistory cat amongst the academic pigeons: the translation of Pre-Folk A was the pot of gold at the end of the preHistory rainbow.

'How can you make zuch a claim, de Nostredame?' challenged

the Doge. 'I understand zhat mitout a key, Pre-Folk A iz untran-
zlatable.'

In answer de Nostredame pulled a second cord, which caused
the dust sheet covering the Column's hexagonal base to fall
away. 'We *have* a key, Your Excellency. Whoever carved this
Column possessed the 4Sight to send us a means of deciphering
the Eddic. Etched into the base is an Old French translation of
the Pre-Folk A verses shown on the main body of the Column.
By studying these inscriptions, it has become possible to translate the previously untranslatable Pre-Folk A.'

Kondratieff couldn't contain himself: he burst into applause,
this taken up enthusiastically by the rest of the audience. As
announcements went, it was world-shattering. At a stroke, the
riddles etched on such Mantle-ite monuments as the Great Wall,
the Sphinx and ExterSteine were made readable.

After bowing his appreciation, de Nostredame waved the room
into silence. 'Thank you . . . you are most generous. And now
my colleague Dr Nikolai Kondratieff will pass to each of you a
translation of the five cantos of the Eddic written on the Column.'

When Kondratieff had distributed the papers, the room went
deathly silent as the attendees made an urgent study of the
translation they had been handed. Finally, de Nostredame
judged that they'd had enough time to assimilate the poem
and he recommenced his talk.

'I will admit that in a number of areas there is ambiguity
with regard to the translation. These I will point out during my
summary of the Eddic. We are told that the poem was composed
by Loci – spelt in the unusual way shown in the translation –
the Trickster god of mythology. In sum, the Eddic tells of the
awakening of Loci and his lust for vengeance on those who had
held him captive; of the fall of the Vanir – the Pre-Folk – through
the machinations of Lilith; of the portents that herald the
approach of Ragnarok; and, lastly, of the coming of the Messiah

who will vie with the Beast in the final titanic struggle that is Ragnarok.' De Nostredame took another, comforting, puff on his pipe. 'I will refrain from making a detailed analysis of the various cantos, simply pointing out a number of features I feel are of the greatest political and religious import. To begin, let us refer to Face Two of the Column . . .'

De Nostredame waited while the Column was rotated. 'The canto carried on this face is entitled "The Vanir Remembered" and here the principal point of interest is the reference to VanaHeimr, the mythical home of the Vanir – the Pre-Folk – and of Lilith. The Eddic reads:

*Look inwards*            *to lost VanaHeimr.*
*Look to the unending river*    *for forgotten VanaHeimr.*
*There lived*             *the Vanir*
*The Elvish godlings*       *who sweetly ruled*
*The Demi-Monde.*

I will admit to some uncertainty here as the Eddic persistently refers to the vanir as "Fragiles". However, in my translation I have preferred the more widely accepted nomenclature, "Vanir". I should also note, en passant, that I had to resist a temptation to substitute the more common appellation "Atlantis" for VanaHeimr but, as the name Atlantis is now replete with a certain romantic hysteria, I have opted for a phonetic rendition of the Old French. I hope you will agree with me when I stress the importance of this canto, since it is the first time in the canon of Pre-Folk history that reference is made to the actual *location* of VanaHeimr. Until this moment, the generally accepted contention was that the land which served as the inspiration for VanaHeimr was lost to us somewhere in the Great Beyond. Now I would suggest, on the basis that we are implored to "look inwards" towards the "unending river", that this fabled land is in all probability located in our own Terror Incognita, which is, of course, surrounded by the circular and therefore unending Wheel River.'

'Zhere is no such place as either VanaHeimr or Atlantis,' said the Doge in a bored voice. 'Zhe reference made to Atlantis by zhe great Quartier Chaudian mage Plato in his *Critias* vos zimply a test for his students, zerving to illustrate zhat an idealised ImPuritan Republic shouldn't just be regarded as a thing of fancy or of intellectual speculation, but could unt should be made real. Zhe idea behind zhis imaginary land of Atlantis has been distorted, however, to zuch an extent zhat it has come to be zeen as real.'

'So you are familiar with the works of Plato, Your Excellency?'

The question from the Lady IMmanual was so unexpected that Kondratieff almost jumped in surprise.

The Doge gave a most condescending smile. 'Of course, younk lady.'

'You will remember, perhaps, that Plato, in his description of Atlantis, made reference to a pillar constructed from the legendary material orichalcum, upon which the laws of that city were carved.'

The Doge chuckled. 'You are not proposing zhat zhe Column ve have standing before us is proof of zhe existence of zhat mythical place?'

'I merely think we should keep an open mind on the subject.'

The Lady certainly was a feisty little piece, decided Kondratieff, but then that was only to be expected.

Not used to being corrected, the Doge gave a disapproving sniff and waved at de Nostredame to continue.

'Perhaps I should point out a number of other notable aspects of the Eddic in the hope that they will not be *quite* so contentious. If we turn to Face Five of the Column . . .'

Kondratieff steeled himself: this was when things could get really tricky.

'. . . we see described the coming of the Messiah and the final struggle between the Messiah and the Beast. This canto contains, perhaps, the most intriguing stanza of the whole poem, in that it describes how we will recognise the Messiah. It reads:

*Know the Messiah*             *as the One who is Two.*
*Know the Messiah*             *by the One with no Shadow.*
*Know the Messiah*             *by the Living Blood.*
*Know the Messiah*             *by the Time of Miracles portended.'*

De Nostredame took another puff on his pipe. 'Suffice it to say that this is the first time in Pre-Folk lore that the Messiah has been described so specifically, and as such it is worthy of much further analysis and interpretation than can be attempted this afternoon. The single point I would make is regarding the translation of the term "Living Blood". This might be better rendered from the Old French as "Daemon", which in turn helps us better understand the statement that the Messiah will be "the One who is Two". The Messiah will be both Daemon *and* Human . . . god *and* mortal.'

As a piece of misdirection it was masterfully done. By not discussing the lines in any meaningful way, de Nostredame had allowed the audience and, most importantly, the Doge to come to their own conclusions . . . their own *erroneous* conclusions. The way the Doge was smiling at the Lady indicated to Kondratieff that she had already made up her mind about just who these lines referred to.

'It vould zeem, younk lady, zhat you fulfil all zhese somewhat obscure predictions. You are a Daemon, unt hence have "Living Blood". And if zhe reports regarding your activities in Varsaw are to be believed, your coming most certainly portended a "Time of Miracles". Most interesting. But vot of zhe phrase "zhe Vun mit no Shadow"? Vot is your interpretation ov zhat, de Nostredame?'

'This remains an enigma, Your Excellency,' de Nostredame lied.

'Ah ha! Zo even zhe great de Nostredame must admit igno-rance. But I can be of azziztance here. Zizter Florence has zeen a former associate of zhe Lady IMmanual' – here the Doge gave the Lady a smile – 'unt has declared him to be bereft of an aura. Zo you zee, de Nostredame, zhe 4Tellings shown on zhe Column are played out to perfection.'

De Nostredame bowed. 'I am grateful to Your Excellency for her elucidation.'

'But if we are zaying, de Nostredame, zhat zhe Messiah valks amongst us, zhen zo too must zhe Beast. Unt as zhe Column states zhat zhe Beast vill come "from zhe North" zhen ve must presume zhis to allude to zhat swine Heydrich.'

'That is a very telling insight, Your Excellency,' observed de Nostredame.

*Telling, but wrong,* Kondratieff added silently.

'Jah, zhe Beast is abroad unt now Ragnarok begins. Unt presumably zhe unzeazonally cold veather ve are enjoying corresponds to zhe "barren Spring" mentioned in zhe Eddic to be zhe time vhen Ragnarok – "zhe Time of Screams" – vill be upon us. Zo zhe chronology is perfect.'

De Nostredame gave an encouraging nod. 'Perhaps now is the moment to move on to the last, and probably the most fasci-nating, of the six faces.'

The sight of the final face of the Column brought gasps from the audience. Here the lines of runic poetry had been replaced by a series of pictograms, the most striking of which was an image of a naked woman standing astride two lions, clutching a snake in each of her outstretched hands. But that wasn't the only idiosyncrasy: the strange geometric pattern of shapes at the bottom of the Column was equally intriguing.

De Nostredame raised an arm and pointed to the naked woman. 'Here we see carved a representation of what I believe to be the Messiah . . .'

'Zo, the Column shows zhat zhe Messiah vill be female?'

'Certainly.'

The Doge was silent for a moment, lost in thought. Then finally she gave a satisfied nod and spoke. 'Jah, you are correct, de Nostredame. It is obvious to me zhat zhis Column celebrates a time vhen zhe female vill be in zhe ascendant. Zhe very shape ov zhe Column – zhe V-shape – imitates zhe shape ov zhe female sexual organs. Jah, zhe Column shows irrefutably zhat zhe Messiah vill be a voman.'

*Excellent.*

'But vot of zhe snakes zhis voman is holding, Professeur? Vot is zheir significance?'

'My own opinion, Your Excellency,' began de Nostredame, sounding a damned sight more confident than Kondratieff guessed he actually felt, 'is that the image on Face Six shows the Messiah disentangling the two helixical strands of the Living as represented by the snakes. It represents her ability to disentwine and then reassemble the most fundamental component of life itself.'

'Interesting. Unt vot of zhe rather mysterious algorithmic inscription shown beneath zhe image of zhe Messiah?'

'As it stands, the "family-tree" design remains undeciphered. One possible interpretation is that it mirrors the work of a modern day scientist named Gregor Mendel, who is now in the employ of the Empress Wu, and who has published a study he has made of plant hybridisation with especial reference to the plant of the common pea or *Pisum sativum* variety. This demonstrates that certain characteristics of the original, parent plants are present in their offspring without any blending or averaging of the original, parental characteristics. These principles of inherited characteristics may be illustrated in a quite satisfactory manner by an algorithm very, very similar to the one shown on the Column.'

The Doge chuckled. 'Are you zuggesting, de Nostredame, zhat zhis wonderful heirloom from deepest antiquity vos wrought by zhe Pre-Folk to preserve zhe zecrets of how to more zatis-factorily grow *peas*?'

De Nostredame ignored the laughter from around the room. 'No,' he protested, 'Mendel's principles may be applied more generally. They govern all aspects of heredity in flora and in fauna.'

'But vhy vould zuch information be contained on a sculpture zelebrating zhe coming of zhe Messiah? No, in zhis matter, de Nostredame, you are in error. Zhis design has, I think, more of an astrological significance rather zhan vun associated mit breeding unt fertility.' The Doge gave another yawn. 'I think I have heard unt zeen enough . . .'

'I have a question,' said the Marquis de Sade quietly.

The Doge waved a hand to grant him permission to continue.

'In Canto Three, Lilith is described as the "Dark Mistress of the Living". May I ask, Professeur de Nostredame, if this confirms that Lilith was a Shade?'

*Bastard.*

The most worrying thing was that the question hadn't been posed in a flippant manner. Kondratieff had the uncomfortable feeling that de Sade suspected the truth.

Fortunately de Nostredame was sharp enough to deflect this potentially embarrassing question. 'Not at all. As I have alluded, some of the phraseology used in the Old French *is* ambiguous. The word "dark" might be construed as both "wicked" or as "Shade". However, on reflection, I am inclined to believe that "dark" refers to Lilith's evil nature rather than her ethnicity. There is little evidence – except that stimulated by racial prej-udice – to support the contention that Lilith was a Shade. If anything, the colour most strongly associated with her is red: she was, after all, the original "Scarlet Woman".' De Nostredame looked around the room. 'Are there any other questions?' he asked.

Suddenly the Doge rose to her feet. 'No more questions. I have zeen unt heard enough.' She turned to the Lady. 'Not only has zhe Zizter Florence zeen zhat your aura is of a divine cast but now zhe lines on zhe Column support your claim to be zhe Messiah in a most remarkable fashion. It tells uz zhat zhe Messiah vill be female, zhat she vill be a Daemon, unt zhat she vill portend a time of miracles. You are indeed zhe Messiah, younk lady, of zhat zhere can be no doubt. I vill be honoured to support your claim of Messiahship in front of zhe Council of Ten.'

*Excellent.*

'Unt now you must come mit me, to reside in my palace. A convent is no place for zhe True Messiah.'

# 27

## The Convent of the Sacred and
## All-Seeing Order of Visual Virgins: Venice
## The Demi-Monde: 27th Day of Spring, 1005

The use of garlic and silver as *apotropes* – devices designed
to dissuade and to dispel spirits and daemons of the night
– although most common in the Quartier Chaud – is a
practice seen throughout the Demi-Monde. WhoDoo
mambos employ them to guard against the most evil of
*loas*, the Grigori; Visual Virgins have them to hand in their
convents to protect against vampyres, whilst the ImPuritans
of the Quartier Chaud display them on their household
shrines to dissuade revenants – those who return – from
entering their homes.

Trying to Pin WhoDoo Down:
*Colonel Percy Fawcett, Shangri-La Books*

The woman who stood watching them was a giantess. She was
far taller than any man Burlesque had ever seen, and some of
the Lascars who had worked the docks in the Rookeries were
colossally big men.

'Fuck me gently, Burlesque,' he heard Rivets whisper, 'that's
a vampyre tart that is, like them wuns in *Gregory the Grigori*.
That's one fucking big woman.' As understatements went, it
was a corker.

On bare feet, the girl glided deeper into the room, and as

she came closer to the halo cast by the gas lamp, Burlesque got a better look at her. By his estimation, she must have been almost six and a half feet in height – or almost a foot and a half taller than Rivets and a good six inches taller than Burlesque himself – and her broad, broad shoulders told him that she had strength to match her size. She shifted her weight onto the balls of her feet, as though preparing to spring, and in doing so flexed her body. From what Burlesque could see, she had a body well worth flexing, especially as all she was wearing was a bolero jacket and a pair of harem trousers made from red silk that glistened in the half-light.

'Gor, clock the charms on that,' observed an admiring Rivets, seemingly oblivious to the danger he and Burlesque were in.

Any further observations Rivets might have been inclined to make about the woman's breasts died in his mouth as she drew a long and very sharp-looking knife from the wide belt that snaked around her trim waist. Automatically Burlesque reached for the pistol he had thrust down the back of his own belt, but before he had a chance to draw it, the woman struck.

There must have been over twelve feet separating her from Burlesque, but astonishingly she covered the distance in one leap. For one breathtaking instant Burlesque couldn't believe what he was seeing. What she had done he knew to be humanly impossible. Nobody, be they man or woman – or even kangaroo – could jump as this woman had just done.

These reflections were abruptly and painfully curtailed as the woman slashed her blade towards him, the knife slicing towards his head at an unbelievable speed. Instinctively he flinched back out of range . . . *almost* out of range.

Just the tip of the razor-sharp blade caught his arm as he dodged, but it was enough to slice an incision in his jacket sleeve and cut into his biceps. With a yelp, he arched away but he knew he was finished. Time slowed. He saw the woman coil back the arm that held the knife for the killing stroke and he braced himself to receive it. But then his life was saved by Rivets.

Instead of stabbing Burlesque, the woman was forced to twist her blade to parry the blow from a large silver candlestick that Rivets had aimed at her head. If his blow had landed, the woman would have been knocked for six, but almost negligently she blocked the downward swing of the candlestick with her knife, and then reached out to grab Rivets by the neck. With one hand she lifted the boy from the ground, holding him at arm's length while he twisted and squirmed, his feet a good foot clear of the carpet. Casually – *too* casually, as it turned out – she raised her knife to cut his throat.

Desperately Burlesque looked around for a weapon, but all he could see was the Chink urn that Rivets had dropped. Without a second's thought, he picked it up and brought it crashing down on the vampyre's head. It shattered, spilling the garlic powder it contained in a great choking cloud. By great good luck, Rivets had stolen one of the *apotropes* the Visial Virgins employed as protection against Grigori. The woman buckled, released her death grip on Rivets and sank to her hands and knees, gasping and retching, her face already blotching into flaming red pustules.

Seeing her weak and helpless, Burlesque didn't hesitate. He kicked her as hard as he could on the side of the head. Behemoth or not, she slumped unconscious onto the carpet, her breath coming in weak gasps.

'Gor, fanks Burlesque, mate,' panted Rivets, as he massaged his bruised neck. 'I fort I was dead meat then, an' no mistake. Wotta vicious cow.' And, as if to emphasise the point, he slammed the toe of his hobnailed boot into the woman's stomach.

Burlesque picked up the vampyre's knife and handed it to Rivets. 'Never mind all that. Cut down some of that curtain rope an' tie 'er up. When she wakes up, she's gonna be in a rare tear.'

'Why not top her?'

Burlesque thought about it for a moment and then shook his head. 'Nah, we can't do that. She's a bird, and anyway, toppin' 'er might upset Odette.'

With a shrug Rivets moved to follow Burlesque's orders, and within a minute he had the vampyre trussed up like a parcel for posting. Satisfied that she was now, as Rivets called it, *whores de combat*, Burlesque heeled across the room and cautiously poked his head out into the hallway. To his astonishment, the butler was *still* standing guard on the front door, shouting at Odette who was *still* banging at it from the outside. All Burlesque could imagine was that the noise the pair were kicking up had drowned the sound of the fracas that had just taken place in the library. He pulled out his pistol and pushed its muzzle against the side of the man's head. 'Ouvrez la porte,' he ordered, and the butler did just as he was told.

Pascal Leroy had never been tied to a chair in his life before, nor had he ever been in the presence of anybody who looked quite so crazy before. The fat man with the beard was one thing, but the shrunken boy who was striding about the room wearing an angry scowl, massaging his bruised neck and kicking furniture, was quite another. This one was a vicious little vandal, who had destroyed the Convent's collection of silver plate by flattening them under his boot so that he could better squeeze them into the pockets of his oversized coat. But even worse, the dwarf kept giving Pascal the most unsettling of looks: he had the distinct feeling the bastard wanted to hurt him.

His peace of mind wasn't helped by the sight of Mademoiselle Armaros lying unconscious on the floor. It seemed impossible to Pascal that these two nonentities had been able to defeat her. He had been assured that Mademoiselle Armaros was a formidable assassin: she was, after all, one of the Grigori. When he had agreed to let the woman into the Convent, in exchange for ten thousand guineas in consideration of his services, he had been told that she could not fail and that she would kill the Lady IMmanual easily and without fuss. All he had had to do was to wait until Machiavelli's Signori di Notte had left the Convent to escort the Lady IMmanual to the Galerie, and then let Mademoiselle Armaros in through the back door. It should have been the easiest ten thousand guineas he had ever earned, but now, here she was, lying broken, bruised and bound on the library carpet.

These thoughts were put very firmly to the back of Pascal Leroy's mind when the bearded man came to stand over him. 'Où est Ella Thomas?' the man asked.

Gamely, Pascal Leroy shook his head. *'Je ne sais pas,'* he responded.

'Où est la Dame IMmanual?' the man persisted, a dangerous tone entering his voice.

*'Je ne sais pas.'*

The bearded man shook his head dolefully. 'Waddya fink, Rivets?' he asked the midget.

The boy stopped his pacing about the room and turned to stare at Pascal. 'I fink 'e just needs a bit ov persuading, that's wot I fink, Burlesque.' He flicked open a very dangerous-looking razor-knife and sauntered over to stand next to Pascal. Leaning down, he used the knife to slice the buttons from Pascal's beautifully embroidered waistcoat. This done, he eased the two sides of it apart, and then cut through his braces. As the boy began to unbutton his trousers – Pascal's eyes widening in horror as he did so – he began to talk in a soothing but infinitely threatening sort of way. 'Wot I'm gonna do, Mon-sewer le Frog, is get yer willy art. Once I've done this, I'm gonna arsk you some questions an' every time you say "Je ne sais pas" I'm gonna slice off an 'alf-inch of your cock. Twiggy-vous le chose? Comprenez?'

Aghast at what he thought he understood the boy to be saying – he could already feel his scrotum starting to shrivel in anticipation – all Pascal could do was nod desperately. 'Monsieur, pleeze . . .' he began, but his pleezes were stilled when the boy put a finger firmly to his lips and winked at him. Then, with a smile, he dug his hand into Pascal's fly and hauled out his penis. It was as embarrassing as it was terrifying, especially when the French girl who had been screaming at him out on the doorstep came over to get a better look at his manhood.

'*C'est très petit*,' she opined, and Pascal coloured in mortification. He had always considered himself a *fortissimo*-class lover.

'C'est vrais,' agreed the one they called Burlesque.

'An' it's gonna be a lot more petit when I'm done,' added the boy. 'I fink iffn I arsk more'n four questions we're gonna run out ov cock to trim. Still . . . when I've run out of sausage, I can start on the sprouts. Vous gonna be a NoN, Mon-sewer.'

Pascal watched, fear stricken, as this Rivets person manoeuvred the tip of the knife until it was scratching at the juncture between his scrotum and his penis. His imagination ran riot. One flick of the boy's wrist and the bastard would geld him. Almost crying with terror, Pascal desperately tried to still his shaking, worried that he might inadvertently lead to his own castration.

'Roight, Mon-sewer le Frog, I fink you parlez le lingo Anglo pretty bien. Do you savvy avec beaucup de understanding?'

Pascal nodded: his understanding might not be 'beaucup' but it was enough for him to get the gist of what was being said. And anyway, whatever the words didn't convey, the knife point his bollocks were balanced on was very eloquent in explaining.

'Roight; question un. Où est Ella Thomas?'

No matter how much he valued his position within the Convent, Pascal Leroy was unwilling to become a NoN simply to protect his tenure. 'The Marquis de Sade 'as taken 'er to the

Galerie des Anciens, there to attend the presentation of an arte-fact most rare,' he answered with as much reluctance as he dared.

'Question ducks: when did she leave cette Convent?'

Pascal glanced at the clock ticking on the library's mantel-piece. 'Monsieur . . . I beg you . . .' There was a tweak of the knife. 'This afternoon; at two of the clock.'

'Very good, Mon-sewer le Frog. Question troys: when will she an' this de Sade item be comin' back to the Convent?'

For a moment Pascal Leroy hesitated, then, prompted by an even more urgent jab of the knife's point, he replied, 'I do not know, Monsieur. I understand that she will afterwards be taken to the Doge's Palace, for an assignation with the Doge.'

'Fuck! We're scuppered, Burlesque,' said the boy, and a flash of anger flickered over his face. 'We can't 'ang around 'ere all night waiting for Miss Ella to show up. There might be more of them vampyre tarts skulking around.'

The bearded man – Burlesque? – seemed uncertain as to what to do next. It was the big woman, the one called Odette, who solved his dilemma. She had been shuffling through the papers on the desk and, obviously having found something of interest, beckoned Burlesque over. They whispered together for a moment and then Burlesque turned back to the dwarf with a smile on his face. 'I don't fink we'll 'ave to wait, Rivets, me old cock.' And with that, he scooped all the papers lying on the desk into a satchel he'd found handy. 'That's it, I think, we can vamoose now.'

'Wot abart the Mon-sewer, 'ere?' asked the boy.

Pascal had only the briefest glimpse of the candlestick the bearded bastard swung at his head before a rather painful dark-ness descended.

# 28

## The Sala del Maggior Consiglio: Venice
## The Demi-Monde: 28th Day of Spring, 1005

There are many fascinating characters in the history of WhoDoo, but none more divisive than Marie Laveau. Born sometime around 800 AC, Marie Laveau is reputed to have been the reincarnation of Lilith, and hence to have been possessed of immense power both as a WhoDoo mambo and as a Seidrkona (a practitioner of Seidr magick). It is rumoured that Marie Laveau was assassinated by the Code Noir, who viewed her as the Beast, the manifestation of Loki here in the Demi-Monde.

**Trying to Pin WhoDoo Down:**
*Colonel Percy Fawcett, Shangri-La Books*

Even Vanka, distracted though he was by the audacity of what he was attempting, had to admit that the Sala del Maggior Consiglio, the great hall where the Council of Ten was meeting, was impressive. Adorned with wonderful artworks and swathed in gilt, the hall was a sight to behold, but what impressed Vanka most was that it was large enough to house the hordes of rich and powerful Venetians who had descended on the Palace to witness the testing of the Lady IMmanual's Messiahship. This was obviously seen as a momentous occasion, an event which anyone who was anyone in Venice wanted to attend.

Vanka was delighted that it was so popular, as crowds meant

lots of unfamiliar people, which, coupled with all the attendees being masked, meant the chances of him being recognised were reassuringly slim. And, of course, the pair of them being in possession of invitations to attend the Great Audience issued by the Doge herself meant that even the Signori di Notte – on full alert after the discovery of a Grigori assassin inside the Convent – were respectfully non-intrusive. That Burlesque had managed to find *two* invitations in the library of the Convent had been a terrific stroke of luck, lucky because it meant that Norma could come with him, and having a friend at his side he found peculiarly reassuring.

And their luck had held: the pair of them had entered the Sala unchallenged and now they found themselves standing wedged in the middle of the hall, compressed by bodies on every side, desperately trying to search out a breeze to relieve the hot, acrid atmosphere that suffused the room. It was so hot that after just five minutes in the Sala Vanka's lime-green silk suit was stained dark with sweat and his curly hair hung limp about his shoulders.

'When are they going to begin?' Norma asked in a whisper. 'If we're made to stand here much longer, we'll all be dead from asphyxiation.'

ABBA must have heard her prayers. Suddenly there was a fanfare of trumpets and a troop of heavily berobed dignitaries stepped onto the stage at the end of the hall. Thankfully, Vanka was tall and, by standing on his toes, he could see what was happening. This, he decided, must be the arrival of the Doge and her Council of Ten, the most important decision-makers in the whole of Venice, and there, at the back of this crowd of dignitaries, was Ella.

She looked marvellous. Encouraged by the sight of the girl he loved, Vanka determined to get closer to the stage. If he was to have any chance of speaking with her, he had to be able to catch her eye and with that in mind he began to lizard his way through the crowd, ignoring the protests of his fellow attendees.

The Lady IMmanual seemed almost abnormally calm, and this de Sade found really quite perplexing. Personal experience told him that those about to be put to the question by the Council of Ten tended to be very nervous: the threat of having their head chopped off, if they were judged to have violated Venetian protocol, had that effect on people. And, from the gossip and rumour circulating in the Palace, there was a bloody good chance that the Lady IMmanual – if she couldn't convince them she was the Messiah – would be ending the day a head shorter than when she began it. Despite the support of the Doge, nobody seemed to think that a *girl* could ever be ordained Messiah. Demi-Mondian tradition had it that the Messiah would be a man and thinking otherwise was a step too far, even for broad-minded Venetians.

And that was why the book some unfeeling bastard had opened was giving such long odds on the Lady being able to avoid the block, so long that de Sade hadn't been able to resist a flutter. But as he trotted behind the Lady IMmanual en route to the Sala del Maggior Consiglio, de Sade judged it to have been a hundred francs well invested. The Lady IMmanual looked and acted like someone destined for the winner's enclosure rather than the chopping block.

She had dressed carefully for the Audience, shunning all the bright fashions of the Quartier Chaud and choosing instead a gown of the purest white. Her dressers had been shocked: white was the colour of burial shrouds, which seemed in the circum-stances to be a tad pessimistic. But the Lady had been adamant. What had she said in response? If she was to play the part of a saint then she would bloody well dress like one. Of course, this being the Quartier Chaud, the gown they had made for her was excessively tight and sported a dangerously low-cut neckline – her breasts unfortunately hidden beneath the shawl she wore about her shoulders – but all in all de Sade was pleased by how his protégée looked. And when it had come to selecting a suitable mask for the occasion, the Lady had been equally adamant that she would stand before the Grand Council unmasked, with her head freshly shaven.

The problem was that it would take more than a tight gown and a shaven head to impress the Council. As de Sade knew to his cost, they were a difficult bunch of bastards to convince, but nevertheless he was quietly confident, especially as the Lady seemed to have a strange certainty about her, and certainty was the one thing that people craved in their leaders and, presumably, in their Messiah.

His hundred francs was safe.

Ella, Vanka was pleased to see, was learning. When he had first met her, she had been a little naïve regarding the tricks of the theatrical profession, but now . . .

If he had been able to speak to her in advance, he would have advised her that in order to be seen as some ineffably spiritual being, she had to act and dress as one. And this was just what she had done. That she had entered the hall unmasked was a master stroke: it marked her out as someone different, whilst simultaneously signalling an innocence, a vulnerability which would make it difficult for anyone to condemn her to death. It also revealed just how astonishingly lovely she was. It would take a real bastard to vote to snuff out the life of such a beauty, but then Venice was stuffed to the gunwales with real bastards.

As he pushed and shoved his way through the crowd, he saw Ella being brought to a halt right in the middle of the stage, standing there flanked by the Council of Ten, by the Doge, and by a guard of honour which seemed to be made up of three Visual Virgins and a small, nervous-looking young man with curly hair.

A silence fell over the assembly as everyone waited with bated breath to hear what the Doge would pronounce in support of this putative Messiah.

Pushing her way through the crowd, Norma decided that as adventures went this was, in her judgement, about as madcap and dangerous as they got. Wandering into a place crawling with Signori di Notte when there were warrants out for their arrest was not a good move, but Vanka was so desperate to see Ella that nothing would dissuade him. And as Norma was finding out, friendship involved standing by your friend even when they did something that defied common sense.

As Norma sidled her way around a particularly fat patrician, she saw the Doge hold up her hands. 'Lords unt Ladies of Venice, patricians: we meet today to make a momentous decision. Zhis girl, zhe vun known as zhe Lady IMmanual, has come amongst us hailed as zhe Messiah who vill lead us through Tribulation unt to Revelation mit ABBA. Zhat she has performed a miracle is not in doubt, since zhere are many reliable witnesses to attest zhat it was she who parted zhe Boundary Layer unt allowed zhose imprisoned in Warsaw to escape zhe vindictiveness of Reinhard Heydrich unt zhe ForthRight. Ve have alzo zhe testimony of Zizter Florence in vhich she confirms zhat zhis girl's aura is more zhan human . . . it is *zupernatural*. But zhere is more: yesterday ve learnt zhat she fulfils zhe prophecies inscribed on Loci's Column.'

There was a murmur around the Sala. That Ella was such a precise fit regarding the prophecies made on the Column was a *very* telling argument in her favour.

'Zo today we must judge her: we must decide vhether she is

indeed zhe Messiah zent to us by ABBA.' The Doge fell silent for a moment. 'Patricians, zhe choice is yours, unt may ABBA guide you in your deliberations.'

With that the Doge stepped back, to leave Ella standing alone at the front of the stage. And then occurred one of those unplanned, impossible, serendipitous *coups de théâtre* that turn the everyday into something astonishing. As Norma watched, a ray of sunshine broke through one of the windows ranged around the ceiling of the hall and speared down onto Ella, enveloping her in a halo of light. Her white gown, covered as it was with white crystals, flared in the sunlight, and for a moment she seemed to have been touched by ABBA.

As the sunlight flamed around her, Ella raised her arms, spreading them in benediction. 'I am the Lady IMmanual,' she announced in a voice loud enough to carry to the very rear of the crowded hall. 'I have been sent by ABBA to give help and succour to the peoples of the Demi-Monde in their struggle against oppression and cruelty. At this very moment, the evil that is UnFunDaMentalism bestrides the Medi, and only the Grand Canal stands between Venice and destruction. I have been sent by ABBA to lead you to salvation.'

*Bloody hell, she's good.*

'I have been sent by ABBA and, as a sign of my coming, He/She has ordained this to be the Age of Miracles. You shall know me by my miracles. So hear me, people of Venice, and believe: I am the Messiah.'

As Vanka watched, a large and well-built man dressed in a suit of burgundy silk, and wearing a mask of uncompromising black leather, strode up the steps to stand on the edge of the stage.

'I am Enrico Dandolo, Administrator of the Arsenal and First Captain of the East Wall.'

'Now there'll be trouble,' Vanka heard one of his neighbours whisper to a colleague. 'Dandolo's a firebrand and he hasn't got any time for messiahs. All this mysticism nonsense will have got right up his nose.'

'Your Most Reverend Excellency, Honoured Members of the Council of Ten, patricians of Venice, I demand the right to speak and to challenge the right of this girl – this self-proclaimed Messiah – to command us, the free-Men and free-Women of Venice.'

There was a nod from the Doge. She had no other option; as Vanka understood it, it was the right of every patrician to speak during a Great Audience, and Dandolo had obviously appointed himself as Ella's chief prosecutor.

'How can any take the claims of this *Shade* seriously?' Dandolo began, 'She comes citing some mumbo-jumbo about being sent by ABBA to lead us to victory over the Beast. But am I alone in thinking that if she has been sent by anyone, she has been sent by Reinhard Heydrich to confuse and perplex us? All this girl seeks to do, with her lies and falsehoods, is to strip Venice bare of its capacity to fight.'

Dandolo turned and looked towards the crowded ranks of patricians. 'I am Captain of the East Wall. I have sworn an oath to defend Venice with my life, and I will not yield that sacred duty to such a pair of untried, untested and unsafe hands.'

There was a grumble of agreement throughout the hall.

'What this girl is *rumoured* to have done in Warsaw is of no import here in Venice. It is impossible that soldiers in Venice will accept the leadership of a Shade *girl* in this matter, especially one tainted with the stench of WhoDoo witchcraft. I and my men have thought to make Venice the richest city in the Demi-Monde, and I will not see this legacy betrayed by one such as her. I was told that today I would see a girl blessed with divinity but all I see is a girl blessed with duplicity. Believe me, she is no messiah.' The disdain in Dandolo's voice was palpable.

With the slightest of smiles, Ella replied. 'Patrician Dandolo seems to doubt me on two grounds: that I am a Shade girl and that I am being untruthful when I say I have been sent to the Demi-Monde by ABBA. The first I cannot correct' – she paused and then hitched her hip coquettishly – 'nor do I suspect many men here would wish me to.' This raised a laugh, and Vanka sensed the crowd warming to her. 'But I resent Patrician Dandolo's implication that women are somehow inferior to men in their ability to fight evil.'

'I do not "imply": I state it,' retorted Dandolo. 'It is recognised that in war it is men who must bear the brunt of the fighting.'

'You are in error, sir. It is not that women are inferior to men in martial matters; it is that they are not inflamed by the curse of MALEvolence. Should they be inclined to fight, you would find women to be more than a match for the likes of you.'

Vanka frowned as he tried to work out just what Ella was about. She seemed to be deliberately trying to provoke Dandolo. And if this was her intention, then she succeeded.

'You insult me and every man who has fought for Venice,' replied Dandolo in an ominously quiet tone.

'Not at all,' answered Ella blithely. 'No more than you insult every woman who has ever had to sacrifice a lover, a son, a brother or a Current to a war prosecuted by incompetent and headstrong captains such as you.'

The gibe struck home, and Dandolo flinched as though he had been physically struck. 'Be careful, witch. If you were a man I would now demand satisfaction.'

Ella's voice took on a more threatening aspect. 'Patrician Dandolo should be more circumspect regarding the challenges he throws down. I fancy, sir, you are as inept in duelling as you are in denying my right to call myself the Messiah.'

For long seconds Dandolo glowered at her. 'I warn you most earnestly, witch, not to talk so imprudently! You are a disgrace to your fair sex. You impugn my reputation as a gentleman and as a patrician. I say again: if you were a man I would cut you down.'

'No, sir: you would *try* to cut me down,' Ella snarled back. 'But you would fail, and I would have you leave here with a scar to remind you that you slander me, my honour and my sex at your peril!'

The fury in Ella's eyes obviously unsettled Dandolo, but such was the man's pride that he refused to be cowed. 'It is all very well for you to hurl these insults at me, confident that you can hide behind your gender. But be in no doubt, ABBA has granted men superiority over women in all matters relating to strength and endurance.'

'Then if I was to best you, would that not be a sign that I am blessed by ABBA? Would you not then be obliged to acknowledge my divinity?'

Vanka couldn't help but smile. It had been so beautifully done. Ella had led Dandolo into a trap, and Dandolo didn't look terribly happy with the situation his own arrogance had put him in.

'You are as conniving as you are beautiful, witch, but your guile will gain you nothing. Honour does not permit me to fight a woman, but if I did, it is impossible that a girl such as you would be able to defeat me.'

Suddenly Ella turned and walked over to the wall behind the stage, every eye in the room following her progress. Two crossed cavalry sabres hung there, doubtless souvenirs of some battle fought in Venice's dim and distant past. She pulled one free, then shucked off her shawl and flexed the blade between her two hands, this making her full and delightfully presented bosom heave. Ella, Vanka decided, could teach even Visual Virgins a few tricks of her own regarding fiduciary sex.

'Perhaps, sir, as your sensitivities do not permit you to fight me, we can establish our relative abilities with the sword by proxy . . . by a trial of skill?' She tossed the second sword to Dandolo, who caught it awkwardly. 'I trust that this, at least, will not impinge too much on your honour as a Venetian gentleman?'

Dandolo tested the blade and then gave a careless shrug. 'I am not averse to demonstrating to you the superiority of the male of the species in matters martial but I am uncertain how this trial of skill is to be conducted.'

'I am informed that how skilled someone is with a sword depends upon the speed of their reflexes. Therefore I propose a contest where my reflexes are pitted against yours, Patrician Dandolo.'

As he removed his jacket, Dandolo sneered. 'I am indifferent to the style of the contest. My sword masters believe that the worth of a swordsman is judged by the strength of his wrist. That is why a woman will never be able to match a man with a blade.' He gave Ella a dismissive smile. 'So, witch, what exactly is this contest you propose?'

She turned to de Sade. 'Monsieur le Marquis, I would be obliged if you would take two apples from the bowl, one in each hand, and then climb up onto the table.'

De Sade was so lost in admiration of the Lady IMmanual's delightful bottom that for a moment he didn't realise she was addressing him. When he pulled himself together he frowned – it was a very peculiar request – and he had to receive a nod of assent from the Doge before he befouled the gorgeously embroidered tablecloth with his velvet pumps. He took the apples and clambered up onto the table, to stand towering over the patricians crowded into the hall below him. It was a some-what embarrassing position to be in but there were compensations, the chief being that he now had an unsurpassed view of the Lady IMmanual's heaving breasts as she stood beneath him. With great reluctance he tore his eyes away from that succulent flesh. It would not do to risk tumescence in front of all these important people.

'What I propose, Patrician Dandolo,' explained the Lady, 'is that the Marquis de Sade will drop one of those apples, and we each, in turn, will demonstrate our skill by skewering it as it falls. This, I believe, will be a telling test of both our skill and our speed of reflex.'

Dandolo shrugged. 'The sabre, as you obviously fail to understand, is a weapon designed to cut rather than thrust.'

'But as we are similarly armed, Patrician Dandolo, then we are both equally disadvantaged. So, do you agree to my proposal or not?'

Another careless shrug from Dandolo, and a supercilious glance towards the other patricians gathered around the hall. 'This is a game for children, but if it amuses you, why not? Shall I go first, to demonstrate the correct technique?'

Ella gave a small bow and backed away to make room for her opponent. Dandolo shuffled his feet until they were about shoulder-width apart, and he was standing square-on to the anticipated descent of the apple. Slowly he drew the sabre back until it was horizontal to his right shoulder, his arm cocked ready to lunge forward.

'I will drop the apple on the count of three,' said de Sade quietly. 'One. Two. Three!'

He let the apple go, and almost instantaneously Dandolo's sabre jabbed forward, sending it spinning across the room. It was retrieved by a young man standing at the very front of the crowd. 'A hit!' he shouted.

There was a round of applause from those in the room and, with a bow of gratitude and an immodest little swagger, Dandolo ceded his place to the Lady IMmanual. He was right to be cocky, decided de Sade: just to hit the apple in flight showed a level of skill he, for one, had never seen equalled.

The Lady IMmanual took Dandolo's position at the end of the table. As she adjusted her stance and brought her sword up ready, de Sade could sense the excited crowd pressing closer to the stage.

'One. Two. Three!'

The apple dropped. The girl struck, her arm moving so quickly that if de Sade had blinked, he was certain he would have missed the pistoning of the blade.

But the apple didn't fly.

There was a gasp of disappointment from the crowd, a gasp tinged, de Sade decided, with just a soupçon of relief. Obviously none of the men gathered in the hall wanted to see Dandolo bested by a girl.

'A miss!' exclaimed Dandolo.

'I think not,' observed the Lady IMmanual, as she brought her sabre back to the *en garde* position. There, some six inches along the blade, sat the apple, skewered dead centre. The Lady turned to Dandolo. 'It would appear that I am the victor, Patrician Dandolo.'

Dandolo scowled and then shook his head. 'Not so, witch. If you were aware of the laws of chance, you would realise that all your success has demonstrated is beginner's luck. It was luck rather than skill that enabled you to pierce the apple.'

'Then we must devise a test which eliminates chance entirely.' The Lady leant over to the fruit bowl, considered for a moment, and then selected two small black grapes. 'If we were to repeat the trial using these grapes, and one of us was successful in making a hit and the other not, would you concede it to be a triumph of skill over luck, Patrician Dandolo?'

A snort of derision from Dandolo. 'What you are suggesting is impossible. To hit such a small target with the lunge of a sabre would require . . .'

'The help of ABBA?' suggested the Lady IMmanual, impishly. 'So I ask you again: if I were to succeed and you were to fail, would that not show that I am blessed by ABBA, and therefore divine?'

As de Sade watched from his lofty position, he saw Dandolo's eyes skittering around the room. He was now a *very* unhappy man. 'Yes,' he agreed reluctantly, 'if you were to perform such an amazing feat, then I would have to concede that you were truly blessed by ABBA.'

A hushed silence fell on the hall as the Lady handed the grapes to de Sade, and announced that as she was the winner of the first round, then Patrician Dandolo was obliged to go first again. This he did with much bad grace, but much determination. His determination did him no good: his lunge missed the falling grape completely, the effort sending him sprawling to the floor. The ripple of laughter that accompanied his fall brought a flush of embarrassment to his face and a snarl of hatred to his lips.

De Sade eyed Dandolo nervously. He was an angry man, and in de Sade's experience angry men could easily be provoked into doing something stupid.

Using his sabre as a makeshift walking stick, Dandolo got back to his feet and brushed the dust off the knees of his trousers. 'I am pleased I amuse you, witch,' he sneered. 'Could we now have the opportunity of seeing if you can do any better?'

For de Sade, the outcome was almost inevitable. The Lady took up her position; he counted *one, two, three*; he dropped the grape; the sabre flashed; and there was the grape skewered on the tip of the sword. But expected or not, his mouth still flopped open in astonishment, amazed that anyone could do what he had just seen done. The rest of the audience was similarly dumbfounded. It was one thing to applaud skill and talent; it was quite another to celebrate what they instinctively knew to be impossible. No one, absolutely *no one*, could have done what the Lady IMmanual had just done. Such a combination of speed, accuracy and hand–eye coordination was inhuman. No, it was more: it was superhuman, and as such it was more frightening than it was awe-inspiring.

Out of loyalty to the Lady, de Sade clapped his hands and shouted 'Bravo', but the rest of the audience refused to be roused. Instead they stood there immobile . . . awestruck.

The Lady IMmanual seemed oblivious to the dazed condition of the gathered patricians. 'So, Patrician Dandolo, it would appear that I have won, and therefore you must acknowledge me for what I am, an emissary of ABBA.'

'What you did was impossible,' stammered Dandolo. 'You are no disciple of ABBA. Rather you are a witch in the employ of Loki.'

'Now, now, Patrician Dandolo, it does not do to show what a bad sport you are. Take defeat like a man, and all that.' She gave a showy swish of her sabre. 'As you say, it is all down to the strength of one's wrists.'

'It is impossible for a woman to be stronger than the man. It is . . . unnatural.' Dandolo growled, and his peevish frown darkened with black anger. 'You are Loki's whore.'

The Lady IMmanual's eyes flashed with anger. 'Perhaps there is another reason for my mastery over you. Perhaps some other affliction is the cause of the weakness of your wrist, and hence of your defeat?'

Like a man who had been slapped in the face, Dandolo stepped back, his face red with anger. Even de Sade – who judged himself indifferent to insults – realised that for a man as splenetic as Dandolo to be accused of masturbation was a grievous insult and one to which he would retaliate.

Dandolo struck.

It was a lunatic move. If Dandolo's sabre had landed, it would have decapitated the girl. But faster than the eye could see, the Lady raised her own blade to parry the stroke and then, in a twinkling, had sliced the tip of her sabre across Dandolo's neck. The Venetian dropped his sword and sank gasping to his knees, his hands desperately clutching at his throat. It was a fatal wound: there was a rattle in his throat, and then he collapsed twitching across the stage. Finally, with one last gasp, he was still.

With a disdainful shake of her head, the Lady IMmanual turned to the audience. 'Let this be a warning, patricians,' she called out, imperiously, 'that even though I am a woman, that does not mean I am unable to defend myself and my followers from wickedness. All those who take up arms against me will perish. Know me, I am the Lady IMmanual, I am the Messiah. Follow me and I will lead you to victory against the Beast that rises in the North. Follow me and I will lead you safely through Ragnarok. Follow me and I will lead you to Revelation. Together we will destroy the ForthRight. Together we will conquer the Demi-Monde and unite it under the blessed creed of IMmanualism. Hear me and know that if any oppose me, I will bring ABBA's fury down on their heads. I will destroy them.'

She paused dramatically and then raised the sabre high above her head. 'I now make this pledge to Venice: I will not allow your city to be ravaged by the ForthRight. I swear to you that not one ForthRight soldier will cross the Grand Canal. ABBA will smite the enemies of IMmanualism and cast them into the waters. I am the Messiah, and I give you this pledge.'

For a long moment she gazed around the hall, and when she spoke again her voice was, if anything, louder and more compelling. 'I have a personal slogan, one given to me by ABBA, that will be adopted by all who accept me as the Messiah: "Unite, Follow, Crush".'

'Unite, Follow, Crush!' was the shout that echoed through the Sala del Maggior Consiglio, and as the cheering of those gathered there rocked the hall, de Sade hopped down from the table, already wondering which whore he would squander his winnings on. He would need something to take his mind off what he had just witnessed. He had never imagined that the Messiah would be quite such a brutal bitch.

Alone of all the people in the hall, only Norma and Vanka didn't join in the applause. Like Vanka, Norma was too shaken – sickened – by what she had seen and heard. This wasn't the Ella she knew. Ella didn't kill people. Ella didn't incite the mob to crush people.

The pair of them standing there, looking bemused and bewildered in that sea of cheering people was what made Ella notice them, and though they were masked, this didn't prevent her recognising her erstwhile friends. Norma saw her turn and point Vanka out to one of her Signori di Notte bodyguards, the look of pure hatred on her face persuading Norma to grab Vanka by the arm and try to hurry him to the exit. Oh, he protested that he had to speak to Ella but when he saw the Signori pushing and shoving their way towards them, even he realised that now wasn't the time to chat. And as the pair of them scuttled out of the hall the question kept nagging at her: why did Ella suddenly hate Vanka – hate *her* – so much? Why was Ella suddenly their enemy?

# 29

## The Future History Institute: Venice
## The Demi-Monde: 28th Day of Spring, 1005

Temporal Intervention is a delicate matter. Even the most nugatory of changes to the TimeStream can, over the course of Future History, have unforeseen and unwelcomed consequences, this being referred to as Temporal Noise or, more whimsically, as the Butterfly Effect. Temporal Interventions must be the minimum actions required to achieve the designated OutCome and must be conducted in total secrecy. If we imagine Future History as a pool of still water and Temporal Interventions as pebbles tossed into that water, then by adhering to the Precept of Minimalism, the changes made must create the lowest amplitude and duration of ripples. Additionally, all Temporal Interventions must be enacted as close (both temporally and spatially) to the desired OutCome as is possible.

*Future History Institute Standard Procedure 017: Rules*
*Governing Temporal Interventions*

It was a shaken Norma who followed an even more shaken Vanka into a nearby bar. Neither of them spoke until Vanka had downed several large glasses of Solution, and Norma had knocked back decidedly more cognac than was good for her.

Eventually, her shock suitably anaesthetised, Norma looked

over to Vanka. 'What the fuck was all that about? Did I or did I not just see Ella Thomas murder a man in cold blood and get cheered to the rafters for her efforts?'

Vanka sat gazing blankly at the wall for several moments before he answered, 'I'm not sure what you mean by "in cold blood", Norma, but the answer to your question is, yes, Ella just killed a man without so much as turning a hair.' He gave a mirthless little chuckle. 'Though, as she's now shaven-headed, that's pretty much what you might expect.'

'I don't really think this is much of a time for levity, Vanka,' snapped Norma. 'And it wasn't just what Ella did to that poor sod Dandolo either—'

'She was defending herself,' interrupted Vanka.

'No, she wasn't! She goaded him into fighting her. She knew what she was doing all along, knew that she'd end up killing him. Fuck it, she *wanted* to kill him!'

'No, I can't believe that. Maybe she's playing some sort of political game we don't really understand. Maybe that guy Dandolo was a bad hat, an UnFunny crypto or something? Maybe—'

'There aren't any maybes about it, Vanka. She killed Dandolo just to make a political point, just to show how strong and tough she is . . . just so she could take her turn at the trough.'

'No, Ella's not like that.'

'Well, the Lady IMmanual sure as hell is. And what I heard her spouting in there was pretty chilling, too. She was talking about bringing down ABBA's fury on her enemies' heads and destroying people. All this "Unite, Follow, Crush" crap she was mouthing is scary stuff. That's the sort of bile I'd expect to hear from Heydrich, not from Ella Thomas.'

Vanka took another long swig of Solution. 'Look, Norma, I was with Ella every minute of every day in Warsaw, and she always abhorred the violence and the misery of war. I can't believe that's the same girl who was pontificating in front of the Council of Ten. Maybe being tortured back in the Bastille has sent her loopy . . .'

'Yeah, she's loopy all right.' She drained her glass. 'I've gotta tell you, Vanka, what Ella did to Dandolo was the last straw. I've had it with violence, I've had it with war and I've had it with killing.' She pulled the Cloverleaf out from her purse and pushed it across the table to Vanka. 'No more violence for me, Vanka. Violence is the oxygen of hatred and I'm having nothing more to do with it.'

'Norma . . .'

Vanka never got to finish his sentence. He was interrupted by the arrival of a breathless newcomer. The man – young, bespectacled and utterly nondescript – leant over the table and, in a conspiratorial voice, whispered a warning. 'My friends, I am Nikolai Kondratieff, and I have been sent to save you. The Signori di Notte dispatched to find and arrest you are only two blocks away from this bar. If you wish to live, you must follow me.'

Kondratieff led Norma and Vanka via a zigzag path through the labyrinthine back alleys of Venice, until, finally, utterly bewildered, they were brought to the rear entrance of a large and imposing building that bordered the Grand Canal.

'I must apologise for the somewhat convoluted route I took to reach the Future History Institute,' Kondratieff explained, as he led them deeper and deeper into the vast building, 'but you will be safe here. This is the most important and most heavily protected building in the whole of Venice, more so even than the Doge's Palace. Housed here is the most precious commodity, after blood, in the whole of the Demi-Monde: information.' He stopped in front of a pair of huge doors and handed a warrant to one of the brutally big guards standing there. Satisfied, the guard gave him a crisp salute, and then levered open the doors.

The hall they entered was enormous. It was at least five hundred feet long by five hundred feet across, but it still gave the impression of being too small. Every square inch of the floor was crammed with rows and rows of clattering machines and rows and rows of shirt-sleeved clerks – hundreds of them – bent over what looked like crude typewriters, stabbing diligently at the keyboards. To Norma it was like a scene from some demented Metropolis and the noise was simply overpowering. The machines – spiderlike contraptions made of brass and steel – whirred and rattled as they absorbed the piles of punched cards the white-coated clerks pushed into them from one side, and then, seconds later, collected when the machine spat the cards out on the other side.

She felt a tap on her arm. 'Let's repair to one of our sound-proofed suites,' Kondratieff shouted, as he pointed to a circular room set in the middle of the hall. 'We'll be able to talk more easily there.'

The room Kondratieff ushered them into might have been quieter but it stank like the very devil, the atmosphere dank with the stench and the smoke of shag tobacco. And the cause of the fug was sitting at a desk littered with papers, sporting an amazingly long beard and puffing away on a clay pipe.

The bearded man appeared not to notice that his room had been invaded, and it took several moments before he finally tossed the paper he was reading aside and, with the words 'Plagiarised crap', raised his gaze and nodded a greeting to his guests.

'Ah, Kondratieff, at last. I am delighted you have successfully evaded the attentions of our secret police.'

He gave a casual wave of his hand, indicating that the arrivals should seat themselves around a large conference table. As Norma shifted the papers that littered the chair Kondratieff had pulled out for her, she felt herself the subject of careful scrutiny by the bearded man.

'And good evening to you, Mademoiselle Williams, this is a *signal* honour,' said Beardy.

'You know my name?'

'Of course. I probably know more about you than you know yourself.'

'Then why is my being here a "signal honour"?'

'Why? Because, amongst other things, it isn't often a girl as beautiful as you deigns to accept an invitation to join me in my parlour. There are rumours circulating amongst the Institute's female undergraduates, to the effect that, though I am somewhat ancient, my sexual powers have not yet fully dissipated. It seems that girls will only attend me if they are chaperoned.' The man gave a wry chuckle and nodded towards Vanka. 'And very sensibly you have followed this advice. Which is unfortunate, of course, as it does somewhat curtail my natural inclination to indulge in all the pleasures made available by an ImPure society.'

'And who do I have the pleasure of avoiding the advances of?' asked Norma.

'My name is Professeur Michel de Nostredame, President of the Future History Institute,' and, with a groan, he levered himself up from behind his desk and came to sit at the head of the table. As he did so, Norma took the opportunity to study her host more carefully. He might be trying to portray himself as some sort of antediluvian buffoon, but Norma suspected he had a penetrating intellect, and the set of his mouth showed him to be a very determined individual. Determined but vague: his grey hair was only vaguely combed, his battered suit was only a vague fit and his cravat – what she could see of it behind his bushy beard – was festooned with the vague spots of the various soups he'd eaten in recent months. And he was old: very, very old.

'I am delighted to welcome you both to the inner sanctum

of the Institute.' De Nostredame gestured towards a window set in one wall of the room, indicating the rows of machines beyond. 'You should consider yourselves privileged; only a very few outsiders ever have the opportunity to see the DAEmon at work.'

'Daemon?' queried Norma.

'Data Analysis and Evaluation machinery . . . DAEmon for short. It's the collective name we have given to the array of Mr Babbage's analytical engines working out there in the hall, engines which allow us to process the vast quantity of data necessary to run our Future History program, HyperOpia.'

Their host took a moment to rekindle his pipe before continuing. 'So, my friends, to business. You will be wondering why I have had Kondratieff bring you here to the sanctuary of the Future History Institute.'

'It might be useful to begin by explaining why we are being sought by the Venetian secret police,' suggested Vanka.

'Ahhh, you must be the famous Vanka Maykov, faux-occultist, survivor extraordinaire and erstwhile companion to the Lady IMmanual.'

'Erstwhile?'

'It would seem, Monsieur Maykov, that your position at the side of – and, presumably, on top of – the Lady IMmanual has been usurped by the Marquis de Sade. Indeed, so precipitous has been your fall from grace that you and your oh-so-attractive colleague are now viewed by the powers that be as malignant political dissidents. It seems that, at the prompting of the Lady IMmanual, you have now been elevated to the rank of a major threat to the quietude of Venice. The streets, as they say, are now being combed.'

'She has so much power?' queried a genuinely shocked Norma.

'You haven't been keeping up with events, Mademoiselle.

According to HyperOpia, after today's performance by the Lady IMmanual in the Sala del Maggior Consiglio, she is now the power behind the throne in Venice.'

'Ella isn't interested in power,' protested Vanka.

'Tush-tush, your sentimentality is really quite touching, Monsieur Maykov, but your Ella no longer exists, her place having been taken by the much more ambitious and belligerent Lady IMmanual. And that is why Nikolai and I had to move with such rapidity to ensure the pair of you stayed out of the grasp of those nasty Signori di Notte.'

'And why did you do that, Professeur?' asked Vanka. 'Presumably, helping us to evade the police is traitorous behaviour.'

De Nostredame paused and then proceeded to spend several seconds restuffing the bowl of his pipe with glutinous black tobacco and then making several futile attempts to ignite it. Eventually, having coaxed his pipe to combust, he continued, 'All in good time, Monsieur Maykov, but first I would ask for your indulgence whilst I ask a question of my own.' He turned to Norma. 'You are a Daemon, Mademoiselle Williams, so I would be interested to hear if in the Spirit World you have the concept of preScience.'

'Prescience? Yeah, sure. Prescience, aka clairvoyance. It's the belief that certain people can see the future. It's all hokum, of course, but there're any number of astrologers and fortune-tellers ready to fool the unwary and turn a buck while they're doing it.'

'I did not say *prescience*, I said pre-*Science*. And while the predicting of the future in *your* world may be hokum, here in Venice it is a respected science, the precepts of which have been verified both experimentally and mathematically. It was preScience that spawned the study of statistics, of gaming theory and of quantum philosophy.'

'You can predict the future?'

'To a very high degree of accuracy – so accurate that preScience is what made Venice the rich and powerful city-state it is today.'

'Okay, I'm impressed.'

De Nostredame sniffed Norma's attempt at sarcasm aside. 'And so you should be.'

'But I've gotta say, Professeur, that I find it difficult to believe, in a world as screwed up as the Demi-Monde, that anybody can *accurately* predict anything.'

'Actually, Mademoiselle, it is because the Demi-Monde is – as you so charmingly put it – so screwed up that we are able to predict the future. PreScience is based on the realisation that the *post-Confinement* Demi-Monde – sealed as it is behind the impenetrable Boundary Layer – is a closed system immune to outside influences. And as most aspects of the Demi-Monde – the quantity of commodity inputs, population growth, the climate and the length of the seasons, for example – are fully predictable, then it is a world which is largely Deterministic in nature.'

'Deterministic?'

'Determinism is the belief that every event is caused by a preceding action, and hence by understanding the cause we can predict the effect. But here in the Institute, preScientists such as Nikolai and myself have taken this notion further and have sought, by mathematical analysis, to extrapolate the present into the future. The result of this analysis is termed Future History.'

'So you're telling me that you've made fortune-telling into a science?'

'A very exact science, Mademoiselle.'

Norma wasn't inclined to give up. 'Ah, c'mon, it's impossible to predict the future. Individual free will negates any and every attempt to anticipate how men and women will act.'

'A persuasive argument – persuasive but wrong.' De Nostredame held up his hand to forestall Norma's protests. 'The reality is that ours is a Clockwork Universe, mechanistic in its workings with every event planned by ABBA. The fabric He/She uses to make our future is woven from the threads of the present.'

'A Clockwork Universe?' asked Norma.

'A phrase coined by the Covenite polymath Pierre-Simon Laplace. Laplace has speculated that as ABBA is omnipotent, omniscient and omnipresent, then He/She knows everything right down to the movement of every atom in the whole Kosmos. What he said was, and here I quote, "For such a Deity nothing is uncertain and the future, just like the past, will be present before its eyes." Laplace contends that an all-knowing ABBA is able to foretell the future with as much certainty as He/She knows the past, and as a consequence the Demi-Monde functions with a clockwork certainty. Hence the tag: a Clockwork Universe. We, with our analytical engines – our DAEmon – have attempted to duplicate the working of this mechanistic universe and in this way we have come to know the mind of ABBA.'

'This is nonsense,' Norma protested. 'For heaven's sake, we can't even get the weather forecast right.'

De Nostredame frowned. 'Of course we can get the weather 4Cast right! Weather 4Casting is taught to first-year students of elementary preScience.'

Norma cursed herself. She had forgotten for a moment that she was in the Demi-Monde, where ABBA – the ABBA back in the Real World – had made things like the weather a little more orderly than where she came from. 'Okay, I'll concede that the weather is predictable but there are still thirty million Demi-Mondians each of whom is possessed of a free will which makes their actions anything but predictable.'

With a sigh, de Nostredame turned to Kondratieff. 'Nikolai, as my pipe seems to be in need of some extensive maintenance, it is time for you to elucidate the mysteries of preScience as it relates to free will.'

Kondratieff stood up from the table, walked over to the window and gazed at the banks of machines chuntering away in the hall beyond. He looked what he was: an academic. His clothes were worn carelessly and he had a far-away look in his eye, but for all that there was some steel about him: this was one man who wouldn't flinch from doing what he thought was right.

'Very well, then let me start at the beginning. Ever since I was a child, I have had two obsessions: mathematical patterns and history. And the DAEmon has given me the opportunity to indulge these obsessions by enabling me to make a *forensic* study of the economic data held in the Venetian Bourse. Analysing these data, I searched for a pattern, a template, a symmetry about what is happening in the world. The results of this enquiry led me to the discovery that Demi-Mondian history is possessed of a peculiar sinusoidal aspect. History, by my calculations, moves in a regular and very predictable manner, ebbing and flowing like the tides in the rivers of the Demi-Monde. And this being the case, the past is a perfect blueprint for the future.'

'That sounds a little far-fetched,' muttered Norma.

Kondratieff shrugged. 'The affairs of the Demi-Monde move in wavelike patterns, with events replicating themselves over and over in fifty-four-year cycles, these economic shifts accompanied by equally predictable patterns of war, social change, fashions . . . everything. This is the Deterministic shape of affairs that ABBA has imposed on the Demi-Monde. ABBA requires – demands even – that ManKind acts in a Deterministic manner . . . in a *predictable* manner. This is why the concept of free will that you propound so forcefully, Mademoiselle Norma, is wrong. The Demi-Mondian does *not* have free will, he or she only has the *illusion* of free will. But in the grand scale of things, each Demi-Mondian is governed by the macroDeterministic forces of history. Only Daemons – like you, Mademoiselle Williams – and their ilk have free will.'

'I can't accept that,' interrupted Vanka. 'Free will is HumanKind's defining characteristic, the thing that separates HumanKind from the animals.'

'The exact nature of free will, Monsieur Maykov, has been the subject of profound, though mostly irrelevant, debate by philosophers, theologians and scientists for many thousands of years. This debate is now closed. The mathematics of preScience demonstrates, unequivocally, that this wave pattern of history is as inevitable as it is predictable, and hence that HumanKind is Deterministic in nature. By the employment of an army of actuarialists and computators' – Kondratieff indicated the rows of clerks beavering away in the hall – 'we are able to evaluate, to an absurdly high degree of probability, the likelihood of specific events occurring – be they wars, blood shortages, famines, the height of men's hats or how far above their ankles the hems of women's dresses might stray. This certainty negates the claim that HumanKind possesses free will.'

Kondratieff took a long steadying breath before continuing. 'Put rather crudely, Determinism is the view that all current and future events are predetermined by events which have gone before. Or else, from a more whimsically theological aspect, as ABBA is an all-knowing and all-powerful deity, He/She *must* know in advance what is to come and how each and every individual will act as they go through life. This is the concept we refer to as Intelligent Design, the concept which underpins the Clockwork Universe.'

Now it was Norma's turn to frown. Kondratieff was right: ABBA – meaning the quantum computer, ABBA – presumably *did* know how each and every Dupe in the Demi-Monde would act, and therefore the Demi-Monde *was* Deterministic. Whilst the Real World might be so chaotic as to be unpredictable, the Demi-Monde was not. Here in the Demi-Monde everything was based on an Intelligent Design, and the Intelligent Designer was ParaDigm CyberResearch's quantum computer, ABBA.

'Intelligent Design,' Kondratieff continued, 'encapsulates the supposition that all actions within the Demi-Monde are fore-seen and prescribed by the omnipotent, omniscient and omnipresent deity we call ABBA.'

*Or rather an omnipotent, omniscient and omnipresent quantum computer called ABBA.*

'And it is through the use of the analytical engines that comprise the DAEmon and of my own HyperOpia program that we have come to know the mind of ABBA and to understand the Intelligent Design that lies behind the functioning of our world. This is the triumph of preScience. We have made the future predictable.'

'But why? To what end?' asked Vanka.

Having finally brought his pipe back into working order, it was de Nostredame who answered. 'A stunningly naïve question, if I might say so, Monsieur Maykov. Surely the answer is obvious: if we know what the future will be, we are able to manipulate the present in order to alter that future. We will be able to make what Nikolai and I call Temporal Interventions.'

'But so what, Professeur de Nostredame?' enquired Vanka. 'What has all this got to do with Norma . . . with me?'

'Because, as I have already alluded, there *are* InDeterminate elements loose within the Demi-Monde, namely Daemons. Daemons are *diaboli ex machina*. And one of these Daemons, the Lady IMmanual, threatens to bring great suffering to the Demi-Monde.'

'How?' asked Vanka.

De Nostredame took a pensive puff on his pipe. 'To answer

that, I must digress for a moment. My studies have shown me that politicians, even ones as sure-footed as Doge Catherine-Sophia, seem, as a class, to possess a blind spot which I refer to as Temporal Myopia. Temporal Myopia is the inherent feature of *all* politicians, being the inclination to deny reality if that reality is politically uncomfortable. Rather than making the *correct* decision, they are inclined to opt for the decision which offers the least degree of political discomfort.' De Nostredame smiled. 'Doge Catherine-Sophia is gripped by Temporal Myopia, and as such is pathologically unable to do what is necessary to protect the Demi-Monde . . . to protect the future. She has been confronted by the need to accommodate the unpredictable actions of a Daemon, and to do this she has convinced herself that because the Daemon – the Lady IMmanual – seems to fulfil all the prophetical requirements of a Messiah, she therefore *is* the Messiah.'

'Why would she do this?' asked Norma.

'Convenience, Mademoiselle,' de Nostredame replied airily. 'Politicians dislike surprises, and get a little obstreperous when something unexpected – something InDeterminate, like a Daemon – comes along to muddle up their plans. The Lady IMmanual being a Daemon is by her very nature InDeterminate, but because she appears to have fulfilled the prophecies regarding the Messiah, the instinct of the Doge is to make her *less* InDeterminate by giving her the mantle of Messiah. As far as the Doge is concerned, the Lady IMmanual is the surprise she knew about in advance.'

'So?' challenged Norma.

'The calculations made by Nikolai and myself indicate that, because of the Miracle of the Boundary performed by the Lady IMmanual, it was *impossible* for the Doge to believe she is *not* the Messiah; it is an *idée fixe*. Nothing Nikolai or I could have done or said would have changed her mind. By coming to this decision and acting upon it, the Doge has increased the probability that the Beast will conquer the Demi-Monde. This is, of course, an unacceptable OutCome, so unacceptable that we have been obliged to take an unprecedented step: to meddle with Future History. We have to make a Temporal Intervention.'

'That sounds to be a risky occupation,' observed Vanka.

'It is *very* risky, Monsieur Maykov, and believe me, it is not something we do lightly. It is, after all, a treasonable offence, but needs must when the safety – nay, the very existence – of the Demi-Monde is at risk.' De Nostredame took another comforting puff of his pipe and then turned to Norma. 'Nikolai went out this evening not to rescue you from the clutches of Machiavelli's secret police but to preserve the life and freedom of the Messiah. By our calculations, we have concluded that if the Messiah lives – if we can help her avoid being destroyed by the Beast – then she has a chance of saving the Demi-Monde from the Beast.'

'Now I'm totally lost,' complained Norma. 'Ella wasn't with us tonight, so how can Docteur Kondratieff have come to the bar to save the Messiah?'

'For the simple reason that Ella – the Lady IMmanual – isn't the Messiah. *You* are, Mademoiselle Williams.'

'Me!'

'Yes, Mademoiselle Williams, *you*.'

'That's ridiculous. I'm a nobody in this world. Fuck it, I don't even want to be here! Anyway it's Ella who's been doing all the fancy stuff. She's the one performing all the miracles and saving people.'

De Nostredame nodded. 'I agree that superficially the Lady IMmanual appears to meet the criteria of the Messiah rather better than you do. But we have recently uncovered a relic, Loci's Column, which dates from the pre-Confinement era of the Demi-Monde and which has led us to re-evaluate your candidacy as the Messiah. Let me give you an example. The text of the prophecy contained on this relic tells us that we will "Know the Messiah, by the One who is Two" and "By the One with no Shadow". I have spoken on this matter to Sister Florence, the foremost Auralist in Venice, and she has confirmed that you, Mademoiselle Williams, have two auras, whilst you, Monsieur Maykov, rather perplexingly, have none.'

'I don't have an aura!'

'Apparently not, Monsieur Maykov, and before you attempt to quiz me on this matter may I say that no one – not even the great Sister Florence – has an explanation for this anomaly. You are, and here I quote some failed Anglo politician whose name escapes me, a riddle wrapped in a mystery inside an enigma. The only thing we are certain of regarding Vanka Maykov is that by his very presence the prophecy contained on the Column is fulfilled.'

'But—' began Vanka.

'I am sorry, Monsieur Maykov, but why this should be, I have no idea. The mysteries of Auralism are quite beyond me. But what I *do* know is that the prophecies go on to advise that we will "Know the Messiah, by the Living Blood".' Here he turned to Norma. 'And through your own admission, Mademoiselle, you are a Daemon. We are also advised that we will know the Messiah "By the Time of Miracles she portends". *Not* by the miracles the Messiah will perform, but by the miracles the Messiah will portend. The final part of the prophecy states that the Messiah will be "Powerful but Unnoticed. Pure but Wilful".'

'Well, I can corroborate the "wilful" part,' muttered a distracted Vanka.

Norma ignored him. 'But surely these prophecies could just as easily refer to Ella.'

De Nostredame nodded his agreement. 'That is so, Mademoiselle, that is so. But there is much more written on the Column than this. You may not be aware that in Demi-Mondian mythology the Dark – the evil side of Nature – is controlled by a deity known as Loki, or Loci as he is referred to on the Column.'

'Yeah, we have the same character in the Real World.'

'A very remarkable but a very useful coincidence. Now both Nikolai and I have long held the belief that the Beast – Loci's representative during the End of Days – will be Lilith reborn. Lilith is, of course, the most reviled figure in Demi-Mondian mythology, the woman who destroyed the purity of the Vanir – the godlike Pre-Folk who ruled this world in ancient times – and provoked ABBA into sending a deluge to destroy VanaHeimr and to imprison the Demi-Monde behind the Boundary Layer. Now the Column gives us many useful hints as to the identity of the Beast. It quite clearly states that "In Lilith I was reborn", and this single line gives us the tantalising suggestion that Loci and Lilith were one and the same, *and* that the Beast will be a woman.'

'I don't wish to sound obtuse, but so what?'

'We also know that Lilith was a Shade. Oh, the Pre-Folk word for "dark" used in the poem is seemingly ambiguous, since it can be construed as either "wicked" or "dark-skinned", but I am sure that it encapsulates *both* meanings. When Loci wrote that Lilith was the "First of the Dark Women", he was telling us that Lilith is a wicked Shade.'

As Norma sat there, she had a terrible feeling about what was coming next.

'I think, my dear, you have probably guessed what I am going to say. The Lady IMmanual isn't the Messiah, Mademoiselle Williams, she's the Beast . . . '

'. . . Lilith reborn.'

'So what?' said Vanka quietly.

'HyperOpia predicts that, left unconstrained, there is a 98.75 per cent chance that the Lady IMmanual will, by the end of the coming Summer, emerge as a Demi-Monde-wide dictator and cause the deaths of seven million innocents in the process.'

'I don't believe it.'

'Whether you believe it or not is irrelevant, Monsieur Maykov, the maths is irrefutable. Although she is a Daemon, and hence at the micro level her actions are InDeterminate, at a macro level we are quite confident about anticipating the effect of her manifestation here in the Demi-Monde. She met all the prophecies made by the Pre-Folk, who were perhaps the most able Future-Historians ever to have lived. By our calculations, the Lady IMmanual is the Beast. The consequential question was, of course, if the Lady IMmanual was the Beast, then who was the Messiah? And the answer to that question, Mademoiselle Williams, is you.'

De Nostredame took a moment to tamp more tobacco down into the bowl of his pipe. 'That is why the Lady IMmanual wants you dead, Mademoiselle Norma. She instinctively realises who – *what* – you are and knows that you are her greatest rival.'

'But what about me?' asked Vanka. 'Ella's ordered that I'm to be killed too and I'm no Messiah. Why's she got it in for me?'

De Nostredame shrugged. 'I don't know, but somehow it would appear that she sees you as a mortal threat.'

'I'd never be a threat to Ella.'

'But you might be to the Beast.'

Vanka lapsed into a shocked silence. Norma understood how he felt: this was all getting rather surreal.

'We have modelled the impact you, Mademoiselle Norma, could make in your role of Messiah using the HyperOpia program and the effect is dramatic. If you were to work in co-operation with Monsieur Maykov in opposing the ambitions of the Lady IMmanual, then it is possible . . .'

'The probability of success is, however, less than 50 per cent,' observed Kondratieff.

'. . . that you could thwart her ambitions and usher in an era of peace and tranquillity to the Demi-Monde. And, of course, by doing so you would save almost seven million people from a terrible and unnecessary death.'

'Define what you mean by "oppose",' enquired Norma cautiously.

'That is for you to decide. You, after all, are the Messiah.'

'Are they settled, Nikolai?' asked de Nostredame.

'Well, they are both in their rooms but Maykov isn't asleep. He's simply pacing his room.'

'Does he suspect?'

'No . . . or rather he is so befuddled by worries about the Lady IMmanual that he can spare none of his thoughts for himself. His love of the girl is quite touching.'

De Nostredame took a contemplative puff on his pipe. 'Love, eh? I have had little experience of it myself but my studies show it to be quite an arbitrary thing.'

'So arbitrary that even HyperOpia failed to anticipate that Maykov and Ella Thomas would form such a close liaison.'

'But then HyperOpia is unable to predict any of Maykov's actions. As far HyperOpia is concerned, Maykov doesn't exist.'

'Indeed. But as always, love complicates matters. His feelings will make it more difficult for Maykov to act when he comes to realise that to save Ella Thomas he must destroy the Lady IMmanual.'

'*If* he ever realises it.'

'And if he doesn't?'

De Nostredame shrugged. 'Then we will be obliged to make another Temporal Intervention, Nikolai. Then *we* must destroy the Lady IMmanual.'

# Part Four
# The Awful Tower
# and the
# Miracle of the Canal

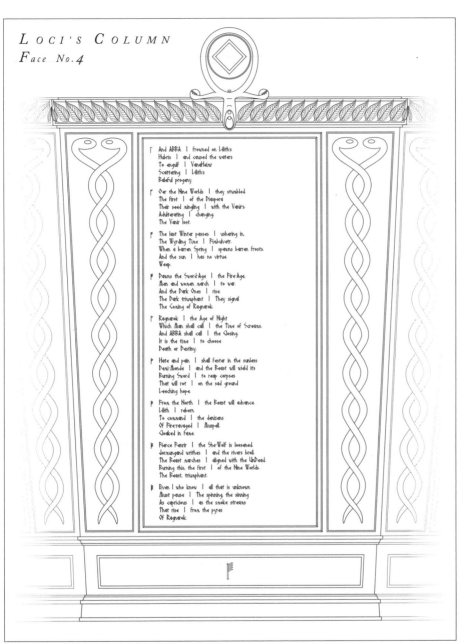

And ABBA frowned on Lilith's
Hubris and caused the waters
To engulf Vanaheim
Scattering Lilith's
Baleful progeny.

O'er the Nine Worlds they stumbled
The first of the Diaspora
Their seed mingling with the Vanirs.
Adulterating changing
The Vanir lost.

The last Winter passes ushering in
The Wyrding Time Fimbulvetr.
When a barren Spring spawns barren frosts.
And the sun has no virtue
Weep.

Dawns the Sword-Age the Fire-Age.
Men and women march to war.
And the Dark Ones rise
The Dark triumphant They signal
The Coming of Ragnarok.

Ragnarok the Age of Night
Which Men shall call the Time of Screams.
And ABBA shall call the Closing.
It is the time to choose
Death or Destiny.

Hate and pain shall fester in the sunless
Demi-Monde and the Beast will wield its
Burning Sword to reap corpses
That will rot on the sad ground
Leeching hope.

From the North the Beast will advance
Lilith reborn
To command the denizens
Of Fire-ravaged Muspell.
Cloaked in fame.

Fierce Fenrir the She-Wolf is loosened
Jormungand writhes and the rivers broil.
The Beast marches aligned with the UnDead.
Burning this, the first of the Nine Worlds.
The Beast, triumphant.

Even I who know all that is unknown
Must pause The spinning, the sinning
As capricious as the smoke streams
That rise from the pyres
Of Ragnarok.

*Diagram and translation reproduced by kind permission of Snore Igbølinn, Cartographer-General to the Court of Her Most Reverend Excellency, Doge Catherine-Sophia*

# THE EDDIC OF LOCI 4: RAGNAROK

PLATE 4

# 30

## The Goldman DigiStudio: New York
## The Real World: 1 October 2018

Eyespies are independently viable, hover-capable and dynamically flexible SurveillanceBots (robotic surveillance cameras) linked to the PanOptika program. Eyespies are never smaller than two centimetres in length, the minimum length of SurveillanceBot declared legal by the League of Nations' Universal Charter of Human Rights and Privacy of 2015. The use of eyespies below this length (so-called 'moteBots') is illegal.

**iSuccess in GCSE-Dip: A Revision Guide to British History**, *ParaDigm Publications*

Aaliz Heydrich stood in the DigiPrep Booth and waited patiently as the PhotoBots hovered around her. She had expected the Real World to be different from the Demi-Monde and she had sworn that, no matter what happened, she would endure these differences with imperturbability and poise. But this particular experience challenged even her redoubtable sangfroid.

To be standing nigh on naked – the swimming costume they had given her to wear was tiny – in a room full of extremely impolite people whilst the images of her captured by the PhotoBots were projected on a super-large Flexi-Plexi was not a pleasurable experience. But Joyce Taylor, the PR expert allocated to 'look after' her by the Kentons, had been insistent that this was a vital first step if she was going to become a PollyCelebrity, and the launch of the Fun/Funs was to get the Polly coverage it needed. According to Joyce Taylor, anyone wishing to be anyone on the Polly had to have a physical appearance that was attractive to his or her target audience and that meant PollyMorphing their image.

'Okay, everybody, could we have a little hush?' shouted Duncan Goldman, the DigiSculptor. 'This is the creative moment, and I don't want any extraneous inputs impacting on my Zone of Scalar Envisionment.'

Aaliz referenced PINC, but PINC couldn't tell her with any great probability of being correct what this odious nuJu was talking about. It wasn't just the man's odd vocabulary and disregard for English grammar that made him difficult to understand, his languid accent was peculiar too. He reminded Aaliz of the rather effete slaves from NoirVille that one or two of her friends' fathers had employed back in the ForthRight.

'So, Joyce darling, this is our raw material – what I call our tabula rasa.'

*Blank slate*, translated PINC helpfully.

'And I have to say that it's not bad, not bad at all. I particularly like the height, which is ideal for PollyCasts. Anything taller and things become a trifle distended.' Goldman wandered over to the Flexi-Plexi, and used a laser pen to indicate parts of the image of Aaliz screened there. 'And as far as I can tell, she's an almost perfect Fifteen/Forty/Forty-Five.'

PINC chimed in to tell Aaliz that Goldman was talking about body proportions: fifteen related to the percentage of total body height represented by the distance from her shoulders to the top of her head, forty to the length of her trunk, and forty-five to the length of her legs.

'Tell me again, Joyce darling, what's the target demographic?'

'Primary Demo is early adoptors, both sexes, within an age span of thirteen to twenty-three.'

'Hmmmm. That's always a tricky one. I would suggest that the IdeoPhantom that hits most of this Demo's decision points is "Classical Dancer". The anthropometric proportions of this Phantom suggest grace, agility and superior intellectual development, all this encapsulated in a rather dishy body outline. And svelteness is so very tomorrow.'

'That sounds ideal.'

'So, let's see how Norma performs when we do the comparison.' Goldman blinked towards his Polly, and immediately an outline of another body was superimposed on the image of Aaliz. 'Oh, bravo, Norma, crural and brachial indices are spot on, and the percentage deviation from the IdeoPhantom's eyeLine is only a meagre 4.7 per cent. It seems hardly worth tinkering with. Maybe the breasts could do with a *little* augmentation.'

Goldman blinked again, and immediately the chest of Aaliz's digital doppelgänger expanded. 'Not too much,' mused Goldman, 'just enough to get the Polly's tit tourists interested.' He turned to Joyce Taylor. 'Happy, Joyce darling?'

'Absolutely. If we could just clean up the tattoo and the perforations.'

It was the work of moments for Goldman to make the tattoo of the Celtic cross on the image's left shoulder disappear, and the small holes left where Aaliz had removed the disgusting jewellery from her ears, nose and eyebrows to miraculously heal.

'And now for the *visage*,' Goldman mused as he zoomed in on Aaliz's face. 'Hmmm . . . not bad. Blue eyes are associated with purity, vitality, honesty – I'd be inclined to leave them.'

Another nod from Joyce Taylor.

'Maybe straighten out her nose just a tad.' The nose shown on the Flexi-Plexi altered before Aaliz's eyes. 'Plump her lips a little – that hint of depravity is always a killer in the teen market. Good but not *that* good is the sort of tip I'm looking for. Let's just check facial symmetry . . .' Immediately two versions of

Aaliz's head were shown, one composed of two left-hand sides and one composed of two right-hand sides. It was apparent that the left-hand side of her face was a little narrower than the right. 'A couple of minor tweaks,' observed Goldman, as he morphed Aaliz's features, 'but we don't want to make her *too* perfect. Imperfection promotes aspirationalism: make someone flawless and the kids give up trying to become them. No one wants to chase the impossible dream.' He stepped back to examine his work. 'Good, that just leaves the biggies: age and hair colour.'

Sorting out the 'biggies' took almost two hours, with Aaliz's image variously sporting black hair, brown hair, blonde hair, long hair, short hair and intermediate hair. In terms of age, it lost two years in search of the 'pre-teen' market, and then had five years added on in pursuit of 'gravitas'. The annoying thing was that, at the end of all their efforts at digital morphing, they chose blonde hair of the shade she was already sporting – okay, so they bobbed it a little – and plumped for the age she already was, namely eighteen. So after three hours' work, the image of Norma Williams that looked at her from the Flexi-Plexi was only subtly different from the real thing. But as Joyce Taylor explained to her at length, on the Polly, nuances mattered.

The first time Aaliz's PollyMorph ImPlant was used was when she was interviewed on 'The Clare Collins PollyCast'. As advised by Joyce Taylor, this was not the gentle introduction to the world of the Polly that she had wished for her client, what with Clare Collins hosting the most viewed chat show in the US and having a reputation as a ferocious interviewer. But as Norma Williams was the President's daughter and, pre-Demi-Monde, had been the darling of the racier PollyGossip mags, an easier debut had proved impossible to manage. There was simply too much Polly interest in her.

As she sat in the studio, waiting for the signal to take her seat opposite the infamous Collins, Aaliz had to admit to a certain trepidation. Though she had Septimus Bole and the might of ParaDigm in her corner, and although she had endured several practice interviews, there was still the possibility that she would screw up and fall at the first hurdle. Collins enjoyed humiliating her guests, and as a staunch Republican she had precious little time for the President. Aaliz's team of handlers had spent a great deal of time wondering what stunts Collins might have hidden up her sleeve, but in the end they had declared themselves 'fireproof'.

But then what they thought didn't really matter. Aaliz had a strategy for dealing with Collins all of her own devising.

She signalled to Joyce Taylor. 'I want my PollyMorph ImPlant pulled. I want to go on the show warts and all.'

Joyce Taylor blinked several times. 'But that's impossible. Everybody goes on the Polly morphed . . . *everybody*. Nobody on the Polly looks like they really are.'

'I know, and that's the whole point.'

'Well, Norma, I don't know if I'm prepared to authorise that,' said the woman stiffly. 'I have my reputation to think about.'

Aaliz leant closer to Joyce Taylor, so that no one else could hear what she whispered in her ear. 'Joyce, don't ever, *ever* tell me "no". I am in charge of this little operation and I warn you, if you don't do precisely what I'm telling you to do, then I will have ParaDigm blackball every one of the artists and companies you represent. They will never get on the Polly again as long as they are associated with you. Now go over there and pull the fucking PollyMorph.'

In the flesh, Clare Collins was at least ten years older than she looked on the Polly and this amazing piece of digital legerdemain was, of course, conjured courtesy of PollyMorphing. By implanting the idealised PollyMorphed vision of herself into the studio MasterPolly, the images of her captured by the

CameraBots were automatically enhanced in real time. The result was that the 'Clare Collins' seen by the Polly audience was decidedly younger, slimmer and facially tauter than the real Clare Collins who plonked herself into the chair next to Aaliz.

'You're Sam Williams's kid, huh?'

'Yes,' said Aaliz, holding out her hand, 'I'm Norma Williams. It's a pleasure to meet with you, Ms Collins.'

Clare Collins ignored the hand. 'Stow the baloney, kid. I ain't in the market for making friends with nuDemocrats or their progeny. So what's this Fun/Funs crock? A last desperate attempt by the President to connect with disenfranchised Middle America?'

'Ms Collins. I—'

Aaliz didn't get any further. The floor manager shouted 'Quiet' and then began the countdown. Clare Collins smiled. 'Well, kid, you better fasten your seat belt and prepare for a rocky ride.'

At the beginning, the interview was strangely muted; it took Collins almost five minutes to hit her stride. 'So, Norma, you've been ill. Rumours on the Polly suggest that you were in rehab trying to beat a Zip habit. Any truth in that?'

'None whatsoever. I suffered from a neurological collapse brought on by extreme stress. It left me comatose for almost three months.'

'Oh c'mon, you don't expect the PollyPublic to swallow that, now do you? You were the archetypal wild child: all sex, drugs and rock 'n' roll. And from what I hear, before you were hospitalised you were cooling on the rock 'n' roll and majoring on the sex and drugs.'

'All I can tell you is the truth, Clare.'

'And what you're telling us is that whilst you were in rehab – sorry, *in your coma* – you found God.'

'That's correct. God came to me and made me understand

that how I had been conducting my life was a sham, that I wasn't realising all the talents He had given me, that I wasn't making the most of my life. God told me I had more to give the world than several column inches a week of prurient Polly gossip.'

'And what is it that God wants you to give the world?' The sarcasm was heavy in Clare Collins's voice.

'Freedom from addiction. He has given me powers to cure people of addiction.'

'Addiction? What sort of addiction?'

'Every sort. I can free people from drug addiction, alcohol addiction and addiction to violence. I can cure people of every and all sorts of addiction.'

'How?'

'By the laying on of hands.'

'Oh, you've got to be joking.'

'Not at all. I will be demonstrating this gift under controlled conditions at the New York Hospital's Drug Dependency Center in two days' time. Maybe you should come along, Ms Collins?'

'I think I'll pass. I'm addictions-lite. But isn't it a fact that this new-found interest of yours in God comes at a mighty convenient time for your father, the President, what with the Midwest primaries due in just a few weeks?'

'This has nothing to do with my father. He's a self-professed atheist and I think he's more than a little perplexed by my finding God.'

'You can't expect us to believe that.'

'Ms Collins, you keep doubting my truthfulness.'

'Oh, c'mon. How can you expect to be taken seriously when just a few weeks ago you were a strung-out goth chick covered in piercings and tattoos?' Collins looked up and smiled. 'I see your father's PR people have had you remove the studs.'

'The scars remain to remind me of how easy it is to fall from grace.'

'Yeah, and I suppose the tattoos have been laser-removed.'

With a sigh, Aaliz undid the top three buttons of her blouse and pulled it from her shoulder to reveal her tattoo and, en passant, that she wasn't wearing a bra. As she was to learn later, ABBA's Saccade Optical Analysis System, which evaluated the level of interest of Polly viewers in each element of each piece of programming they sampled, showed a 50 per cent increase in attention whilst Aaliz was performing her little striptease.

'You see, Ms Collins, with me what you see is what you get, and what you hear is the truth.'

'Honey, you're too good to be true.'

Aaliz stayed silent for a moment, letting the tension build, letting the CameraBots move in closer as they searched for emotion. Emotion was the lifeblood of the Polly and soon, Aaliz decided, the Polly viewers would have it in bucketfuls.

'You continue to question my probity, Ms Collins. You continue to imply that I am lying, even when I have admitted that, yes, I took drugs; that, yes, I've slept with a great many men and women; and, yes, mine has been, up until now, a useless and a squandered life. I have been perfectly frank with you, Ms Collins, but you refuse to accept what I say as the truth. And by doing this you imply that *you* are more trustworthy and more truthful than me.'

It must have been Aaliz's tone that alerted Clare Collins that something was going down that wasn't in the script. But with thirty-seven million PollyViewers watching live, Aaliz knew her interrogator didn't have much thinking time. Collins shot a quick glance at her producer, but all he did was shrug.

'Well, I've got a reputation for getting to the bottom of things, for letting the PollyPublic see people for what they really are.' She looked distinctly uncomfortable. The golden rule of interviewing was that whoever asked the questions controlled the interview, and much to Clare Collins's discomfort, she was the one who was having to do the answering.

ROD REES | 353

'But why should people trust *you* to ask the questions, when you are so adept at hiding yourself and your motives from them?'

The CameraBots hovered closer, but this time it was Clare Collins they were focusing on. The producer knew good Polly when he saw it.

'I don't know what you're talking about. Look, I'm here to interview you, to find out about the real you.'

'But you're not prepared to reveal the *real* Clare Collins and have her scrutinised, are you?'

'I don't know what you're talking about.'

'When I came on this show, I refused to be PollyMorphed. I wanted the PollyPublic to see me, warts and all. But you won't do that, will you? Are you scared to let the viewers see who you really are, Ms Collins?'

The colour drained from Clare Collins's face – not that the Polly viewers would notice, as PollyMorph automatically compensated for sudden changes in skin tone. Aaliz knew why she was shocked: PollyMorphing was a closely guarded secret, and discussing it in public *verboten*. And the reason was simple: the process could add ten or more years to a PollyPerformer's career, and it was a damned sight cheaper and more effective than surgery or Botox.

'I don't use PollyMorphing.'

'Oh, c'mon Ms Collins, you don't expect the PollyPublic to believe that, now, do you? And if you can't be honest about your appearance, why should the PollyPublic believe you're being honest with your questioning?' With a shake of her head Aaliz turned away from Clare Collins, and stared directly at the nearest CameraBot. 'Decide for yourself whether I'm telling the truth by Pollying into ParaDigm's coverage of me at New York Hospital's Drug Dependency Center on Wednesday next. And I promise that, unlike Clare Collins, nothing will be PollyMorphed. With Aaliz . . . with Norma Williams, what you see is what you get.'

# 31

## A back room of the Maison d'Illusion: Paris
## The Demi-Monde: 30th Day of Spring, 1005

In a world seemingly in thrall to violence and war, the preaching of a 'second way', a philosophy that celebrates peace and harmony and which promotes a turn-the-other-cheek solution to the curse of MALEvolence, was inevitably going to be the subject of derision and ridicule. But the success of the first Normalists in using civil disobedience and passive resistance to oppose and disrupt the ForthRight's occupation of the Medi made many think again. The 'Peace Corps' of Aaliz Heydrich soon became a political force to be reckoned with.

**Normalism: Why Violence Is Never the Answer:** *Percy Bysshe Shelley, Canal Publications*

Since Norma had been in the Demi-Monde, she'd experienced any number of frights and shocks, but as she peeped out from behind the stage curtains at the hundred or so stony-faced women waiting to hear her speak, she had to admit that this was the scariest. If she failed now, Ella – the Beast – would be triumphant.

She made a nervous adjustment of her gown – quite modest by ImPuritan standards – absent-mindedly patted her freshly dyed blonde hair and then leant closer to the curtain, to listen to Odette make her introduction.

'Many of you will know me. You will know me as the fire-brand Odette Aroca, captain of the Market Girls regiment. I fought shoulder to shoulder with you when the UnScreweds marched on the Bastille to free Jeanne Deroin and Aliénor d'Aquitaine, who I am pleased to say are with us here tonight.' Odette paused to allow a round of applause. 'It was my regiment that was first inside the Bastille, and it was girls from my regiment who shot Grand Inquisitor de Torquemada.' More applause. 'At that time I was impatient with those of you who counselled a more softly-softly approach. I demanded that we fight fire with fire, and the results of that impetuosity are hanging by piano wire from the lamp-posts that line the Champs-Élysées: hundreds of men, women and children slaughtered by the ForthRight to revenge my lust for violence.'

*Pretty powerful stuff*, thought Norma. If Odette got any more cathartic, she'd be running a transactional analysis class rather than a political meeting.

'After the taking of the Bastille, I was pursued by Checkya agents and escaped to Venice. It was there that I met a remarkable woman; a woman who changed my life; a woman who is intent on opposing the evil of UnFunDaMentalism, but who is determined to do so without plumbing the same depths of wickedness the UnFunnies have. She, more than any, knows the extent of the political and moral corruption within the ForthRight. She is a woman who had been party to Reinhard Heydrich's most intimate and most gruesome secrets. Ladies, I give you . . . Aaliz Heydrich.'

When de Nostredame had told her she was the Messiah, it had taken a real effort on Norma's part not to burst out laughing. It all sounded too ridiculous for words, but what hadn't been ridiculous was when he'd gone on to say that it was her responsibility to oppose Ella – to oppose the Beast. That had been

deep-breath time. Something told her that this was one responsibility she wouldn't be able to shirk. Before, when she had
acted as a spoiled, useless, brain-dead good-time girl, nobody
had got hurt, but now, if she fucked up, seven million Demi-
Mondians would die.

Scary stuff.

When she had sat down to think about *how* she would go
about putting a spoke in the Lady IMmanual's wheel, she had
come to realise that this was a pivotal moment in her life. People
– lots and lots of people – were relying on her and she was determined not to let them down. And the one thing she realised
was that to oppose the Lady IMmanual was one thing, but to
*fight* her was quite another. Fighting, she decided, was useless.

The one good thing about her time in the Demi-Monde was
that she had learnt how utterly futile war and violence really
were. In her view, violence wasn't the answer, violence was the
problem. This was the belated conclusion she'd come to after
enduring the misery of Warsaw and seeing Ella murder a man
in front of her. Now she knew she no longer wanted any part
of the mockery that violence made of civilisation. Now she
realised that the ideas her father had tried so diligently to introduce her to – the teachings of people like Mahatma Gandhi and
Martin Luther King – weren't as uncool as she'd complained
they were. Now she understood that it took real courage to
reject violence. And now she had a chance to do some of the
things Percy Shelley had only had the guts to talk about doing.

Percy Bysshe Shelley . . .

She'd desperately tried to expunge him from her memory.
Dishy, talented and totally unreliable, he'd been the one who
had kept her returning to the Demi-Monde, he'd been the
reason she'd ended up in this muddle.

Just thinking about the guy made her heart flip. God, he had
been so beautiful and she had loved the man so very much. She

could still remember the first time that he had kissed her. It had been the only time in her life she'd ever been kissed with *real* purpose by a man. Sitting side by side in the Prancing Pig – not the most romantic of settings to be sure – he'd leant over to her, brought his fingertips to her cheek, turned her face gently towards his and butterflied his lips against hers. Oh, she'd read the soppy romances that described the impact a hero's first kiss had on a heroine but she'd always dismissed this as so much fanciful nonsense. It wasn't. So many emotions were provoked by that kiss that it was impossible for her to recall them accurately. The biggest remembrance she had was the sensation of falling, of tumbling *into* Shelley, as though, somehow, they were merging. It was like fainting in stereo. It was the most profoundly emotional, the most profoundly romantic, the most profoundly erotic ten seconds of her entire life.

How had Shelley described it? It had been bliss, the infinite joy of a debut kiss.

*Debut . . .*

Now that brought her up short. She had never thought of it before but Shelley had known her for what she was, known that she was a faux-rebel, a plastic punk, known that though she had a tabloid reputation for being a wild child the reality was far different. She was all front and no substance, never having had the confidence to really kick over the traces.

And that, she realised, had been the lure of the Demi-Monde. The eNorma who had been conjured when she had entered the Demi-Monde had been more *real* than she had ever been. Gone was the gawky, slump-shouldered, mono-syllabic teenager. The girl whose computer showed her walking (walking? Hell no, eNorma glided) through the streets of the Rookeries, when she had first switched on the Demi-Monde, was Norma as she would like to have been, if she'd had the courage. It was Norma as she would have looked and acted if she'd been on the receiving end of an economy-sized injection of chutzpah, if she'd had a shot of industrial-grade courage. For Norma, the doppelgänger that was eNorma was fantasy made real and breathtakingly exciting and unbelievably bloody scary because of it.

The question that had nagged at her was simple: how could she look so wonderful, act so confidently, and be so alluring in a computer game and yet be so diffident and unsure in real life? And it was the search for the answer to that question that had persuaded her to keep coming back to the Demi-Monde: real-Norma was identical to the eNorma – the same height, the same figure, the same looks, the same everything – but in the Demi-Monde she was transformed into this . . . super-woman. It had been very perplexing and very intriguing.

And then, of course, there had been the buzz associated with meeting a living, breathing Percy Shelley, her favourite poet and the man of her dreams. The man of her dreams who had betrayed her to Crowley and thrown her to the UnFunDaMentalist wolves. But in retrospect, had all that suffering been such a bad thing? Experiencing the pain and the panic had forced her to grow up. Until she'd experienced at first hand the Demi-Monde's more outré attitudes and beliefs, it had been impossible for her to know what life was all about and to appreciate evil. Without the experience of life in the raw – and nowhere was life rawer than in the Demi-Monde – she would have remained a cypher, a mere observer of life. The Demi-Monde had forced her to engage with the world . . . to become a player.

Her time in the Demi-Monde had re-modelled her, re-made her into something beyond her imagining, and if she was destined to die here in the Demi-Monde, she was determined that she would die trying to do something good.

Vanka hadn't been convinced by her new-found determination. When she had told him that if Demi-Mondians were ever to possess true free will, they had to be free of the threat of violence, he had looked at her like she was crackers.

'You believe that?' he'd asked with more than a hint of mockery in his voice.

'Of course. What we have to do to face down the Beast is refuse to cooperate with our would-be oppressors, but we must do this in a non-violent and a civilised manner.' Here Norma had to give a wry smile, as she mangled Edmund Burke's great epigram. 'The only thing necessary to prevent the triumph of evil is for good men and women to do nothing, but to do it in a resolute and stoic manner. We must have the peoples of the Demi-Monde meet hate with politeness; violence with peace; and punishment with imperturbability. Together we must work, all of us, to stop the machine of violence and destruction that is the ForthRight.'

'But how will stopping the ForthRight help defeat the Lady IMmanual?'

'Because it will show there's another way, the way of peace. If we're successful, when the Lady IMmanual comes to power people will already have realised how specious violence is, so she'll be politically neutered.'

Vanka looked decidedly dubious.

'So what do you call this creed of non-violence of yours?'

'I haven't given it a name yet.'

'Try "Normalism",' he laughed, and the tag had stuck.

Vanka hadn't been laughing so much when he'd realised that promoting Normalism would require them leaving Venice. The Lady IMmanual might be trying to kill him but he was reluctant to give up on his love. In the end it had been Burlesque who had weighed in with the most telling argument.

'The important fing, Wanker, is that we all get out ov Venice

before them Signori di Notte items come banging on our door.
I've 'eard some 'orrible fings about them bastards. Seems they
could teach the Checkya a fing or two about fucking a suspect
over. An' once we're in the Medi we can 'elp Miss Norma 'ere
spread 'er soppy message about not fighting and such, and get
the Medi into a real tizwaz. Doin' that is going to 'elp Miss Ella.
It'll mean, even if she is this Beast fingy, that she won't 'ave to
fight 'cos the ForthRight Army is going to be too busy sortin'
art the muddle we make of things. To save Miss Ella, Wanker,
me old cock, we've got to defeat the ForthRight.'

It was a persuasive argument, so persuasive that finally a
reluctant Vanka had agreed to accompany Norma back into the
Medi. It was there that Burlesque's girlfriend, the formidable
Odette Aroca, came into her own. The girl had been tasked with
gathering the leaders of the UnScrewed-Liberation Movement
for a clandestine meeting where, as she told potential attendees in breathless whispers, they would meet 'someone quite
astonishing'. In the end she had managed to persuade a
hundred women to brave the curfew to attend a meeting in the
back room of a rather seedy bar called the Maison d'Illusion.

So tonight Norma would make her first foray into politics.
And she was wetting herself.

The idea of posing as Aaliz Heydrich had come while she had
been talking to Odette and explaining to her that getting any
political message across needed a spokesperson who would grab
people's attention. Unfortunately, she'd added ruefully,
Normalism didn't have any celebrity endorsement.

'Oh, I think we have,' said Odette with a laugh. 'I remember you telling me, Norma, that you once posed as Aaliz
Heydrich . . .'

That was when Norma had realised that *she* was the solution
to this particular problem. Who better to promote a message

of opposition to Reinhard Heydrich's UnFunDaMentalism than his own daughter? It would be a remarkably powerful marketing message: the father rejected by the dutiful daughter. Moreover, with the real Aaliz lost somewhere in the Real World, Heydrich and Crowley would have the devil's own job proving that Norma *wasn't* Aaliz Heydrich. It would be the biter bit.

With one last plumping up of her hair, Norma strode onto the tiny stage to face her audience. Her *stunned* audience.

The women making up that audience sat in shocked silence, staring at her, the expressions on their faces a mixture of astonishment and fear. Astonishment that it was the poster girl of UnFunDaMentalism – and the impassioned and unwavering leader of the RightNixes, the ForthRight's youth wing – who was standing in front of them. And fear because wherever Aaliz Heydrich went, the Checkya were never far behind.

But it was astonishment and fear mixed with a little awe. Aaliz Heydrich was, after all, a genuine, twenty-four-carat, grade-A celebrity. The image of the beautiful Aaliz Heydrich adorned the covers of magazines and her appearances, speaking on behalf of her father, were made in front of massed crowds. Aaliz Heydrich attended the opening nights of plays in the West End, and she was seen in the most fashionable nightspots arm in arm with famous actors and troubadours. Aaliz Heydrich was a *star*.

There was an awkward attempt at a round of applause, which Norma raised her hand to still. 'I am Aaliz Heydrich,' she said simply, as she stood in the centre of the stage, 'and I thank all you courageous women for braving the curfew to attend this meeting. You should be in no doubt that I understand what you are risking to be here. I know you have had to dodge the Checkya patrols, fearful that if you were arrested you would face imprisonment or worse. I too face these perils, though mine are made more terrible by the knowledge that it is my own father who seeks my destruction.'

Norma paused to allow the nervous chattering provoked by this statement to subside.

'As you know, I have stood loyally at my father's side all of my life. I have been the dutiful, obedient daughter. But there came a time, quite recently, when the knowledge of the perversity and the wickedness betokened by UnFunDaMentalism made it impossible for me to remain quiet or to remain dutiful. The catalyst for this change was when I saw the misery and the pain heaped on the citizens of Warsaw. The suffering of those poor people, as they resisted the onslaught of the SS, is almost impossible to describe, but through witnessing this suffering I came to realise that war – *all* war – is wrong. If the only way a people can be converted to a religion is at the end of a gun, then that religion is corrupt.'

A tentative round of applause.

'But I would say more: if a religion or a political creed does not allow freedom of opinion and freedom of expression, then it is corrupt. It is only by criticism and open debate that the truth will triumph. You in the Quartier Chaud were blessed with a great thinker, Mary Wollstonecraft, whose teachings that violence is barbaric, inefficient and wasteful are as potent and as valid today as they were when she first postulated them all those centuries ago. Now, at last, the time has come for the mitigating and moderating influence of women to be felt throughout the Demi-Monde. Now, at last, the time has come for this senseless cycle of war and political violence that has plagued our world to be broken.'

More applause, but this time it was a trifle more enthusiastic.

'We must oppose war and violence, by rejecting war and violence.'

'How?' came a question shouted from the back of the room.

'We must first understand that to oppose the ForthRight will be difficult and will require sacrifice. I declare it to you flat out: those who join me must be prepared to die. Although ours will be a Quiet War, a non-violent war, there will still be casualties. What I am proposing is that we withdraw all our cooperation from the occupying forces of the ForthRight; that we engage in a well-orchestrated campaign of civil disobedience and passive resistance.'

A bemused silence fell on the audience.

'We must not collaborate with evil. We must wage peace. Like all good ImPuritans, we must make love, not war!'

Now that got a cheer!

'Anything that supports the wicked and illegal occupation of the Medi by the ForthRight must be resisted. We must refuse to pay our blood tax, as this finances the ForthRight; we must refuse to deliver mail addressed to the ForthRight forces; we must refuse to serve ForthRight soldiers in restaurants and bars; we must refuse to collaborate in *any* way with the ForthRight. And we must do all this whilst practising non-violence. We must express no anger when we are beaten; we must not resist when we are arrested; we must be forever polite and stoical . . . and, most of all, we must be prepared to die in as noble a fashion as we are able.' Norma paused. 'It will be difficult, but my belief is that ultimately it will make the Medi ungovernable. My colleagues, who, like me, believe in the creed of non-violence we call Normalism, are, even as I stand here, taking this message of civil disobedience and passive resistance to the people of the Medi. We are determined to show the Demi-Monde that the ForthRight can be humbled without having to resort to the gun or the bomb. But we need your help. So I ask you now: are you with me?'

As one, her audience rose to their feet to applaud her. Now Norma was a leader, and she had never felt more alone in all her life.

*

After the meeting, Burlesque took Odette for a stroll along the bank of the Thames. Perhaps promenading past cranes and all the other dockside paraphernalia wasn't terribly romantic, but Odette was quite content to spend an hour or so just walking arm in arm with her beau.

It was strange for her to feel so contented doing something so simple. She had gone through life being angry with every*one* and every*thing*, so to feel calm and at peace with herself and the world was really quite perplexing. But she was – and this she put down to being in love, knowing that finally she had found a man who was a perfect fit for her, a man who was phys- ically, mentally and emotionally the left to her right, the up to her down.

Love was an odd thing, Odette decided. But then so was Burlesque.

When she had been younger she had always dreamt that one day a prince on a white charger would come and sweep her off her feet but she had never thought that her prince would be fat, gap-toothed and prone to flatulence. But the peculiar thing was that now she had met Burlesque she wouldn't trade him for the world. Burlesque made her laugh, and laughter, she had come to realise, was the key to love. To be truly in love you had to *enjoy* being with your man.

Even Burlesque's inability to speak French wasn't that much of a problem (especially as she spoke more English than she was prepared to admit); she just loved the way he *tried* to communicate with her. And anyway, like all true loves, they seemed to know instinctively what the other wanted.

She gave Burlesque a kiss on the cheek and sent a silent prayer to ABBA, thanking Him/Her for bringing Burlesque into her life.

Their strolling eventually brought them to the Pons Fabricus and as they stood there for a moment gazing out over the iron bridge, watching the sun set, Burlesque began to speak in his strange mixture of French and English.

'Ma cherie, j'ai un idea qui est un real corker. Quand Mademoiselle Norma parle beaucoup de bollocks au sujet de civil disobedience et passive resistance, je pense elle pulling mon jambe, mais maintenant peut-être que elle parle n'est pas daft. Je see un way de fucking up les UnFunnies sans le bang-banging. Comprenez?'

'*Oui,*' Odette giggled and gave Burlesque a bigger kiss and slid her hand towards his codpiece.

'Get off, you randy Frog tart, you. Okay . . . Odette, qu'est-ce que le Frog pour "spanner"?'

True love or not, Odette was thrown for a moment. '*Pardon?*'

'Wot's a spanner? Un wrench?' He tried to mime the tools. '*Clé?*'

'Bon, puis je veux un grand clé, un really fucking grand clé.'

A smile tugged at Vanka's mouth as he gazed out of the window towards the majestic Awful Tower, which stood so tall and magnificent over night-time Paris. As he had read in *The Stormer*, the Tower was to be the centrepiece of the celebrations scheduled for the 60th day of Spring marking the unification of the ForthRight and the Medi. There would be marching by soldiers of the ForthRight, a ceremonial Puff Past of armoured steamers and a huge fireworks display. Even Heydrich would be in attendance to witness this demonstration of the ForthRight's power.

And all Norma's efforts wouldn't be able to prevent it happening.

Oh, he was proud of what Norma had achieved. She had spoken well at the meeting and the way she and Odette Aroca – now, what a revelation *that* girl was – had organised the delegates had been a sight to behold. With their energy and commitment, there was just a chance – a slim chance, but still a chance – that they might be able to mobilise the Medi behind this hare-brained scheme of Norma's. But, though Vanka had a natural aversion to violence of any kind, he still couldn't believe that a policy of civil disobedience would be enough to defeat the ForthRight.

In his opinion, the problem Norma faced was the same one the Varsovians had had when they fought the SS through the streets of Warsaw. It wasn't enough to simply avoid defeat; people needed the occasional victory to remind them of what they were struggling for, and to give them the encouragement to *keep* struggling. In other words, they needed to *win*. And, as Vanka saw it, simply smiling and being polite while the Checkya kicked your head in didn't – in most people's books, anyway – constitute a victory. People of the Medi needed proof that the ForthRight was being defeated.

Vanka needed it too. If the ForthRight could be defeated in the Medi, then the war would be over and there would be no need for Ella to carry on playing the Lady IMmanual. She could revert to being the girl he loved. She could be Ella Thomas again.

A thought flared in Vanka's head, sputtered for a moment, then burst into life as a fully formed 'good idea'.

*Perfect.*

He looked around at Rivets, who was sharing the garret room with him. 'Have you ever had a job, Rivets?' he asked.

Rivets looked up from the bed he was lounging on, paused in the process of picking his toenails, and frowned. 'Job? Wotcha mean, Vanka?'

'I mean, have you ever had a job which necessitated you going to work in the morning, toiling all through the day, and then coming home at night?'

Rivets laughed. 'Don't be daft, Vanka. Waste ov time, iffn you ask me, 'specially when there's so much stuff lying around just waiting to be pinched. Anyway, wot the fuck would I wanna get a job for?'

'Because it would help Miss Norma bring down the ForthRight.'

Rivets shrugged. 'Well, iffn it'll do that, I'm willing to give anyfing a shot.'

Vanka rewarded Rivets with a smile. Now all he had to do was persuade Norma to take her clothes off in a good cause. After all, it was she who was always banging on about Normalism being about 'Love Not War'. Now she'd have a chance to show just how good she was at playing the seductress. He had the sneaking feeling she might be *very* good at it.

# 32

## Paris
## The Demi-Monde: 45th to 49th
## Days of Spring, 1005

```
TO DOCTEUR NIKOLAI KONDRATIEFF FUTURE HISTORY
INSTITUTE VENICE PO BOX 27/54 + + + CODE NOIR
AGENT ADVISES <<ONE WITH NO SHADOW>> IS IN MEDI
OPPOSING FORTHRIGHT + + + PLS ADVISE WHICH ASPECT
OF THE PHRASE SAFE/UNTHREATENED U DID NOT FUCKING
UNDERSTAND + + + PWR OF BEAST GROWS + + + IT IS
YR DUTY AS A DEMI-MONDIAN TO ENSURE <<ONE WITH NO
SHADOW>> IS BROUGHT HARMLESS TO JAD + + + ETHOBAAL
```

**PAR OISEAU**

*Copy of PigeonGram message sent by Doctor Jezebel Ethobaal*
*on 45th day of Spring, 1005*

### 45th Day of Spring

'I understand from my enquiries, Monsieur Girard, that your Ministry is seeking to employ help in its mailroom.'

Gaston Girard shuffled uncomfortably in his somewhat over-stuffed chair, gimleted by the hard and unrelenting stare of the strange and unsettling girl sitting across the desk from him. Strange and unsettling but remarkably attractive, and Gaston Girard had a soft spot for young and attractive girls . . . and occasionally a very hard spot.

Yet the fact remained that this young girl – Girard doubted she was much over eighteen – was a very *determined* young girl. She had, after all, browbeaten his secretary until she had been given an appointment with him, and as he was the head of administration of the Medi's Ministry of Works, such appointments were granted only very begrudgingly. Of course, Girard could still have declined to see her, but she was very pretty and had a sparkle in her eye that suggested . . . suggestions.

That he had a weakness for French spoken with a foreign accent was another reason why Gaston Girard had granted this interview. The way this Yank so exquisitely mangled his mother tongue was simply irresistible.

But even now, with the interview hardly begun, Gaston Girard was wary. Beautiful and alluring though the girl undoubtedly was, he had an instinct that she would prove difficult, demanding and even dangerous. He had a nose for these things. Famous in the Ministry for his commonsensical approach to business, Gaston Girard was an extremely unimaginative man, except, that is, when it came to his dealings with young girls – and then he could be *very* imaginative.

Generally, though, caution triumphed over imagination, and he was so nonplussed by the forcefulness of this Norma Cartwright that he had half a mind to give her his most apologetic smile and inform her that the position she was enquiring about had been filled.

But, ever a fool for a heaving bosom, Girard shooed away any suspicions and smiled. 'Indeed we have such a vacancy, Mademoiselle Norma, though I am at a loss to understand how this very junior position could interest a gentlewoman such as yourself.' Girard's voice was deep and grave and like everything about him – including his grey hair, his conservatively cut suit and his lugubrious expression – was designed to cultivate an air of steadfast trustworthiness.

Mademoiselle Norma smiled sweetly, wriggled her pert bottom on her chair, and shuffled herself nearer to Girard's desk. He watched every movement with a wide-eyed fascination, the girl being possessed of an exquisite figure most charmingly displayed in a green velvet jacket and skirt. This wonderful body was complemented by a face – what he could see of it behind her coquettish half-veil – of such breathtaking loveliness that it even managed to soften the hardness of her blue eyes and the very determined set of her alluring mouth. These delightful features were framed by a puff of blonde hair. She was, in sum, a treat.

'Oh, I'm not looking for a position for myself . . . not that sort of position, anyway!' She gave a charmingly mischievous giggle. 'I am newly arrived from the ForthRight, Monsieur Girard,' she explained in a smoky voice, 'having been accompanied to the Medi by my younger brother, Robert. My father has sent us here in anticipation of the unification of our two Sectors, in order that we might perfect our fluency in your wonderful language. To this end, my father has asked me to assist my brother to secure a position here in Paris, of a kind which will demonstrate to him how necessary hard work and diligence will be, if he is to thrive in this rather contrary world. When I heard of the position your department is seeking to fill, well, it seemed perfect for him.'

It was a strange request but these were strange times, and as he mulled it over, Girard was not inclined to consider it frivolous. A father determined to set his son to work, to teach him the ways of the world seemed to him an admirable ambition. But it was not an ambition with which he could assist, and he spread his hands to indicate his helplessness. 'Alas, Mademoiselle, much as I am inclined to aid so charming a visitor to Paris, such is the unsettled political and economic nature of the world that the powers that be have issued an edict stipulating that all positions within the civil service of Paris must be filled by persons born in the Medi. As a consequence, my Ministry is only permitted to employ Quartier Chaudians. It is a policy known as "Looking After Our Own" and as your brother is not one of our own, I am not able to look after him.'

The girl seemed not one wit deterred by Girard's demurral. She smiled again and edged even closer to the desk, leaning forward so her succulent breasts were temptingly within reach. It took an act of will for him not to reach out and caress them, but such ImPure familiarity was nowadays rather frowned upon. 'Of course, my father is more concerned with little Robert gaining a proper insight into the world of commerce than with his being rewarded financially. And as Robert would refuse all reimbursement, it is a moot point whether he would, technically, be "employed".'

'Your brother would not require to be paid?' asked a dumbfounded Girard, whose experience of good fortune persuaded him that it only touched those other than himself.

'Not one centime.'

'Ah,' said Girard, and it was an 'Ah' replete with much meaning. If the brother of this angel would work for nothing, then his unpaid salary could be used to supplement Girard's own. Certainly the thirty francs or so the boy would earn each week was not a fortune, but it was thirty francs better in his pocket than in someone else's. 'That, of course,' he mused, as greed struggled with prudence, 'is an interesting consideration, but really, Mademoiselle, it is impossible. The potential for scandal is considerable, you see.'

'How unfortunate. I am sure that working under a man as powerful and potent as yourself would be a rewarding experience for any boy . . . or any *girl* for that matter. I myself, for instance, would deem it an honour to service . . . to serve you.'

Girard wondered for a moment whether he had heard this girl aright. No, it was impossible. 'I am sorry, Mademoiselle?'

Norma Cartwright lowered her sad, sad eyes, then drew a

lace handkerchief from the sleeve of her jacket to dab them. 'You should know, Monsieur Girard, that my father is ill at the moment. The pressures of political life, you understand. So I am most concerned that nothing occurs that might exacerbate his already fragile condition. I know how he frets about little Robert, and, as a dutiful daughter, I am inclined to do *anything* which might settle my brother in a suitable position, and thus bring my father some peace of mind.'

Her emphasis on the word 'anything' was almost undetectable, but after twenty years of picking his way so adroitly through the intricacies of Ministry politics, Girard was alive to the subtlest of nuances. The hairs on the back of his neck – and other places – bristled with excitement.

'Anything?' The word limped out of Girard's mouth, as he struggled with the thought that this might, finally, be his lucky day.

Mademoiselle Norma Cartwright said nothing, but simply gazed at Girard with an amused half-smile adorning her lovely face. Then she stood up from her chair and went to stand by the window, gazing down to the street below. 'You really have no idea, Monsieur Girard,' she said finally, 'how important it is that I have my brother safely positioned within the Ministry.'

And to Girard's amazement she began to slowly unbutton the front of her close-fitting jacket. 'Today, Monsieur, is my nineteenth birthday and it is traditional to give gifts on such a day. If you were to assist me in this matter, then you would receive a very special *cadeau* . . . a very special *cadeau* indeed.' Unbuttoning finished, Norma Cartwright drew her jacket apart, revealing herself naked beneath. Girard sat stunned by the sight of such wonderful flesh. Norma Cartwright was beautiful when clothed; she was mesmerisingly lovely semi-naked. Girard was sure he had never seen breasts to equal those that this strange young woman was flaunting so openly.

'This body, Monsieur Girard, will be yours on the same day that Rivets . . . er, Robert takes up his position in the mailroom. Do we have a bargain?'

All Gaston Girard could do was nod.

Claude Poisson, Directeur Général of Mitraille de Medi, the largest scrap-metal company in the Quartier Chaud, gazed towards heaven and for the first time in his life believed that somewhere up there ABBA was smiling back down on him. As far as he could estimate, the Awful Tower contained 10,550 tons of premium-grade steel, and in today's market – with all the talk of war, embargoes and production shutdowns – that had to be worth . . .

Poisson cursed the three bottles of finest blood-claret he had shared that lunchtime with Monsieur Vanka Kruchkov of the ForthRight's Procurement Commission. The wine had completely befuddled his abacus-like ability to calculate francs and profits. But what he did know was that, reduced to scrap metal, the Awful Tower was worth a lot – a fucking lot. A 'fucking lot' so big that it would set him up in that mansion off the Bois de Boulogne which he had his eye on and persuade Naughty Nancy, principal dancer at the Folies-Bergère, to become his mistress. A 'fucking lot' so big that he could feel himself stiffening just at the possibility of such a prize being within his grasp. Naughty Nancy with her marvellous mouth was a prize beyond compare. He might even be able to afford her sister, too.

'*C'est une grande, grande tâche,*' he muttered, as he tried desperately to estimate how many men and steamers would be necessary to dismantle the Tower.

'Too big a job for Mitraille de Medi, perhaps?' came the question from his side.

Cursing himself for his faux pas – he hadn't realised Kruchkov was standing within earshot or that he understood French – Poisson vigorously shook his head. '*Mais non,* Monsieur

Kruchkov, with Mitraille de Medi you are dealing with the biggest and the longest-standing of all the firms trading in scrap metal throughout the whole Quartier Chaud. Be of no doubt that if we are awarded the contract it will be executed with an aplomb most expeditious.'

'How expeditious?' asked Kruchkov.

Poisson studied his interrogator for a moment. He seemed *very* young to have been entrusted with such a large and politically sensitive project as the dismantling of the Awful Tower, and with his long hair and frivolous attitude he certainly did not possess the seriousness one normally expected of such a high-ranking official. But then all Russkis were rumoured to be a trifle eccentric, and this Kruchkov had implied earlier that his family connections were lofty. Still, it would do no harm to check out his bona fides.

He shrugged in that oh-so-eloquent way only Frenchmen are capable of. 'Given access to the site, with a team of, say, forty men equipped with the most modern steam-driven chisels, and a fleet of ten of the biggest steamer lorries . . .' He scratched his chin: he hated giving estimates when he was pissed. 'Two months,' he said finally.

Kruchkov stood silently assessing him for a long moment, then suddenly held out his hand in that oh-so-eloquent way only Russians are capable of. 'Well, it's been a pleasure meeting you, Monsieur Poisson, and thanks for lunch. My Commission will be in touch.' The Russian then turned on his heel, signalling that the meeting was over.

Poisson felt faint as images of future nights spent locked in the arms – and other parts – of Naughty Nancy vanished in a puff of reality. 'Monsieur Kruchkov, please' – he made a grab at the Russki's arm – 'have I said something which has mayhap offended you?'

The Russian paused, then gave an indulgent smile. 'Not at all, Monsieur Poisson. It's just that you seem not to have grasped the urgency the ForthRight ascribes to this project. That edifice,' and here Kruchkov made a sneering glance towards the Tower, 'is a carbuncle on the face of this great city, it is a ridiculous monument to the discredited philosophy of ImPuritanism. As such, its dismantling will be symbolic of the rejection of ImPuritanism by the Medi and of the sacrifice demanded of its CitiZens if UnFunDaMentalism is to triumph over the decadent philosophies at large in the Demi-Monde. The Provisional Government of the Free UnFunDaMentalist Medi wants the Awful Tower gone, and it wants it gone not in two months but in two weeks.'

'Two weeks?' Poisson felt the fug in his mind disperse as he struggled with the problem of how to dismantle such an enormous structure in such a ridiculously short time.

'I have had discussions with ForthRight-based scrap-metal companies, and they believe a two-week timescale is feasible.'

*Bastard Anglos.*

Swiftly Poisson recalculated, doubling, then trebling the number of men and machinery he would deploy, but still he couldn't come anywhere near the two-week deadline. As he felt the sweat of panic begin to pool in his armpits, he racked his mind desperately trying to magic up a solution.

'There is one way, Monsieur Kruchkov, but it is brutal . . . barbaric . . .'

'Yes?' prompted Kruchkov.

'We could use explosives: blasting gelatine. The Tower could be dismantled in a moment but we would need two weeks to collect and remove the steel debris.'

'Ah.'

'*Mais oui*, ah. We could destroy these supports' – he pointed to the nearest of the four base columns holding up the Tower – 'and by doing so topple the structure along the Champ de Mars. It will create, as the Anglos might say, the biggest fucking mess, but it will be of the effectiveness most remarkable.'

'And Mitraille de Medi has the expertise to undertake such a demolition?'

'*Mais oui.*'

'Then, on that basis, your company would seem to be worthy of inclusion in the tender.'

'Tender?'

'Of course, Monsieur Poisson. This contract will be awarded by tender.'

'And who will be responsible for deciding the winner of the tender?'

'Why, me, as it happens.'

Claude Poisson felt a weight lift from his shoulders. He was an expert in bribing civil servants.


## 46th Day of Spring

Captain Peregrine Jenkins was more than a little suspicious of this rather elegant Russian, Kruchkov.

He had been called into the major's office to be introduced to the man, who, it seemed, was intent on selling the major a device which he claimed would turn the Puff Past to be performed by Jenkins's steamers in celebration of the signing of the Declaration of Unification into an 'unforgettable triumph'. The device in question was unprepossessing. It looked like a ball of soap six inches in diameter, and was, as far as Jenkins could see from the examples laid out on the major's desk, available in three colours: red, blue and green.

'These coloration tablets,' the major explained, 'if placed into the boilers of our steamers, dissolve at two hundred and twelve degrees Fahrenheit and colour the steam when it emerges from the funnel either red, blue or green.'

The penny dropped. It had been announced in *The Stormer*

that to signify the Unification of the ForthRight and the Medi a new flag had been commissioned which superimposed a ForthRight Valknut symbol on top of the Medi's *tricolore*. And as the *tricolore* was coloured red, blue and green, it was comfortably within even Captain Jenkins's limited intellectual compass to see the patriotic possibilities of Kruchkov's coloration tablets.

But whilst Jenkins might have been condemned to go through life in a haze of stupidity, this did not prevent him being naturally suspicious, especially where the well-being of his beloved steamers was concerned. 'Isn't it against ordinance thirteen of Standing Instructions Regarding the Operation and Maintenance of Armoured Steamers to place *any foreign body or substance within the boiler of said steamers which might be injurious to the efficient operation of aforesaid steamers*, sir?'

Major Tomlinson gazed at Jenkins as he might gaze at a backward child. It was a look Jenkins was familiar with, his father having used it all the time. 'You will be pleased to know, Jenkins, that Mister Kruchkov's coloration tablets have been fully tested and certified by the ForthRight Ministry of War.' He pushed a heavily stamped and sealed certificate across the desk towards his subordinate.

'But Captain Jenkins is correct in wishing to confirm that the coloration tablets will not impair the effectiveness of his steamers,' noted Kruchkov. 'Perhaps I might suggest that tomorrow my forewoman attends the captain, and he is able to test my device for himself?'

## 47th Day of Spring

Rivets didn't like working. He didn't like having to get up at seven in the morning, in order to be at the Ministry of Works' mailroom by eight. He didn't like having to put on the suit Miss

Norma had bought for him (what a stroppy cow she had turned out to be). He didn't like having to wash (or being washed – Miss Norma had nearly taken his fucking skin off with that scrubbing brush). He didn't like his *chef*, the officious boss of the mailroom, Monsieur Anton Henry, who had the unnerving habit of turning up just as Rivets was doing something he shouldn't be. He didn't like being called Robert. And, most of all, he didn't like the way that fat fuck Gaston Girard kept sidling up to him and asking how his sister was, all the while winking at him.

'So, Robert,' explained an excessively didactic Monsieur Henry, 'in this sack are the many letters destined for the attention of the managers and directeurs 'oo manage this great Ministry. You, my leetle man, are to delve into the sack, remove the letters and then place them in these holes of pigeons. *C'est facile, n'est-ce pas?*' Monsieur Henry made to pat Rivets on the head, which Rivets decided would be a slight too far. He would have to put one on the Frog. Fortunately, the grease he'd larded on his hair – it stuck up at the back otherwise – deterred him.

When Monsieur Henry had departed and Rivets had got a fag on, he started on his task. He worked diligently sifting through the mail and popping the letters into the requisite holes, all the while keeping an eye out for any letters destined for the attention of the Minister himself. As it turned out, there were nearly thirty of them that morning. Those with a stamp indicating that they came from outside the Quartier Chaud Rivets ignored, but any posted locally he studied with more attention. He eventually found the one Vanka had told him to be on the lookout for, and slipped it in his pocket.

The steamer arrived at the Steamer Park bang on the dot of ten o'clock and Kruchkov's forewoman turned out to be a very sizeable and enormously strong Frog who had, surprisingly, a rather petite and attractive young girl as her *assistante*. Indeed the *assistante* was so attractive that Captain Jenkins was persuaded to modify his usual brusque demeanour and be almost polite. He directed the two girls to the test steamer, waited while the steamer sergeant broke the seals on the boiler and then watched as the large forewoman clambered up onto the side of the vehicle and dropped a coloration tablet into the water tank.

The test was a great success. The steamer chugged around the parade ground shrouded in bright red steam and the effect was such that even the crews desperately trying to scrape the mud and rust from their own steamers paused in their work and applauded as the test machine puffed by.

The forewoman's *assistante* came to stand disturbingly close to Captain Jenkins, and then began talking to him in surprisingly good English. 'There is one problem, Monsieur le Capitaine,' she said amiably.

Jenkins's brow furrowed. He always had difficulty solving problems.

'It's our experience that the coloration tablets have an effective life of only ten minutes, so if they are inserted into the boilers here in the Park, they will be expended before the steamers are more than halfway to the Champ de Mars where they will be performing their Puff Past.'

'I see, but it's no real problem. I can have the steamers' BoilerMen nip out and insert them en route.'

'Of course, but isn't that a solution lacking a certain *élégance*, a certain *je ne sais quoi*? Perhaps you would permit me to suggest an answer to this dilemma?'

'Mademoiselle, please.'

'The symbol of Liberté has been commandeered – purloined rather – by those terrible and most unpatriotic women who count themselves members of the UnScrewed-Liberation Movement. Would it not be a coup if you were to reclaim Liberté

– if, as a signal of the *entente cordiale* between our two great states, Liberté was to ride at the front of the steamers waving the flag of the Union and, at the appropriate time, dropping a coloration tablet into the boiler?'

'I am not sure if I quite understand what you're suggesting.'

'Would you allow a demonstration?'

'Certainly. Why not?'

'Then I must change. To perform as Liberté, I must look like Liberté.'

Remarkably, this pretty young girl – Norma Dubois – had a costume and a *tricolore* tucked away in the back of her steamer lorry. And Captain Jenkins had to admit that it was a very fetching costume indeed, being particularly taken by the way her right breast was left bare. Major Tomlinson, who had wandered over to see why all the steamer crews had downed tools, seemed to agree with him. He watched, google-eyed and open-mouthed, as the *assistante* rode on the front of the steamer while it chugged up and down the parade ground, waving her flag as she went.

When finally she hopped down from the front of the steamer, she was greeted by a round of applause and cheers from the gathered crews. She gave the major a smile and bobbed a deep curtsy. His Adam's apple bobbed in appreciation. 'Very nice,' he muttered, though Jenkins was unsure as to whether he was referring to the girl's performance as Liberté or to the rather pert breast on display. 'Captain Jenkins has been explaining your idea to me, Mademoiselle, and I must say it sounds very jolly. But tell me, young lady, will you be able to find twenty girls willing to play Liberté in quite such an enthusiastic manner as yourself?'

The girl's lovely brow furrowed. 'Only twenty? Does that mean you will not have the full might of your regiment of steamers on parade?'

'Unfortunately not, my dear. Captain Jenkins does not have the manpower to clean and repaint any more than twenty of them in the thirteen days remaining before the Ceremony of Unification. A great shame, of course.'

What the major said was perfectly correct. Jenkins had more than one hundred and fifty armoured steamers lined up in the Jardin de Robespierre, and most of these were veterans of the Battle for Warsaw. Theirs had been a hard life, and they had the bashes, scratches and scrapes to prove it. Even working his crews and the maintenance corps day and night, two weeks wasn't long enough to get the steamers painted and polished to a standard that would make them fit for inspection by the Great Leader.

The major's comment sparked a rapid and somewhat heated exchange, all in incomprehensible Frog, between the *assistante* and her forewoman. Finally the *assistante* turned to the major. 'Major, we believe it is our duty as good Medis to come to the aid of the ForthRight. If you would permit, Mademoiselle Odette here would be honoured to provide, at no expense, the services of a dedicated team of cleaners and renovators to help make your steamers perfect in both form and appearance. And, to adorn such symbols of ForthRight power and potency, I will recruit one hundred and fifty of the most beautiful girls in Paris to ride upon them.'

The major licked his lips, obviously contemplating the sight of one hundred and fifty girls clad as the *assistante* was. His Adam's apple started jiggling again.

'And afterwards,' Norma continued, 'perhaps there could be a *célébration* of our own?'

'And what form would this celebration take?'

'That would be a surprise, Major,' she replied, a little too flirtatiously for Jenkins's liking. 'But if you wish, Major, I might tell you my plans in secret.'

With that both Norma and the major repaired to the major's office.

## 48th Day of Spring

'More wine, Monsieur Kruchkov?' enquired Claude Poisson.

The Russian shook his head. Today he was all business. 'I understand from the Minister of Works that you have been making enquiries about me.'

The bottle froze in Poisson's hand. That this mysterious Kruchkov knew that he had written to the Minister demanding assurances of the Russki's bona fides was disturbing. He had thought he had made it plain in his letter that his enquiry was a confidential one, but then, he supposed, even a minister had to be careful when dealing with the nephew of Lavrentii Beria.

There was no point, Poisson decided, in dissembling. 'You are correct, Monsieur Kruchkov. As you might imagine, with a project so large and unorthodox as the dismantling of the Awful Tower—'

'Monsieur Poisson,' Kruchkov interrupted, in a voice which had suddenly become excessively precise and deliberate, 'when we began our discussions I made it perfectly clear that confidentiality was a prime consideration in this matter. You even signed a confidentiality agreement confirming you understood that divulging any details of this project would be a violation of state security. Do you remember that?'

The mouthful of blood-claret Poisson was in the process of enjoying suddenly turned sour. The juxtaposition of the word 'violation' with 'state security' was enough to chill the SAE, especially as the man doing the juxtaposing had the ear of that murderous bastard Beria. Images of meat hooks and piano wire suddenly came to dominate Poisson's imagination. All he could find the strength to do was give a meek nod.

'Then you will know that this letter' – here Kruchkov delved into the inside pocket of his jacket and produced the selfsame letter that Poisson had sent to the minister – 'violates that undertaking. This letter describes in detail the project to dispose of the Tower – a revelation that could be interpreted as treason. Do you know the penalty for treason, Monsieur Poisson?'

'*Oui, Monsieur*,' said Poisson, his mouth suddenly so dry he could barely talk. His arsehole began twitching in nervous anticipation of the arrival of the Checkya, too.

'Good. So can I take it that there will be no repetition of this deplorable lapse of judgement?'

'Yes.'

'Then let us not let this little faux pas spoil our mutually profitable relationship.' With that, and to Poisson's great relief, Kruchkov tore his offending letter into small pieces, deposited the fragments in the ashtray, and then set them alight. This done, he raised his glass. 'So, a toast – to a fresh start.'

'A fresh start,' echoed Poisson, as he wondered whether it would be appropriate to fall to his knees and kiss the feet of this wonderfully forgiving man.

'To business.' Kruchkov pulled a second envelope out of his pocket. 'This is the notification confirming that Mitraille de Medi has won the tender to demolish the Awful Tower, to remove the scrap metal resulting from the demolition, and to sell said metal on the open market. The ForthRight Ministry of Works will pay one hundred thousand guineas on completion of the demolition, which must be accomplished within thirteen days of the date on this contract – that is, one day after the Ceremony of Unification. Proceeds of the sale of the scrap metal will be divided on a fifty-fifty basis between the Ministry and Mitraille de Medi. Do those terms seem acceptable?'

Claude Poisson decided he would kiss the feet, the arse, or anything else the Russian might wish kissed. It was an amazingly generous contract, one which would make him rich beyond his wildest dreams, and he had entertained some pretty wild dreams in his time. All he had to do was get Kruchkov to let him have that envelope. Unfortunately, the way Kruchkov was hanging on to it signalled to Poisson that negotiations were far from over.

'Monsieur Poisson' – Kruchkov leant forward in a conspiratorial manner – 'have you ever paused to consider how hard is the lot of those who toil so diligently for the public good? Have you ever thought how civil servants, by their selfless desire to serve the ForthRight, sacrifice themselves on behalf of their fellow citizens? Have you, Monsieur Poisson, have you?'

'Er . . . no, not really.'

'Then perhaps you should, Monsieur Poisson. Take my situation as an example. I am a Grade Four bureaucrat and earn a paltry one thousand guineas each season, a mere peppercorn of a salary.'

Poisson sat silently waiting for Kruchkov to put the bite on, but if the man expected him to believe that it was possible to buy the exquisitely tailored suit and marvellously crafted boots he was wearing on a bureaucrat's wage, then the Russian must think that he was as green as the emerald that nestled amidst the froth of the man's cravat.

'So I must look to the generosity of people such as yourself to make my lot more endurable.'

Now it was Poisson's turn to extract an envelope from inside his jacket. He handed it over, as surreptitiously as he was able, to the Russian. 'I trust this is a sufficient indication of the admiration I feel for men such as yourself, Monsieur Kruchkov. It is a symbol of my thanks for your selfless service.'

'And how many times am I being thanked?'

'Ten thousand.'

'Excellent. But I trust there will be more thanks once the scrap metal is sold. After all, Monsieur Poisson, with scrap steel trading at one hundred guineas a ton, you will be receiving over half a million guineas as your share of the contract.'

'Shall we say, 5 per cent of the gross sales value?'

'Shall we say . . . ten per cent?'

The two men shook hands across the table, and as Claude Poisson sat back contentedly in his chair he wondered whether Naughty Nancy might not have *two* equally naughty sisters.

Kruchkov made to hand Poisson the contract and then paused. 'There is one other thing. The Checkya insist that the explosives to be used in the demolition are held in secure bond until they are employed. This is a matter of state security, you understand.'

Poisson wasn't sure he did understand, but he was so mesmerised by the contract being waved in front of him that he'd stopped thinking clearly.

Kruchkov continued, 'I will have one of my men, named Bartholomew Bubble, come to your depot tomorrow to collect the blasting gelatine.'

'Of course,' purred Poisson as the contract was finally placed in his hand.


## 49th Day of Spring

Rivets felt decidedly put upon. When he had agreed with Vanka to take a job, he had thought it would be *a* job, not two of the damn things. But as soon as he'd left the Ministry's mailroom, Vanka had secured him a new position with the Bureau de Feux d'Artifice, the Medi's premier maker of fireworks.

New job or not, Rivets still didn't like working. He especially didn't like work which involved him having to scamper like a monkey along the long steel beams of the Awful Tower, ducking and diving through the metal latticework to tie the fireworks in position. It was just as well that he didn't have a fear of heights, because dangling a hundred or more feet from the ground, with just a length of rope strapped around his waist as a safety harness, was not an occupation he'd recommend to those who suffered from vertigo. And there were a lot of fireworks to install. As his foreman had told him proudly, to Bureau de Feux d'Artifice fell the responsibility of turning the Awful Tower into a spectacle that would make the Ceremony of Unification an event that would never be forgotten.

But if the duties he was asked to perform seemed odd, what was odder was the interest in his non-existent sister evinced by the Directeur of the Bureau de Feux d'Artifice. This Alain Brun item – a skinny, nervous individual – seemed obsessed with this mythical creature. On his first day on the job, the man must have approached him at least six times to enquire how Rivets's sister was, when she would be recovered from her illness, and if it would be appropriate for him to visit her to offer his solic-itations. Even Rivets's evasive answers hadn't dampened the man's enthusiasm, and as the days had gone by, his questioning had become even more persistent and fervent.

Rivets was just enjoying a fag when a steamer arrived at the foot of the Tower and a man, who looked suspiciously like Burlesque Bandstand wearing a wig and a pus-green mask, hopped down from the cabin to seek out Monsieur Brun. It was not a happy meeting, and what followed was a pantomime of gestures and stamping of feet (from Monsieur Brun) and the waving of official-looking papers (by Burlesque). But after much heated debate, it was Monsieur Brun who capitulated. He glanced around, and his eye settled on Rivets.

'Robert,' he yelled.

Rivets took a moment to register that he was being summoned by his working name. He swung himself down to the ground, untethered the rope and trotted over to Monsieur Brun, touching the peak of his cap as he went.

'Robert, as you are the only worker I 'ave 'oo speaks the perfect Anglo, you are to 'elp this mens, 'oo is the representative of the ForthRight Ministry of Propaganda, to unload the fireworks they carries in the back of 'is steamer. It would appear that our ForthRight *amis* are of the unconfidence regarding the ability of the Bureau de Feux d'Artifice to make the spectacle *magnifique.*' A sniff from Monsieur Brun. 'They wish to supplement our efforts with four devices of their own. Monsieur Bartholomew Bubble 'ere will instruct you as to where those devices must be placed.' Monsieur Brun gave 'Monsieur Bubble' a dismissive glance. 'However, Robert, if you have any of the big doubts, please speak to me and I will give you my own suggestions as to where Monsieur Bubble might place 'is fireworks.'

So, for the next hour, Rivets had the back-breaking job of lugging the four packages very, very carefully out of the steamer and over to the base of the Awful Tower, where 'Monsieur Bubble' positioned one at the bottom of each of the four supporting piers. Rivets felt so knackered at the end of it that when Burlesque carefully – very, very fucking carefully – attached the fuses to the fireworks, he had real trouble in remembering which was which. All he knew was that the fuses to the right-hand pillars should be lit first, and the fuses to the left-hand ones should be lit five seconds later. In the end it was Burlesque who volunteered to haul the fuses over to the Chef de Batterie – the man responsible for igniting the fireworks in the correct order – and to give the firing sequence.

When they'd finished, Burlesque seemed very happy with himself. He even bought Rivets a pint to celebrate, though Rivets wasn't quite sure what it was that Burlesque was so keen on celebrating.

# 33

## Paris
## The Demi-Monde: 50th Day of Spring, 1005

Such were the depleted blood reserves of the ForthRight that for a moment in Spring 1005 the Sector's currency appeared about to crash and hyper-inflation cripple the economy. It was Comrade Commissar Horatio Bottomley who saved the ForthRight's bacon. It was Bottomley who, by the use of inspired financial legerdemain, conjured the RentenGuinea from thin air. The RentenGuinea was not backed by blood – as the Guinea had been – but by mortgages on Sector-owned land and property and by bonds underpinned by ForthRight-based plant and machinery. A chimera this backing might have been, but it steadied the markets and allowed Heydrich enough time and wherewithal to develop his V-weapons and to attack the Coven.

A History of ForthRight Finance:
*John Maynard Keynes, ForthRight Publishing*

### 12.30: The office of Vice-Leader Beria in the Élysée Palace

Commissar Peter Havelock – the Checkya officer in charge of Counter-Intelligence in the Medi and Officer Commanding Security at the Ceremony of Unification – was grateful that officers in Counter-Intelligence wore brown uniforms. He had never seen Vice-Leader Beria so agitated, and an agitated Beria scared the shit out of him. The bastard sat behind his desk evincing all the serenity of an unexploded bomb.

'Are all our troops inside Paris?' Beria asked suddenly.

'About half, Comrade Vice-Leader. There have been some difficulties in securing coal for the steamers needed to transport them and their equipment. The Frogs have taken to hiding it.'

'Hiding it?'

'Yes, the Frog merchants began by refusing to accept ForthRight guineas in payment for the coal, as they claimed our currency is devaluing too fast. And then, when the Coven's coal embargo was announced, they said that the price we were offering didn't reflect the true value of such a "scarce commodity". After that, supplies just seemed to vanish.'

Beria let out a long, exasperated sigh, as he struggled with the idea that coal stocks could 'vanish'. 'Have you tried making an example of these Enemies of the Revolution?'

'I have had a hundred of them hanged. The problem I face is that if I hang any more of the bastards, there'll be no one left to unload what little coal there is.' Havelock waited a moment to let Beria absorb this depressing fact of life. The Vice-Leader's penchant for stringing up anyone he thought to be impeding the Occupation was nigh on out of control. There were at least five thousand of the poor sods decorating the Champs-Élysées already. 'The upshot, Comrade Vice-Leader, is that half of our steamer regiments are marooned in the Hub, waiting for supplies of coal to be carted in from the ForthRight.'

Havelock saw Beria's dead eyes flick towards the calendar on his desk, doing the same thing Havelock himself did every morning: calculating the number of days remaining until ThawsDay, the sixtieth day of Spring, the day on which the Hub nanoBites woke from their hibernation. Any steamer crews caught in the Hub on ThawsDay had better be able to levitate.

Beria took a moment to light a cigarette, and Havelock was amazed to see his hand tremble slightly as he did so. Things must really be bad if the normally imperturbable Lavrentii Beria was so upset.

'The important question, Comrade Commissar, is if there will be sufficient coal to allow the armoured steamers to parade on Unification Day. Comrade Leader Heydrich considers it essential that there is an appropriate display of ForthRight military might on the glorious day when the Medi is officially absorbed into the ForthRight. He believes that such a display will do much to persuade the population of the Medi that their idiotic espousal of Normalism is futile. They will come to understand that the ultimate victory of the ForthRight and the triumph of UnFunDaMentalism is ordained by ABBA Himself.'

So, it was the antics of these Normalists which was perturbing the Vice-Leader! But Havelock supposed there was a lot to be perturbed about. The Normalists had appeared out of nowhere and had succeeded in totally disrupting the functioning of the Medi. But what was worse, it was a political movement that appeared to be growing stronger by the hour. Aaliz Heydrich had proven herself to be as adept a leader as her father.

'There are still ten days remaining until Unification Day, Comrade Vice-Leader, so rest assured that the Army of the ForthRight will be parading in its full strength.'

'Is everything else in order regarding the preparations for the Ceremony of Unification?' Beria demanded.

'Absolutely, Comrade Vice-Leader,' replied Havelock. Not that there was any way he would have replied to the contrary. He was no fool. 'We have supervised the building of the VIP stand that will accommodate the two hundred and fifty dignitaries invited to the ceremony. I have searched it myself, and it is now under twenty-four-hour guard. It is impossible that any malcontent will be able to place a bomb under it or anywhere near it.'

'Assassins?'

'All VIP attendees have been requested not to wear swords and firearms and each has been issued with an invitation which my officers will scrutinise before they are permitted to take their places on the stand. As for a sniper using a rifle from distance, we have cleared and occupied all possible vantage points surrounding the Champ de Mars.'

'The crowd?'

'The crowd will be confined to the edges of the Champ de Mars, where they will enjoy an excellent view of the festivities, but will come no closer than fifty yards from the VIP stand. I have requested Senior CitiZen Robespierre to provide the names of pro-UnFunDaMentalist groups, and these will be positioned nearest the stand. I will have five hundred plain-clothes Checkya agents mingling with the crowd, looking out for terrorists, and five thousand uniformed Checkya officers nearby, in case of . . . difficulties.'

Havelock checked his notebook. 'We have rounded up all known dissidents – Normalists, UnScrewed-Liberationists, and diehard ImPuritans – and placed them in protective custody in the Bastille, where they will be shot.'

'Excellent. So what is the programme of events celebrating the Ceremony of Unification?'

'Departing at four o'clock in the afternoon from the Élysée Palace, there will be a triumphant cavalcade through the streets of Paris where the Great Leader and yourself, as well as representatives of the Medi Senate and of the ForthRight government, will be cheered by the people of the Medi in a spontaneous demonstration of love and thanks for their delivery from the evil embrace of ImPuritanism. Members of the ForthRight Army, uniformed as Medi infantry, will line the street to ensure there are no demonstrations of dissent. The cavalcade will consist of ten steamers with cavalry escort. You, Comrade Vice-Leader, accompanied by Senior CitiZen Robespierre, will be in the first steamer accompanying Great Leader Heydrich. Comrade General Skobelev and Senator Torquemada will be in the second.'

'Torquemada's wound?'

'He has been persuaded to abandon the sling. There will thus be no evidence of unfortunate events that occurred when the Bastille was stormed.'

'Good. And security during the cavalcade?'

'The steamers will be discreetly armoured and hence utterly impervious to attack by handguns or grenades. Each steamer will be flanked by hussars of the Reinhard Heydrich's Own cavalry regiment.'

'Good.'

'Once at the Champ de Mars – or the Champ de l'Union, as it is to be renamed – there will take place a series of events and pageants: marching by the Heydrich Guards regiment, dancing by the ForthRight Ballet company, and the popular French singer Maurice Chevalier will give a rendition of patriotic songs.'

'Patriotic songs?'

'They have been carefully vetted for anti-revolutionary sentiments, and censored accordingly, Comrade Vice-Leader. He will sing three songs, each a harmless piece of puff in praise of love and young women, of whom Monsieur Chevalier seems inordinately fond. Then there will be two speeches. The first will be given by the Great Leader, pledging the ForthRight to defend the Medi from the enemies of peace and freedom, and committing the ForthRight to helping the Medi resist the evil of non-UnFunDaMentalist thought. The second will be made by Senior CitiZen Robespierre . . .' Havelock hesitated for a moment.

'There is a problem?'

'Senior CitiZen Robespierre is reluctant to take the advice of the Checkya propaganda section regarding both the content and most especially the *length* of his speech. He seems to be of the opinion that, being Senior CitiZen, he has some sort of

ROD REES | 393

power to overrule our suggestions. When I pointed out that his was a titular office, he became somewhat agitated.'

'Fuck him. Is there anything incendiary about his speech?'

'Not per se, Comrade Vice-Leader, but it is very pompous and *very* boring. And I have had to *insist* that his condemnation of the nuJus be made more vehement.'

'Then it seems perfect. The people will understand that their current leadership is overblown and incompetent, whereas their new masters aren't. The Great Leader's speech, by comparison, will be remembered as a masterpiece of brevity and efficiency. So, after the speeches, what then?'

'Senior CitiZen Robespierre will request the unification of the Medi with the ForthRight and together he and the Great Leader will sign the Declaration of Unification. Then, in a symbolic act, the Senior CitiZen will hand over the three keys of the city-states of Paris, Barcelona and Rome, which you, Vice-Leader, as Head of the Provisional Government of the Free UnFunDaMentalist Medi, will accept into your safe keeping. The Great Leader will then announce that henceforth the Medi is officially part of the ForthRight. As these words are spoken, the Awful Tower, now renamed the Reinhard Heydrich Tower, will be festooned in a display of pyrotechnics never before equalled in the history of the Demi-Monde. It will be a fireworks display seen throughout the Quartier Chaud and will serve as a beacon proclaiming the unassailable power and strength of the ForthRight.'

'Are the fireworks safe?'

'We have employed the Medi's leading manufacturer of fireworks, the Bureau de Feux d'Artifice. They are a *very* reliable company. Their installation is now complete, and the Tower itself is under twenty-four-hour guard.'

'Excellent, Comrade Commissar, it appears you have displayed your customary organisational diligence, and be assured that, if these events proceed as flawlessly as you have related, you will be appropriately rewarded.'

A hugely relieved Commissar Havelock saluted, spun on his heel and marched out of Beria's office. He had a lot to do and a lot of things to double-check. It was one thing to be rewarded if things went well, but it would be quite another to be rewarded if things went badly.

## 12.45: The Pons Fabricus

Captain Jeremiah Greene watched as the ForthRight Corps of Engineers tried – *very* carefully – to ease the first of the gigantic Krupp mortars across the Pons Fabricus. It was a delicate job, as each of the mortars, designed specially to pummel Venice to powder, weighed over twenty tons. Although Captain Greene, as the officer in charge of the operation, had had the foresight to consult with a construction engineer, Comrade Engineer-Captain Banks, before commencing the crossing, and although said construction engineer had confirmed – in writing – that he believed the bridge would take the weight, the groans and the creaks he could hear did not fill Greene with confidence.

Inch by inch, the first of the mortars was hauled onto the bridge. Of course, the weight of the gun was compounded by the weight of the huge steamer-crawler necessary to pull the thing and as he stood at the end of the span, watching as the steamer-crawler crept along, dragging the trailer bearing the Krupps mortar behind it, Greene found himself praying more fervently than he had ever prayed before. He knew that the alternative route to Venice was even more challenging, especially as it would necessitate traversing the HubLand. There might be ten days still to go before ThawsDay, but the men stationed in the Hub were already getting nervous.

And Greene fully understood their nervousness. The rumour

circulating throughout the army was that the enormous weight of the steamer-crawlers plus the mortars they were dragging would gouge ruts so deep into the Hub's surface that the nanoBites would be brought out of their hibernation prematurely. The men were getting what the army called 'Nibblers Feet'.

'We've reached the middle of the bridge,' Greene heard Comrade Engineer-Captain Banks murmur. 'Once we're over this bit . . .'

Greene raised his telescope and studied the driver of the steamer-crawler. As far as he could see through the thick haze of steam that shrouded the vehicle, the man was doing exactly as he had been ordered, bringing the crawler and its cargo across the bridge smoothly and slowly. For the first time that morning, he felt almost optimistic.

Greene's optimism was incredibly short-lived. Suddenly there was the ear-splitting scream of steel scraping on steel, a loud bang of snapping cables, and a ping as a foot-long rivet whizzed past his ear. Then slowly – majestically almost – the steamer-crawler lurched to one side as the bridge buckled beneath it and then plunged into the Thames.

'Those Normalist bastards must have sabotaged the bolts holding the bridge together,' someone gasped.

As a pall of steam rose from the hissing wreck, the living corpse that was Comrade Engineer-Captain Banks vomited over the side of the bridge. Greene ignored him, lost in thought as he tried to remember whether he'd packed his platform-soled anti-Nibbler boots. He had an awful feeling he was going to need them.

## 13.00: The docks along the Quai d'Orsay

Odette Aroca had never felt quite so proud or important in the whole of her life. But there was more to it than that, she felt *fulfilled*. Here she was leading a group – well, more than a *group* actually, since there were at least three or four hundred Normalists making up the crowd marching slowly behind her – of like-minded people determined to do everything in their power to *peaceably* resist the forces of oppression and violence.

And if the amount of abuse currently being showered on her and her fellow demonstrators by the drivers of the ForthRight convoy they were holding up was any indication, then these tactics were proving very effective indeed. For about the fifth time in as many minutes, the red-coated sergeant in charge of the convoy came over to parley with Odette.

'Mademoiselle,' the sergeant began in excellent French, 'I'm telling you for the last fucking time. Unless you and your people stop clogging up this street with your slow marching, I am going to have to arrest you.'

'Arrest me for what, Sergeant?' asked Odette, a look of sublime innocence on her face. 'I am merely promenading, Sergeant – taking in the sights, the scents and the joy of Paris, the most beautiful city in the Demi-Monde.'

'Don't give me that bullshit. You and your pals are fucking up the unloading of these barges by preventing my steamer-lorries from getting to the docks.'

'Which steamer-lorries, Sergeant?' simpered Odette.

'*Those* fucking steamer-lorries,' said the sergeant, angrily stabbing a finger in the direction of the phalanx of vehicles huffing and puffing along behind the crowd of Normalists.

'Oh, *those*.' Odette gave an impish little smile. 'I had no idea that we were interfering with the operation of the Thames docks.'

'Like fuck, you didn't. I've only told you about fifty fucking times.' Suddenly the sergeant drew his pistol from his holster and aimed it at Odette's head. 'All right, party time's over. If you don't clear this road right now, I'm going to shoot you.'

Odette sighed. It was inevitable that their protest would be met by violence, and even by murder. As Norma had told her, the ForthRight was addicted to violence as a means of keeping power. She had also warned Odette that non-violence wasn't, as many thought, synonymous with meekness; rather it was synonymous with a quiet – a fatalistic – strength. The disciples of non-violence had to be as ready to die for their cause as any soldier.

This was Odette's moment of truth.

'Then you must shoot me, Sergeant. If you believe that your religion and your beliefs demand that the appropriate punishment for the crime of walking slowly is murder, then you must shoot me. If you believe that by refusing to fight you I am the embodiment of evil your superiors tell me I am, then you must shoot me. *But* if you believe that no sane religion or government would ever order its officers to commit murder, you must holster your pistol. The decision is yours.'

The sergeant hesitated, and this brief hesitation saved him from the need to make that decision. The few seconds he stood there trying to make up his mind were long enough for his cogitations to be interrupted by the bustling arrival of a soldier.

'The steamers have run out of coal, Sarge. The steamer drivers say they can't do the unloading today. They've gone cold-boilers.'

'Fuck.'

'We'll disperse now, Sergeant,' said a smiling Odette Aroca, as she and her fellow demonstrators began to wander off.

## 19.30: The office of Vice-Leader Beria in the Élysée Palace

It had been a fucking *awful* day, decided Beria as he sat in his darkened office, comforting himself with a glass of Solution and mulling over the current crisis that was besetting the

ForthRight. First there was the delay in getting the army into the Medi, then the collapse of the Pons Fabricus, and finally the news that the docks were out of action because of Normalist demonstrations.

Yeah, *crisis* was a fucking accurate description for what was happening. And the crisis was all because of those fucking Normalists, all because of this bitch who was posing as Aaliz Heydrich. All because of the Daemon, Norma Williams.

*Fucking Daemons.* He rang the small brass bell that stood on his desk.

The Andrei Zolotov who entered the room in answer to the summons looked markedly different from the jaunty and impudent rascal of only a few weeks ago. But then, Beria supposed, a close brush with death tended to be a sobering experience.

'How is the wound, Zolotov?'

Instinctively, Zolotov raised his fingers to his left shoulder, where he had taken the bullet during the mêlée in the Maison d'Illusion. 'The doctors tell me it's healing well, though it aches like the very devil.'

'Are you fit enough to resume your duties?'

'Yes, thankfully, my sword arm was undamaged. I am ready and *very* willing to revenge myself on that witch the Lady IMmanual for the humiliation she inflicted on me.'

'Ready, willing, but, not very able. You have been a disappointment to me, Zolotov,' said Beria quietly. 'I gave you the task of killing Burlesque Bandstand, and you failed. I gave you the task of killing the Lady IMmanual, and you failed. Normally such serial failure would result in . . . retribution. The ForthRight cannot – will not – tolerate failure. But I am moved to give you one final opportunity to prove yourself. The ForthRight has another task for you, which I believe will do much to slake your thirst for revenge and which will confirm that you are a loyal servant of the ForthRight. But I stress, this is your last chance. You do understand me, don't you, Zolotov?'

'Perfectly, Comrade Vice-Leader.' And for once in his life, Andrei Zolotov looked like he *did* understand.

'You have heard, no doubt, of the Lady Aaliz Heydrich?'

This was the most delicate moment in the whole interview, and for once Beria was pleased that Zolotov was such an uncaring wretch. It wouldn't do for him, or for anybody outside the Leader's closest circle, to enquire *too* seriously as to why the oh-so-patriotic and oh-so-dutiful Aaliz Heydrich had suddenly gone renegade.

'Of course. She's the daughter of our Leader.'

'Do you know her?'

'I was introduced to her at Dashwood Manor. She's a rather attractive little piece, if I remember, though possessed of a keen tongue. I am not generally drawn to girls with sharp tongues. I prefer length to sharpness.'

'Yes, she is both sharp and very, very dangerous. She has been designated a major threat to the ForthRight. She has been declared a nonNix.'

'A *nonNix*?'

'Indeed, I have a death warrant authorising her elimination, signed by the Leader himself.'

'Remarkable,' mused Zolotov. 'May I ask why?'

'The Lady Aaliz has become delusional. She has rejected UnFunDaMentalism, and has appointed herself the leader of these damned peaceniks who are plaguing our efforts to pacify the Medi. I wish you to infiltrate the Normalists and assassinate Aaliz Heydrich. Only when this is done are you permitted to turn your attention back to the task of dealing with IMmanual and Bandstand.'

Zolotov stubbed out his cigarette in Beria's ashtray. 'Then the quicker the girl is dead, the better for all concerned.'

# 34

## Paris
## The Demi-Monde: 60th Day of Spring, 1005

Doubt about our ability to predict history is due to HumanKind's epistemic limitations, that is, their inability to perceive and understand *everything* about the Demi-Monde. It is the Demi-Mondians' limited understanding of the movement of the rocks and pebbles in our temporal avalanche that has led them to the erroneous conclusion that this movement is random. Once this misconception is acknowledged, then Quantum-InDeterminism becomes Quantum-Determinism and *everything*, big and small, becomes predictable. At that moment of revelation we are able to see ABBA's Intelligent Design of the Kosmos in all its awe-inspiring glory. Of course, there are still those naysayers who – despite all the evidence to the contrary – deny the existence of ABBA, to which Laplace famously replied 'I have no use for that hypothesis'.

A LayPerson's Guide to preScience:
*Nikolai Kondratieff, Future History Institute Press*

### 16.00: The Élysée Palace

When the convoy of armoured steamers bringing the Great Leader to Paris – via a hastily repaired Pons Fabricus – had finally arrived at the Élysée Palace, Heydrich was not in the best of moods. He was so unhappy that he spent the hour immediately following his arrival in an urgent meeting with Comrade General Skobelev. Although he was not invited to the meeting, Beria overheard much of what was said. Indeed the voice of the Great Leader was raised to such an extent as he harangued his subordinate that Beria would have been surprised if half of Paris hadn't heard him.

Skobelev had emerged red-faced and shaking from the meeting. Now it was Beria's turn.

'Skobelev has agreed to bring forward the attack on Venice, Comrade Vice-Leader,' snarled Heydrich, by way of a greeting. 'I understand that the convoy bringing the Krupps mortars to Paris has now almost completed its journey across the Hub, and has not yet encountered any problems with nanoBites. My experts believe that the unusually cold Spring has prolonged their hibernation. The mortars will be in place along the Grand Canal within five days, and the bombardment of Venice will begin then.' Heydrich paused to collect his thoughts and to warm his arse by the fire. It was a bitterly cold day and there was no coal rationing in the Élysée Palace. 'Now, Comrade Vice-Leader, listen to me very carefully. Any Medi CitiZen, particularly any of these fucking Normalists, caught thwarting or in any way hindering the deployment of Skobelev's mortars is to be shot on the spot. I will tolerate no more excuses, no more delays regarding the conquest of the Quartier Chaud. Is that instruction clearly understood?'

'Yes, Comrade Leader. But may I ask how the army is to haul the mortars once they are in Venice? We used all our remaining reserves of coal to fuel the steamer-crawlers currently traversing the Hub, but once in Venice they will be obliged to go cold-boilers.'

'I have stripped the ForthRight of all its strategic reserves of coal. This coal is on barges crossing the Thames, sufficient to enable the steamer-crawlers to drag the mortars into position.

I have made Comrade General Skobelev aware of the sacrifices the people of the ForthRight are making in order that this precious resource is available to the army.'

*Yes, I heard you.*

'It is also necessary to liberate the supplies of meat held here in the Medi. It is intolerable that the people of the ForthRight should go hungry because of the misguided actions of a group of Normalist fanatics in preventing the export of foodstuffs. Tomorrow, Comrade Vice-Leader, the Checkya will occupy the Medi's Industrial Zone and expedite the delivery of meat and grain to the ForthRight. Again, anyone opposing you will be shot.'

Heydrich paused, obviously having run out of things for Beria to do which involved shooting a lot of Medi CitiZens. 'What is the news regarding the assassination of the Daemon Norma Williams?' he asked finally.

'I have infiltrated a crypto into the ranks of the Normalists. He is to be granted an audience with the Daemon posing as your daughter.'

'When?'

'Before the end of Spring.'

'Excellent. At least there is *some* good news.'

Beria took advantage of the Leader's raised spirits to mention Robespierre. 'Senior CitiZen Robespierre is waiting in the anteroom.'

'Why? What does that prick want?'

Obviously diplomacy wasn't high on the Great Leader's agenda. 'To accompany you to the state steamer in order that the Ceremony of Unification might begin.'

## 16.32: The Quartier Chaudian Hub

Anxiously, Captain Jeremiah Greene scanned the convoy of steamer-crawlers chugging slowly across the Hub towards Porte

Saint-Martin. The thirty vehicles that comprised Convoy One were already safely inside Paris, but because of a breakdown when they were crossing the Hub Bridge, the thirty crawlers that made up Convoy Two, commanded by Greene, had been delayed. Delayed for so long that the Convoy's crawlers were still puffing and panting across the Hub on this the 60th day of Spring, ThawsDay, and nobody – nobody in their right mind, that is – came anywhere near the Hub on ThawsDay. That was when the nanoBites woke from their hibernation and after one hundred and fifty days of fasting the bastards were so hungry that they would eat anything – *anything* – sinking more than six inches below the surface of the HubLand. And from what Jeremiah Greene could see, the way the caterpillar tracks of the steamer-crawlers were chewing up the Hub would make them the *plat du jour* when the nanoBites came to dine.

'Keep your steam up,' Greene screamed at his steamer-crawler driver.

'I *am* keeping my fucking steam up,' came a bellowed reply, the tension in the air making everyone forget military etiquette.

Greene decided to ignore the driver's insolence and turned instead to his sergeant, who was standing at the front of the steamer, anxiously examining the Hub for signs of subsurface life.

'See anything?' he asked.

'Not a dicky bird, Captain. Maybe it's just too cold for the nanoBites to come out of hibernation.'

The sergeant's optimism was interrupted by a strange rustling noise that suddenly enveloped the entire Hub. It sounded to Greene akin to the noise dried leaves made when they were blown about, which was odd because there were no dried leaves to be seen, and not even a breath of wind. A moment later this rustling sound was accompanied by a shriek of tortured metal, as the steamer-crawler to his left began to lurch around in a most peculiar manner. As Greene stood gawping, the machine gradually sank deeper and deeper into the ground. He couldn't believe his eyes. Not even something as heavy as a steamer-crawler could sink into the frost-hard Hub.

'Nibbler attack!' the sergeant screamed in his ear.

It was a scream which brought Greene to his senses: the steamer-crawler wasn't sinking; it was being *eaten* from below.

Greene grabbed his megaphone. 'Crew of Number 37, abandon crawler.' He turned back to his sergeant. 'Unhitch the mortar tow.'

'But, sir . . .' The look on the man's face was eloquent. To abandon the Krupps mortar they had struggled to bring all the way from London was an act of treason.

'Do as you're fucking well told, or we're all fucked!' screamed Greene, who had made the instant decision that facing a firing squad for dereliction of duty was infinitely preferable to being eaten alive by nanoBites.

The sergeant used his boot to kick open the coupling that connected the steamer-crawler to its tow and, free of its burden, the crawler jumped forward, almost toppling Greene off his perch. Now, without the dead weight of the mortar, the crawler began to power its way across the Hub at almost twelve miles per hour.

Greene leant down into the turret. 'BoilerMan,' he shouted at the top of his voice, since his megaphone was now serving as a nanoBite hors d'oeuvre, 'give me as much steam as you can. Your life depends on it!'

'But the boilers!'

'Fuck the boilers, just pour it on.'

A moment later the pistons began pounding back and forth even more frantically. Feeling a whole lot safer, Greene turned his attention back towards the crew escaping the stricken crawler 37. There were six of them sprinting across the hundred yards of open HubLand that separated their half-eaten steamer from Greene's vehicle. Army lore had it that nanoBites wouldn't attack a running man, as the contact his feet made with the surface was so fleeting that they didn't have time to react. But, like most army lore, this rumour turned out to be bollocks.

What happened to the fleeing crew members was horrible but simultaneously fascinating. Each of the escapees suddenly stopped dead, and then seemed to be sucked into the ground, all the while screaming as they were devoured by the nanoBites. And they were devoured surprisingly rapidly: by Greene's estimate, it took each man just twenty seconds to be converted from a living breathing human being into a stain on the ground.

The destruction of the crew of steamer-crawler 37 signalled a general awakening of the nanoBites and even travelling at twelve miles per hour, Greene's steamer-crawler wasn't immune from attack. Just two hundred yards from the sanctuary of Porte Saint-Martin, the machine suddenly staggered to a halt as its partially devoured tracks spun off. The munching sound of Nibblers at dinner enveloped the whole vehicle.

'Abandon crawler,' Greene screamed, not at all impressed with the hint of panic inflecting his voice. Determined to be the captain who *didn't* go down with his steamer, he leapt to the ground and, sobbing and crying, raced as fast as his boots would allow him towards Porte Saint-Martin.

When she had heard that he might be serving in the Hub, his mother had provided her beloved son with what the manufacturers called 'anti-Nibbler' boots, which, according to the promotional literature, guaranteed wearers ten minutes' immunity from nanoBite attack. The boots were equipped with solid steel platform soles four inches thick and, as Greene now discovered, they made running *very* difficult. He only hoped the manufacturer's estimate wasn't just advertising puff.

He made it, but only just.

As a sweat-soaked, exhausted and near-deranged Captain Jeremiah Greene staggered through Porte Saint-Martin to the safety of Paris, he found that the soles of his boots were gone, and two of his toes were missing. But he was alive.

Greene was the only survivor of the nanoBite attack on steamer-crawler Convoy Two.

## 17.30: The Champ de Mars

Beria found it a very long, a very boring and a very painful celebration.

The meandering procession through Paris had been a trial. For security reasons, Havelock had insisted that the bulletproof windows of the steamer remained sealed for the whole two-hour cavalcade, thus turning the cabin into a smoke- and cinder-filled sweat-box. When Beria finally alighted at the Champ de Mars, he was tired, dirty and his dress uniform had been reduced to a sweat-soaked rag that stuck to his body in a truly loathsome manner. His mood hadn't been helped by being confined for over an hour with a morose Heydrich and a nigh-on-hysterical Robespierre.

Beria also regretted not having used the bucket Havelock had placed in the cabin before he'd relinquished the privacy of the steamer, but the thought of pissing in front of Robespierre was inimical. In Beria's opinion, it didn't do for underlings to see their betters engaging in bodily functions, but in retrospect, not using the bucket might have been a mistake. He just hoped that he would be able to control his bladder for the rest of the celebrations.

The events preceding the speech-making seemed never-ending. The marching of the red-jacketed Guards was predictably flawless and predictably boring, and after half an hour watching them wheeling and turning in front of the VIP Stand and being forced to listen to the pounding of their infernal brass band, Beria found that his face had become set in a rictus of a smile and his head was near splitting with pain. But his head wasn't the only thing in danger of splitting: he really *had* to take a piss.

The dancers from the ForthRight ballet company were pleasant enough. The piece they performed was apparently called 'An Ode to UnFunDaMentalism' which promised to be deathly dull, but as the middle part showed girls clad in nothing much at all – supposedly representing 'ImPuritanism' – being chased around by a gang of lusty lads – supposedly representing 'UnFunDa-Mentalism' – it turned out to be a rather jolly affair. So much so that Beria made a mental note to have the entire chorus line – the girls, not the boys, since there seemed to be a dash too much of the zadnik about them for his liking – brought back to the Élysée Palace, where he would personally initiate them into the less publicised wonders of UnFunDaMentalism.

It was while Maurice Chevalier was yodelling to the gathered throng that Beria's urinary problems became almost unmanageable. He had never been overly fond of 'crooners' and what other, meagre, virtues this Chevalier item had as an entertainer were lost on Beria as he struggled to stop from wetting himself. He wondered if he might be able to slip away before the speeches began, but the stand in which the grandees were sitting was packed. To squeeze his way out in an unobtrusive manner was almost impossible, so his only alternative was to cross his legs and pray to ABBA that Chevalier got a move on.

After Chevalier came the speeches . . . the very *long* speeches.

Beria listened to the Leader's speech, with one hand in the pocket of his trousers. He hoped it made him look suitably stylish, but the real reason he did this was that it enabled him to use his thumb and forefinger to squeeze his penis, inflicting such pain on the organ that it persuaded his bladder to stop its moaning. Admittedly it did funny things to his voice, and

THE DEMI-MONDE SPRING | 408

when he replied to the inane questions being asked by the superannuated woman seated next to him, his answer came out abnormally high-pitched. But that was a small sacrifice to make: he was wearing light grey uniform trousers, and the prospect of the colour changing from grey to black in front of thirty thousand people – never mind hundreds of newspaper daguerreotypists – did not appeal.

Then Robespierre got up to speak.

## 17.35: The Quai d'Orsay

It was the proudest day of Captain Jenkins's life. The regiment's steamers had never looked better. The teams of cleaners, painters, panel-beaters and polishers delivered by Kruchkov's forewoman had done a marvellous job and now, as the one hundred and fifty steamers chugged their way along the Quai d'Orsay on their way to the Awful Tower, they shone and sparkled in the evening sunshine. The crowds standing on either side of their route had been enthusiastic too, but this he put down to the presence of a flag-waving Liberté perched on the front of each steamer. It was a shame that the flag-makers hadn't been able to deliver the new ones in time, but he guessed no one would notice the absence of the Valknut on the tricolores the girls were waving.

As the first steamer passed Avenue de Robespierre, he gave a toot on his whistle, a signal for the girls to insert the coloration tablets into their steamers' boilers. Within moments, the three columns of vehicles were shrouded in a haze of red, blue and green steam. And then the girls did something quite unrehearsed: they jumped down from the steamers and ran off into the crowd. As Jenkins was puzzling this over, the first of the steamers exploded.

## 18.05: The mansion of M. Claude Poisson, Bois de Boulogne

In anticipation of the fortune that would soon be his, Claude Poisson had secured – with the help of an unbelievably expensive mortgage – the much coveted mansion on the Bois de Boulogne. Into this he had installed – at unbelievable expense – Naughty Nancy. Now, with a glass of vintage Solution in his hand, he stood on the mansion's top-floor balcony, gazing out at the Awful Tower, ready to salute the edifice's last glorious act, before it was demolished tomorrow. In less than twenty-four hours the Awful Tower would be no more.

If he had been asked, Poisson would have admitted to just a *little* confusion regarding the authorities' attitude towards the Tower. On the one hand, all week the newspapers had been trumpeting that the Tower – tall, strong, imperious and very masculine – was the perfect symbol of UnFunDaMentalism. But on the other was the oh-so-pragmatic attitude evinced by the ForthRight's Monsieur Vanka Kruchkov, which would see it toppled and converted into weapons destined to help the war effort.

But in a way, he supposed, it made a sort of garbled sense. As Monsieur Kruchkov had explained, from tomorrow the Tower would become the embodiment of the sacrifice the ForthRight would be demanding of its citizens during the struggles to come.

Poisson took a sip of his Solution and turned to check the clock ticking so ponderously in the salon. The firework display would be starting in just a moment. 'Nancy,' he called, 'they'll be setting off the fireworks soon.'

He watched, lost to lust, as the girl oozed out of the salon, slowly and artfully unbuttoning her red blouse as she walked. As she shucked the blouse from her shoulders to display her magnificent breasts, Poisson decided that, expensive though she was, Nancy was worth every fucking – a *very* apt adjective – franc she was costing him. She came to stand next to him on the balcony, where she unfastened her skirt, letting it flutter to the floor and pool around her feet. Now, save for her stockings, she stood absolutely naked before him.

'The fireworks are about to start,' Poisson uttered in a strangled voice.

Nancy smiled. 'There's only one banger I'm interested in setting off, Claude,' and with that she dropped to her knees and began to untether the laces holding Poisson's red-and-pink-striped codpiece.

## 18.09: An apartment on the Champs-Élysées

Alain Brun arrived early at the address the wonderful Mademoiselle Norma Cartwright had given him for their tryst, his eagerness to partake of her succulent body overcoming the objections of his Current that he should be taking her to see the firework display. When the girl finally responded to Brun's impatient tapping on her door, she rewarded all his fervent imaginings by being dressed in a disturbingly tight and revealing gown of the deepest, most lascivious purple. Barely had the door closed before he was grappling with her, nuzzling at the copious amount of flesh she had on display, whilst simultaneously muttering confessions of undying love and lust.

But tease that the girl was, she would have none of it, insisting that their lovemaking must wait until she had seen the firework display. After all, she explained, her brother had contributed to its creation, had he not? And hadn't Alain himself told her what a spectacle it would be?

It was thus a sour Alain Brun who allowed himself to be

manoeuvred over to the window, which gave a splendid view of the Champ de Mars. His irritation was somewhat assuaged by Mademoiselle Norma making no objection to him fondling her splendid derrière while they waited for the show to commence.

## 18.10: The Champ de Mars

The twenty-five minutes that Robespierre spoke were without doubt the longest and most uncomfortable minutes of Beria's entire life, and during that time he developed an abiding hatred of the man. Indeed, in the course of Robespierre's seemingly never-ending speechifying the only way he could take his mind off the increasingly painful protests coming from his groin was to daydream about how he would torture the fucker if and when he ever stopped talking. He had just decided that death by asphyxiation via the use of molten lead being poured down the bastard's throat was his preferred option when, miraculously, Robespierre ended his speech.

'I would now like to call upon Comrade Leader Reinhard Heydrich and Vice-Leader Lavrentii Beria to sign the Declaration of Unification that will meld our two great Sectors together.' Robespierre looked towards Beria. 'Comrade Vice-Leader . . . if you would join me and the Comrade Leader here on the podium.'

Beria stood awkwardly. The pain in his penis was excruciating and he was sure that his face had gone bright red with the effort required to keep himself from pissing down his leg. He squeezed even harder on the tip of his cock, damming the urine and, by so doing, inflating the bloody thing to bursting point. But somehow he found the will to smile, and taking the pen he was offered by Robespierre, he scrawled his name at the bottom of the document.

'And now,' announced Robespierre in his horrible, piping

voice, 'I will present Comrade Vice-Leader Beria with the three keys to the city-states of Paris, Rome and Barcelona. I hand them over so that you may hold them in your safe keeping, as a symbol of our Union and our unity.'

Robespierre picked up a velvet cushion on which lay three golden keys, and thrust it towards Beria. Beria looked at the cushion as a rabbit might look at a fox. There was no way he could take it with only one hand: if he did that, he would undoubtedly drop the cushion, and that would be a diplomatic faux pas of cataclysmic proportions. Taking a deep, deep breath, and trying to stand sideways-on to the crowd, he released his grip on his penis and held out both hands to accept the proffered keys, wondering, as he did so, if he was the first man in the history of the Demi-Monde to take possession of three city-states while piping hot piss streamed down his leg. Further embarrassment was saved by the detonation of the fireworks.

## 18.16: The Champ de Mars

Senior CitiZen Maximilien Robespierre felt himself suffused by a glow of almost beatific satisfaction. The whole event – the procession, the marching, the dancers, Maurice Chevalier's singing and the speeches – had gone off perfectly, but the fireworks were a masterpiece. As he stood at the dais acknowledging the 'ooh's and the 'ahh's of the crowd – and one unfortunate 'arghhh' when a VIP was struck by an errant rocket – he knew that this ceremony would truly mark the moment when the Medi took UnFunDaMentalism to its bosom. If the ForthRight could conjure an event of such scale and of such stupendous spectacle, and manage it with such exactitude and efficiency, then none would be able to stand against it.

He was more than ever convinced that harnessing the

fortunes of the Medi to the rising star that was the ForthRight was the best thing for him to have done. Certainly, there were some wrinkles still to be ironed out in the relationship, but that was only to be expected. Once he'd had a longer tête-à-tête with Reinhard Heydrich, things would get sorted – not least of which would be putting this oaf Beria firmly in his place. The man stank: if Robespierre wasn't mistaken, there was a distinct whiff of urine about him. And the way he had scuttled off just as the fireworks were starting . . . the man was a boor!

A huge shower of sparkling lights erupted from all sides of the Tower as the firework display moved towards its crescendo. Feeling altogether satisfied with life, Robespierre waved benignly to the crowd and basked in the glory of their adulation.

## 18.18: A second apartment on the Champs-Élysées

In the apartment above the one occupied by Norma and Monsieur Alain Brun, Vanka, Burlesque, Odette and Rivets stood by the window, each taking a moment to enjoy a bumper of Solution.

'Good work, all of you.' said Vanka, raising his glass in a toast. 'We've helped strike a blow for Normalism, and we've done it without costing anyone their life.'

Burlesque said nothing, his eyes glued to the Tower. A quiet smile of satisfaction dressed his lips.

## 18.19: The Champ de Mars

Tomorrow, Beria decided – as he eased off his clammy and soaking-wet trousers and accepted the fresh pair his valet handed him – he would make Havelock suffer for the oversight of not providing toilet facilities for the VIPs. The only privacy he had been able to find in order to change was under the VIP Stand, and he was convinced that by tomorrow the gossip going around the ForthRight would have it that Comrade Vice-Leader Beria had been seen skulking beneath the stand while attempting to look up the skirts of the female dignitaries.

As he did up the final button of his flies and eased his way into a clean jacket, Beria was just grateful that the whole palaver was now coming to an end. Soon he would be back at the Élysée Palace, teaching a troupe of ballet dancers the *real* meaning of the expression 'reverse turn'.

## 18.20: The Champ de Mars

The Chef de Batterie breathed a sigh of relief as he came to the final four fuses. Lighting them, he gave himself a mental pat on the back: everything had gone amazingly well – almost *too* well. The fuses flared and he stood back to watch the grand finale.

And then things went terribly, terribly wrong.

The twin explosions that took out the left-hand pair of the four giant legs at the base of the Awful Tower were so enormous that they blew him off his feet and deposited him in a clump of rose bushes almost twenty metres from where he'd been standing. It took him a moment to recover from the shock and to wipe the dust and debris from his eyes. And what he saw when he'd done this was terrifying. From his seat in the bush, he watched in horror as the Awful Tower shuddered and then began to pivot gradually, gracefully, en route to destruction.

It was the second pair of explosions that ultimately did for the Chef de Batterie. These took out the two remaining legs of the Tower, shaking the ground sufficiently to send chunks of paving slabs flying through the air. It was a piece of pavement hitting him square between the eyes that caused the Chef de Batterie to lose any further interest in life.

## 18.21: The mansion of M. Claude Poisson, Bois de Boulogne

'*Merde*,' said Claude Poisson, watching in awed trepidation as the Awful Tower crumpled towards the ground twenty-four hours earlier than was planned. Even the ministrations of Naughty Nancy's marvellous mouth were insufficient to prevent him going flaccid with fear.

## 18.21: An apartment on the Champs-Élysées

'*Merde*,' said Alain Brun, shocked and stunned by the way the Awful Tower began to pitch forward. Instinctively he knew that this bitch Mademoiselle Norma had something to do with what was happening, but when he turned around she had vanished.

## 18.21: The Champ de Mars

'*Merde*,' breathed Senior CitiZen Robespierre, watching the great and supposedly indestructible Awful Tower shake for a moment under the impact of the explosions, and then begin to topple towards him. As best he could judge, it was going to land dead centre across the stand full of dignitaries. He was a dead man.

## 18.21: The Champ de Mars

Beria heard the sound of pounding feet above him as the panicking VIPs struggled to descend the stairs on either side of the stand. He knew instinctively that something bad was happening, but even he didn't expect that that something would be the arrival of 10,550 tons of premium-grade steel on top of his head. The last words Lavrentii Beria uttered, as he pissed himself for the second time that evening, were '*Yob tvoiu mati.*'

## 18.21: A second apartment on the Champs-Élysées

*Oh fuck*, thought Vanka, realising how pissed off Norma was going to be. The Awful Tower was toppling the *wrong* way: it was toppling *towards* the VIP Stand rather than away from it. This, he decided, was hardly passive resistance. Burlesque must have got the fuses muddled up.

## 18.21: A second apartment on the Champs-Élysées

*Fucking great*, thought Burlesque Bandstand, watching 10,550 tons of steel complete its descent onto Comrade Vice-Leader Beria's head. He raised his glass to salute the fucker's demise. Nobody fucked with Burlesque Bandstand and got away with it.

# 35

## The Grand Canal: Barcelona/Venice
## The Demi-Monde: 70th and 71st Days of Spring, 1005

TO DOCTEUR NIKOLAI KONDRATIEFF FUTURE HISTORY
INSTITUTE VENICE PO BOX 27/54 + + + CODE NOIR AGENT
REPORTS SUB ROSA DISCUSSIONS BETWEEN IMMANUAL AND
SELIM + + + COVERT OBJECTIVE OF IMMANUAL TO OPEN
TEMPLE OF LILITH IN NOIRVILLE HUB + + + IMPERATIVE
REPEAT IMPERATIVE COLUMN NOT ALLOWED TO BE TAKEN TO
TEMPLE + + + YR BEST ASSISTANCE IN THWARTING THIS IS
DEMANDED + + + ETHOBAAL

**PAR OISEAU**

*Copy of PigeonGram message sent by Doctor Jezebel Ethobaal*
*on 70th day of Spring, 1005*

Comrade General Mikhail Dmitrievich Skobelev's reputation within the army was that of being the bravest of the brave. Not the sharpest of blades, admittedly, but certainly the most courageous man in the whole of the ForthRight. But today Skobelev felt anything but brave. Watching the Leader stalk backwards and forwards across the floor of his office in the Élysée Palace, he knew that his life hung in the balance, and that the manner of his demise could be extremely messy. He had learnt, during his time as a member of the PolitBuro, that it was possible to gauge the Leader's state of anger by how loudly he spoke, and contrarily, the quieter he was, the angrier he was. And this morning Reinhard Heydrich was very quiet indeed: quiet and ghastly-looking.

The Leader had survived the fall of the Awful Tower by mere inches, but the debris that had showered down on him had left its mark. Even now, ten days after the attack, his head was still bandaged, his left arm was still supported by a sling, and deep bruising still covered most of the left side of his face. It had been a miracle he had survived, and that was exactly how it was being played in *The Stormer*: 'Great Leader Spared by Intervention of ABBA'.

Of course, the newspapers in the other Sectors had been rather less generous in their comments. A headline Skobelev had seen in the *Venetian Visualiser* still rankled: 'ForthRight Humbled as IMmanualists Bury Beria'.

*Bastards. Inaccurate and inflammatory!* It had been the Normalists who had done for Beria, not the IMmanualists.

'So, Skobelev,' the Leader began at length, in a voice barely more than a whisper, 'let me see if I correctly understand what happened during the Ceremony of Unification. Despite the best efforts of the Checkya, terrorists managed to infiltrate bombs into the Awful Tower, one of the most closely guarded structures in the entire Demi-Monde, and to detonate those bombs at the culmination of the ceremonies. Those explosions caused the Tower to collapse onto a stand packed with two hundred and fifty dignitaries especially invited to witness this demonstration of the ForthRight's strength. Am I correct thus far?'

'Yes, Comrade Leader.'

'Amongst those crushed to death were Comrade Vice-Leader Beria, two bishops from the Church of the Doctrine of UnFunDaMentalism, and a number of members of the Medi Senate – including Senior CitiZen Robespierre and Grand Inquisitor Torquemada. In total the butcher's bill was forty-five dead and seventy-three seriously injured. I suppose we should also add to the death toll those – like Commissar Havelock – who have been executed for their incompetence in permitting such an attack to take place. Is this an accurate summation of the humiliation the ForthRight has suffered?'

'Yes, Comrade Leader.'

'Compounding this, these same terrorists managed to penetrate army security and plant bombs in the boilers of ninety-five of our armoured steamers, and by doing so blow said boilers to buggery and beyond. At a stroke, our arsenal of serviceable armoured steamers has been halved. Is this also an accurate summation of the humbling experienced by the ForthRight?'

'Yes, Comrade Leader.'

'It also appears that the demolition of the Awful Tower was used as the signal for a general uprising against ForthRight forces occupying the Medi. I am informed that Paris, Rome and Barcelona are now . . .' Heydrich picked up a report from his desk and flicked through it to a marked page. '. . . in a state of "quiet uproar". *Quiet uproar*, Comrade General, is this a military term with which I am unfamiliar? Or perhaps it is a euphemism? Perhaps "uproar" means rebellion? Could it be that the Medi Districts are now in a state of rebellion against their legitimate and ABBA-ordained masters?'

Skobelev didn't like the way Heydrich was fingering the heavy crystal ashtray that rested on his desk. The man had a reputation for throwing things at those who annoyed him.

'It might be a little premature to classify it as "rebellion", Comrade Leader,' he stammered. 'Although the people are now following, en masse, the directions of the renegade Aaliz Heydrich . . .'

Skobelev prepared to duck, but Heydrich seemed indifferent to his daughter being termed 'renegade'.

'. . . what is taking place is more civil disorder than outright rebellion.'

'Disorder,' Heydrich mused, as he matched a cigarette and blew smoke towards the ceiling. 'I have an aversion to disorder, Comrade General. It is a Leader's task to bring certainty and precision to the running of the Sector he governs, and disorder indicates that he is failing in this duty.' Suddenly he hurled the ashtray at the wall, where it shattered with a loud bang. Skobelev ducked anyway: practice made perfect. 'I will not tolerate disorder in any part of the ForthRight. Do you understand me, Comrade General?'

'Yes, Comrade Leader.'

'This disorder will be crushed. The regular army will work in conjunction with the Checkya to eliminate all dissident factions in the Medi, and I do mean *all*. Any Medi CitiZen giving a member of the ForthRight forces of occupation so much as an unpleasant look is to be instantly shot.'

With a trembling hand, Heydrich raised a glass of Solution to his lips and took a long swallow. 'I have also learnt, since my release from the hospital yesterday, that thirty of our new Krupps mortars were lost in the Hub, eaten by nanoBites.'

There was no point in denying it. 'That is correct, my Leader. Although Convoy One, with thirty of the mortars, reached Paris safely . . .'

*Thank you, ABBA.*

'. . . Convoy Two was delayed and was still in the Hub when the nanoBites awoke from hibernation.'

'Am I right in supposing that the thirty mortars we saved are now deployed around Venice?'

'We are hopeful that they will be fully operational within ten days . . .'

'Mikhail Dmitrievich,' Heydrich interrupted, somewhat flummoxing Skobelev who had never been addressed in such familiar terms by the Great Leader, 'may I ask you a personal question?'

Skobelev spread his hands. 'Of course, Comrade Leader.'

'Good,' said Heydrich quietly. 'So tell me: are you tired of life?'

'I'm sorry?'

'I asked whether you are tired of life.'

'Why, no.'

'Then why the fuck are you giving me this shit? I don't want to hear "hopefully"!' Heydrich's voice rose to a scream. 'JUST TAKE FUCKING VENICE! BECAUSE IF YOU DON'T TAKE VENICE, I WILL HAVE YOU AND YOUR FAMILY SHOT. *NOW* DO YOU FUCKING UNDERSTAND?'

As Skobelev stood there shaking, he realised that he did indeed fucking understand.

'Yes, Comrade Leader.'

'I DEMAND that the destruction of Venice commences tomorrow.'

'Yes, Comrade Leader.'

*Fuck it.* Come Hel or high water, the bombardment would start tomorrow, otherwise Skobelev would ensure that his journey to the Spirit World was made in the company of every one of the officers serving on the Venetian front.

'Very well.' Heydrich took another, longer, swig of Solution. 'Now hear this, Skobelev. I want Venice pulverised in punishment for the insults the ForthRight has suffered at the hands of these Normalist terrorists. Do you understand?'

Skobelev nodded. His mouth was so dry that he seemed to have lost the power of speech.

The Great Leader fell silent for a moment, presumably steeling himself for what he was going to say next. 'There is more bad news. It would appear that the duplicitous Coven, sensing our weakness, is now refusing to supply coal to the ForthRight. This, as you will understand, Skobelev, is an unacceptable state of affairs, and hence we have no alternative but to *take* the coal we need by force. To do this, the ForthRight

Army must invade the Coven and seize its coal mines and it must do this by early Summer, before our coal stocks are exhausted.'

Inwardly Skobelev groaned. This wasn't just bad news, this was *fucking* bad news and not just because 'early Summer' was the time when the monsoon rains were at their heaviest. No, the big problem was that it would necessitate fighting a war on two fronts. It was the touchstone of all ForthRight foreign policy that everything be done to avoid having to fight two Sectors at once. That had been the cause of defeat in the Great War of 512, and no one wanted to revisit *that* particular level of political mortification.

'With the greatest of respect, my Leader, the army will find it difficult to deal with the subjugation of a recalcitrant Medi, the destruction of Venice *and* the invasion of the Coven. Our forces are stretched as it is.'

He got ready to duck.

Seemingly careless of Skobelev's concerns, Heydrich accepted a fresh cigarette and a new ashtray from an aide. Only then did he deign to reply. 'That is why, Comrade General, it is imperative that the current situation in the Quartier Chaud is brought to an expeditious conclusion and Venice is subjugated before the end of Spring. But do not overly concern yourself about the Coven. Our scientists in the ForthRight have not been idle and soon we will unleash an array of Vengeance Weapons the like of which have never been seen in the Demi-Monde. These will be used to vanquish all of the ForthRight's foes, including those LessBien witches in the Coven.' Heydrich smiled. It was a horrible smile. 'But whether you will be around to see their deployment, Skobelev, depends upon your success in taking Venice . . .'

Captain Jeremiah Greene shifted his weight on his walking sticks, trying to ease the aching of his foot. The doctors had told him that losing two toes wasn't that serious, that he'd be walking normally in three or four weeks and that he should think himself lucky to have avoided death by nanoBite. 'Lucky' wasn't quite the word Greene used when he woke up screaming in the middle of the night, tormented by nightmares of being eaten alive by Nibblers. His hair had gone white, too.

He was brought out of his reverie by a *crack*, as a shot rang out from the walls surrounding Venice.

*Fucking snipers.*

Building the gabions that protected the army's thirty remaining mortars from counter-fire by the Venetians had been hot work. The Venetians were no fools and had anticipated that they might one day be besieged from the Medi side of the Grand Canal, and hence had refused to permit any building encroaching nearer than one hundred yards to the Canal itself. It was in this empty killing zone that Greene's sappers had been building their gabions, which made them perfect targets for the Venetian snipers. In their rush to meet the deadline set by the Great Leader, the ForthRight Army had lost more than five hundred men building the gun emplacements. But now, thankfully, the mortars were in position.

As he cowered behind one of the emplacements, his officer, Major Yuri Borissov, came scuttling up. 'The bombardment will commence at dawn tomorrow,' Borissov advised his captain.

'But we're not ready! I think—'

'Don't think, Captain Greene,' his major snapped. 'Thinking is frowned on in the ForthRight Army. Here we celebrate obedience and sacrifice, and thinking is seen as a very Under-Mentionable trait.'

Greene gave a doleful nod, trying to keep his expression impassive as he did so. He might be stupid but he knew a warning when he was given one.

'And for your information, the bombardment *will* begin at

dawn tomorrow come what may. Any mortar crew unable to fire will be shot as traitors to UnFunDaMentalism. That is the express order of Comrade General Skobelev. Tomorrow, the ForthRight will begin its "Shock and Or" campaign against the pagan Venetians.'

'Shock and Or?'

'Yes. The weight of the bombardment and the unrelenting destruction visited on a city will be such that it *shocks* the population into understanding that resistance is futile.'

'And the "Or"?'

'That is the next stage: surrender *or* we will carry on pounding you to dogshit.'

'I see. And this is the military doctrine which will be initiated at dawn tomorrow?'

'Correct. We have thirty mortars each capable of firing a one-ton shell every ten minutes. This means that one hundred and eighty tons of high explosives will be landing on Venice every hour. Give it five days, Greene, and the place will have been blasted back to its Mantle-ite foundations. Venice will have ceased to exist.'

De Sade stood beside the Lady IMmanual atop the city walls gazing at the ForthRight Army scurrying like so many ants on the far side of the Grand Canal. This, he decided, was one of those pivotal moments in history: tomorrow the fate of the Demi-Monde would be decided. More . . . it would be the moment when he had to make up his mind whose side he was on. If he chose right, Venice could be his, but if he chose wrong . . .

He handed the Lady his telescope and pointed down to the huge stone and brick emplacements that the ForthRight Army – despite the best efforts of the Venetian sharpshooters – had succeeded in throwing up along the far side of the Grand Canal.

'Tomorrow morning, I reckon, my Lady. I've been watching

the UnFunnies' steamers chug back and forth for the last day or so, delivering mortar bombs. That means the attack must be imminent.'

'Mortars? That's unusual. They didn't use mortars when they attacked Warsaw.'

De Sade shrugged. 'Nasty pieces of work, mortars. The six or seven ranging shots the UnFunnies have fired did a Hel of a lot of damage; one of them took out most of the San Polo district. And our intelligence tells us they've got thirty of the brutes down there, enough to pulverise Venice to dust, and then some.'

'So what to do?'

'To save Venice? I think that will need one of your miracles, my Lady. Maybe you could destroy the ForthRight Army. Send a plague of poisonous locusts . . . that sort of thing.'

The Lady IMmanual smiled. It was really quite an unpleasant smile, one that betokened condescension and arrogance.

'I did promise the people of Venice that I would protect them from the ForthRight, didn't I? You really think that the only thing that can save Venice is a miracle?'

De Sade gave a nod.

'Then to perform a miracle it will be necessary for the Doge to issue orders that the Bank of Venice be cleared. I can only work my magic in a Blood Bank.'

'The Lady IMmanual hath requested that she be granted leave to enter the Bank of Venice, Your Most Reverend Excellency, and there to perform a ritual most strange and esoteric.'

'Vhy? To vot end?'

'It would seem that she hath the full intent of discomfiting the ForthRight Army that is now encamped beyond our walls,' answered Sister Florence.

'Unt how will she do zhis?'

'By the performing of a miracle.'

Doge Catherine-Sophia took a long swig of Solution and then lapsed into a fretful silence as she cogitated on this piece of disturbing intelligence. By the way her aura wavered Sister Florence could see that the burgeoning power of the Lady IMmanual was worrying the Doge. But then, she supposed, no one liked to be usurped, and the growing popularity of the Lady IMmanual made that eventuality ever more likely.

Oddly it was the events in Paris rather than in Venice that had reinforced the Lady IMmanual's reputation with the Venetian hoi polloi. Even though she had had nothing to do with the destruction of the Awful Tower and the assassination of Beria, the newspapers in Venice had given her the credit for inspiring the attack. *The Venetian Visualiser* had even gone so far as to suggest that it had been IMmanualists, *not* Normalists, who had perpetrated what it called 'this courageous and audacious humiliation of Heydrich and his thugs'. As the *Visualiser* suggested, the attack could hardly be the work of the non-violent Normalists if fifty people had been killed; rather it must have been that firm and resolute Defender of Freedom the Lady IMmanual who had done the deed. Thanks to the *Visualiser*, the Lady had been acclaimed as the saviour of Venice, and her prestige waxed while that of the Doge waned. The talk on the streets was that the Doge Catherine-Sophia should stand down, to make way for Doge IMmanual.

'Unt zhe aim of zhis miracle?'

'To make the most sudden and complete destruction of the artillery positioned on the far side of the Grand Canal, Your Most Reverend Excellency.'

The Sister watched the Doge struggle with the political implications of allowing the Lady IMmanual permission to attempt such a miracle. If she granted permission and the Lady was successful, then her own position as Doge would be untenable, but if she refused permission and the ForthRight Army was to bombard Venice, then her position as Doge would be forfeit. Heads the Lady won, and tails the Doge lost.

'Unt vhat is your opinion regarding zhis matter, good Zizter?'

'You have little option, my Doge, but to allow the Lady to save Venice. But I most earnestly entreat thee to mark the Lady IMmanual most carefully. She is not all that she wouldst have us believe her to be.'

'You have seen changes in her aura?'

Sister Florence nodded. 'When she did put Patrician Dandolo most brutally to the sword, for a fleeting instant I did perceive a darkening of her aura which, methinks, betokens deep connivance. Thus prompted, I have given much consideration to her these past days, and I now believe that she holds her true colours in most devious concealment.'

'Hmmmmp,' snorted an obviously dissatisfied Doge. 'You must zee, Zizter Florence, zhat I am unable to act merely on zuzpicion unt conjecture.'

'Prithee, my Doge, her actions, in claiming the success of the Normalists as her own, are not those of an honourable person.'

'No politician is honourable, Zizter; all of uz are adept at claiming credit for anozzer's success. Zhis is not zhe mark ov perfidiousness, merely zhe zignal zhat zhe Lady IMmanual is an accomplished statesvoman. If I chop her for zhat, I must chop every member of zhe Council of Ten.'

'My Doge, I beg thee, be most wary of this woman. Her aura is unique. Never have I seen an aura of such depth, of such intensity or of such brilliance . . .'

'But?' prompted the Doge.

Sister Florence stifled a smile. Drunk or not, Doge Catherine-Sophia had sensed the unsaid. 'The colour of her aura is strange. I have made close enquiry of the Convent's archives, but there is no account of any being possessèd of a silver aura. It is true the WhoDoo mambos associate the colour silver with those perverse creatures of mythology the Lilithi, but other than that there is no evidence to provoke my disquiet. But nevertheless, I am minded that whilst silver is most certainly a divine hue, it is also one which speaketh of that which is hard, unyielding, inhuman.'

'But if she is truly zhe Messiah, it is to be expected, is it not?, zhat she would have an unworldly cast.'

'Indeed, my Doge. Mayhap I am still befuddled by the gross experiences I did endure in Paris at the hands of the erstwhile assassin Zolotov. Mayhap my metaphysical senses are disturbed, but now when I gaze on the Lady I am possessèd not by a sense of being uplifted but rather by a sense of dread.'

'I need more conclusive proof zhan zhat of her ill intentions.'

'Then I must see her in congress. Only then will her true aura be all revealèd.'

'But how? You tell me zhat she has avoided all pleasures ov zhe flesh zince she came to Venice.'

'And that in itself is of the greatest significance, my Doge. Methinks she is thus contrary in order to prevent her aura being examined at the point of orgasm.'

'Maybe Daemons don't like to be vatched vhilst zhey are fucking?' The Doge paused to take a long, reflective sip of her Solution. 'But you Visual Virgins are experts in zhe erotic arts, are you not? Perhaps you could arrange things zo zhat zhe Lady IMmanual is unable to resist zhe overtures of her vould-be lovers. Zhere are aphrodisiacs, are zhere not?'

'But their use is illegal, my Doge! ImPuritanism demands that erotic acts are unsullied by artificial excitements.'

'Pah! In matters of state security nothing is illegal. Zee to it, good Zizter. Perhaps ve should perform zhis interrogation by seduction on Walpurgisnacht?'

'It is the most cunning of suggestions, Your Most Reverend Excellency . . .'

Sister Florence let her sentence trail away. There really was no need to finish. Walpurgisnacht was the night that marked the end of Spring and the advent of Summer and, as was traditional in Venice, it was the night for role reversal, when the women portrayed Evil and the men Good, and everyone had an enjoyable time as Good came – during the course of a very tiring night – to dominate Evil.

'To do this, we must employ a most subtle seducer, my Doge, one who is much blessed by ABBA in the arts of amatory allurement. A *fortissimo*-class love-maker. Might I suggest Giacomo Casanova?'

Though there was still an hour remaining before dawn, a large and hushed crowd waited patiently as the Lady IMmanual and de Sade climbed the huge stairway leading to the bank's massive front doors, the word having gone out that the Lady was to perform her promised miracle and save the city from destruction. De Sade was surprised there were so few Signori di Notte agents on hand to protect the Lady but then he supposed that nowadays she didn't need protection. Anyone moving against the Messiah would be torn apart by the mob. Not a pretty way to die and he shuddered at the thought of it.

Inside, the bank was eerily silent: all the screens in the transfusion booths were still and the only sound, as the couple walked into the hall, was the echoing clack of their footsteps reverberating around the colossal chamber.

'This is one big bank.'

'Indeed, my Lady, it is the biggest bank in all of the Demi-Monde, bigger even than the banks in Warsaw and in Berlin.' De Sade pointed towards the domed ceiling far, far above their heads. 'It's so big that clouds have been known to form in the bank's cupola.'

The Lady IMmanual shivered in the chilled air. 'Which booth shall we use?'

De Sade laughed. 'Any you wish. We're the bank's only customers.'

The Lady wandered over to the nearest booth and placed her hand into the indented shape to the left of the booth's keyboard. Immediately the screen set into the wall in front of her began to operate, the sound of the symbols as they rotated filling the hall with their clattering.

**THE BANK OF VENICE WELCOMES**
**ELLA THOMAS**
**PLEASE ENTER YOUR PASSWORD**

The Lady IMmanual typed her answer too quickly for de Sade to see what her password was, but whatever it was, it worked.

**PASSWORD ACCEPTED**

Immediately the screen prompted:

**WHICH SERVICE DO YOU REQUIRE?**
1.      WITHDRAWALS
2.      DEPOSITS
3.      TRANSFERS
4.      OTHER

The Lady hit the '4' button and then typed:

**IM MANUAL**

The response from the screen was instantaneous. The letters twirled again.

PLEASE BE ADVISED ELLA THOMAS THAT YOU HAVE GRADE 8 (CAPTAIN OR ABOVE) STATUS. IN ACCOR-DANCE WITH PROTOCOL 57 THIS ALLOWS SUCH INDIVIDUALS, WHEN DEPLOYED IN THE DEMI-MONDE[®] AND FACED BY MORTAL DANGER, TO MAKE EMER-GENCY ONE-HOUR CHANGES TO THE DEMI-MONDE'S CYBER-MILIEU. IN ORDER TO PRESERVE THE DUPES' PERCEPTION OF THE LOGICALITY OF THE DEMI-MONDE[®] SUCH CHANGES MAY <u>NOT</u> VIOLATE THE NATURAL LAWS PREVAILING IN THE DEMI-MONDE[®]. ALSO NOTE THAT BEFORE SUCH CHANGES ARE MADE PERMANENT THEY MUST BE RATIFIED BY THE DEMI-MONDE[®] STEERING COMMITTEE. IF SUCH RATIFICATION IS NOT RECEIVED BEFORE ONE HOUR HAS ELAPSED, THE AMENDMENT TO THE CYBER-MILIEU WILL BE ANNULLED.
PLEASE ENTER 'YES' IF THESE CONDITIONS ARE UNDERSTOOD AND ACCEPTED.

The Lady IMmanual pressed 'YES', and de Sade was surprised to see her give a sigh of relief. It was as though she had been half-expecting that ABBA would deny her, and she would no longer be able to work her magick, but she quickly recovered her equanimity. A list of choices relating to the **AMENDMENT OF CYBER-MILIEU CHARACTERISTICS** spun up on the screen, from which the Lady selected:

14.     SCALAR CHARACTERISTICS

A moment later came the instruction:

**PLEASE USE THE MUTOSCOPE VIEWER**

The Lady IMmanual leant forward and spent several seconds looking into the viewer, then, sensing de Sade's curiosity, she beckoned him to take her place. Peering through the viewer, de Sade saw that ABBA had displayed a map of the Demi-Monde which showed the world's principal topographical features.

'Look at the Grand Canal,' he heard the Lady IMmanual whisper in his ear, and out of the corner of his eye he saw her fingers roll a ball set into the keyboard. Immediately the map shown in the mutoscope viewer changed, the viewer focusing in on a smaller and smaller area. It was as if he was tumbling down from the heavens towards the Demi-Monde beneath – tumbling until he found himself looking at an area that encompassed just the Grand Canal, the detail so precise and so wonderfully rendered that he might be looking down from a balloon.

The Lady IMmanual worked the ball again, and immediately the edge of the Grand Canal was highlighted.

'Now watch,' the Lady ordered, then once again she flexed her fingers over the ball and, magically, the Grand Canal was shown wider. Astonished, de Sade stood away from the viewer and watched as the letters rolled.

**WHEN IS THIS SCALAR AMENDMENT TO THE GRAND CANAL TO BE INITIATED?**

The Lady checked her watch and then her fingers worked the keyboard:

**IN 47 MINUTES**

Dawn!

CONFIRMED

'It's done, de Sade, and soon the guns threatening Venice will be lying at the bottom of the Grand Canal.'

De Sade smiled. 'Now that, my Lady IMmanual, is something I have just *got* to see.'

And so, it seemed, did the rest of Venice.

'I don't understand,' said Captain Jeremiah Greene, as he scanned the walls of Venice shortly before dawn.

'What don't you understand, Captain?' asked Major Borissov as he finished his first cigarette of the day and flicked the butt away, the sparks flaring pink in the pre-dawn darkness.

'I don't understand, Major, what all those Venetians are doing standing along the top of the walls.'

'All *what* people?' said the major, as he snapped open his own telescope and used it to examine the walls that ran along the far bank of the Grand Canal, some half-mile or so away.

Atop the walls there were thousands of Venetians standing, gazing towards the ForthRight Army making its final preparations to bombard the city. They made a disturbing sight: it was as though they were waiting for something special to happen but what that special something was, Greene didn't have a clue. All he knew was they really put the wind up him.

'What are they looking at?' asked Major Borissov, as he made a surreptitious check that his fly was firmly buttoned. 'They must be mad.'

'Maybe they think it'll be safer up there on the wall than in the city proper,' suggested Greene. 'Maybe they know that our mortar shells will clear the wall.' He made another quick study of the spectators through his telescope. 'It's bloody spooky, if you ask me.'

It was a sentiment shared by most of the other ForthRight

soldiers gathered on the bank of the Canal. There were mutterings about 'witches' and 'miracles', and the men began to cluster more closely behind the gabions. One or two of them made the sign of the Valknut across their chests, to ward off the evil eye.

Major Borissov looked around and obviously didn't like what he was seeing. He pulled out his watch to check the time. Thankfully it was only a few minutes to dawn.

'Prime mortars,' he shouted, and the gun crews scurried to their weapons, stuffing pieces of ragged cotton into their ears as they ran: mortars were noisy brutes. Once there, they hauled the tarpaulins from their guns, made sure that the firing charges were in place and then loaded the guns with shells. Then the gunners took hold of their firing ropes and turned to the major, waiting for his instruction to fire.

'Prepare to fire!'

Major Borissov raised his arm and the gunners drew the slack from their firing ropes.

'Four!' shouted the major. 'Three! Two! O . . .'

It was a peculiar sensation. One moment Captain Greene was standing on a hard-paved surface and the next . . . he wasn't. Instead, he found himself splashing around in the middle of the Grand Canal. But he was in good company. The rest of the ForthRight Army, and their guns and their horses and their steamers, seemed to have joined him in enjoying an early morning dip.

*How peculiar*, he mused, as he heard the cheers of the Venetians drifting across to him from the other side of the Canal. *Perhaps I should have learned how to swim.*

# Part Five
# Walpurgisnacht

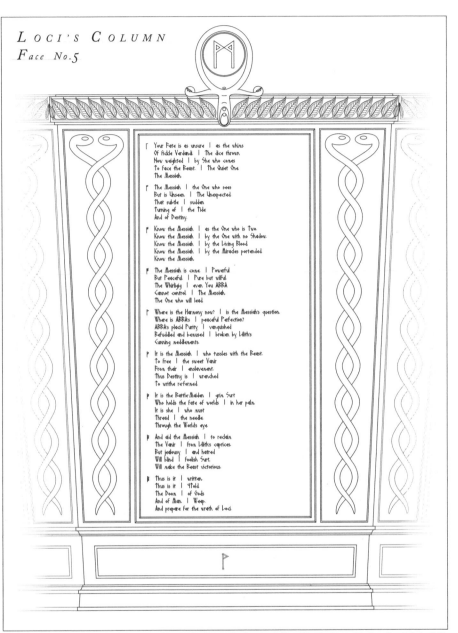

*LOCI'S COLUMN*
*FACE NO.5*

Your Fate is as unsure | as the whims
Of fickle Verdandi | The dice thrown
Now weighted | by She who comes
To face the Beast. | The Quiet One.
The Messiah.

The Messiah | the One who sees
But is Unseen. | The Unexpected
That subtle | sudden
Turning of | the Tide
And of Destiny.

Know the Messiah | as the One who is Two.
Know the Messiah | by the One with no Shadow.
Know the Messiah | by the Living Blood
Know the Messiah | by the Miracles portended
Know the Messiah.

The Messiah is come | Powerful
But Peaceful. | Pure but wilful.
The Whirligig | even You ABBA
Cannot control | The Messiah.
The One who will lead.

Where is the Harmony now? | is the Messiah's question.
Where is ABBA's | peaceful Perfection?
ABBA's placid Purity | vanquished
Befuddled and bemused | broken by Lilith's
Cunning meddlements.

It is the Messiah | who tussles with the Beast.
To free | the sweet Vanir
From their | enslavement.
Thus Destiny is | wrenched
To writhe reformed.

It is the Battle-Maiden | grim Surt
Who holds the fate of worlds | in her palm.
It is she | who must
Thread | the needle
Through the Worlds eye.

And aid the Messiah | to reclaim
The Vanir | from Lilith's caprices.
But jealousy | and hatred
Will blind | foolish Surt,
Will make the Beast victorious.

Thus is it | written.
Thus is it | 9Told.
The Doom | of Gods
And of Men. | Weep.
And prepare for the wrath of Loci.

*Diagram and translation reproduced by kind permission of Snore Igbolinn, Cartographer-General to the Court of Her Most Reverend Excellency, Doge Catherine-Sophia*

# THE EDDIC OF LOCI 5: THE COMING OF THE MESSIAH
PLATE 5

# 36

## New York Hospital's Drug Dependency Center: New York
## The Real World: 3 October 2018

The attack on Edinburgh was carried out in order that the citizens of the decadent and anti-Christian countries led by Babylon Britain were punished for having spawned the Great Beast. This abomination, which the infidel British call ABBA, was foretold in the Seventh Prophecy of Prophet Kenton the First. The Beast seeks to control and conquer the peoples of the world, and to do this in the name of Satan. We, Christ's Crusaders, will not rest until the Beast and its Master, the AntiChrist, have been destroyed and cast back into the Pit from whence they came. This is our First Act.

*Transcript of the Polly broadcast made by Christ's Crusaders immediately following the execution of the 'Dirty Nuke' terrorist attack on the city of Edinburgh, Scotland on 12 December 2014*

As Joyce Taylor described it, Aaliz's Polly confrontation with Clare Collins had 'kicked up a shit storm', with celebrity PollyMorphing becoming the number-one topic of searches on the Polly and any number of 'before and after' outings of PollyCelebrities taking place. Norma Williams became simultaneously the most popular *and* the most reviled Polly personality on the planet, but as Joyce Taylor observed, 'as long as they're talking about you, it really doesn't matter what they're saying'. But, fortunately for Aaliz's peace of mind, when Septimus Bole had ABBA make an examination of the Polly chatter, it seemed that the words most often used in connection with Norma Williams were 'honest', 'upfront' and 'ballsy', and that, as far as Aaliz was concerned, was a fine result.

So it came as no surprise that a veritable herd of reporters, accompanied by a swarm of hovering CameraBots, were waiting for Aaliz when she arrived at New York Hospital's Drug Dependency Center two days later.

She was greeted by the head of the hospital, a miserable-looking man going by the name of Milton Lord. 'The hospital isn't used to suffering this sort of mayhem, Miss Williams,' he said as he pushed his way through jostling reporters, 'and I trust that the hospital board hasn't been duped into cooperating in some cheap publicity stunt.'

'Oh, believe me, Dr Lord, this is all deadly serious. Do you have your candidate patients ready?'

'Yes. ParaDigm's lawyers have had them sign their disclaimers and your friend Septimus Bole has sent the indemnity I asked for, so everything is in order. You have some powerful friends, Miss Williams.'

'Just as long as I'm able to operate under controlled conditions. I don't want there to be any dispute as to the validity of the results.'

'I am afraid you are being a little disingenuous, Miss Williams. We could have Jesus Christ and all of heaven's angels supervising your little experiment, and there would still be those who refuse to believe. But having said that, the way things have been organised should keep scepticism to a minimum.'

The doctor described how this would be achieved at the press conference. 'The hospital was asked to provide an environment whereby the ability to eradicate addictive behaviour claimed by

Miss Williams could be tested under controlled, scientific conditions – conditions which precluded cheating or connivance. To ensure this, twenty patients were selected by lot from the hospital's inmate population and given the chance to participate in this trial. All, I am happy to say, volunteered.'

*Hardly surprising*, Aaliz mused, *considering how much they were offered by ParaDigm.*

'The names of these volunteers,' the doctor went on, 'were withheld from Miss Williams and her representatives until one hour ago, when certain legal formalities had to be finalised. Since that time the volunteers have been held incommunicado, supervised by the hospital's own eyeSpies. It is my intention to have one of the members of the press corps gathered here today draw a number which will correspond with the patient to be treated by Miss Williams. I will now place counters inscribed with the numbers one to twenty into this bag.' Having done this, Dr Lord held the bag out at arm's length towards the audience of media hacks. 'Would one of you care to select the patient who will assist Miss Williams in her experiment?'

It was one of the younger and prettier of the assembled journalists who was finally persuaded to draw one of the lots. 'Fourteen,' she announced, before returning to her chair and to media obscurity.

Dr Lord turned to the Flexi-Plexi behind him and activated his Polly. 'Please display the details of patient number fourteen.' Immediately a 3D image of a man – thirtyish, quite podgy and with a face that had a bashed-about look to it – appeared on the wall. 'This is patient Burl Standing, six-month resident of our intensive care wing. Part of Standing's sentence for pimping and drug dealing was commuted on condition that he received treatment for his Zip addiction, but unfortunately he has failed to respond to counselling, therapy or medication. Whilst disappointing, this is not unexpected. Zip addiction is particularly tenacious, and Standing – emotionally, physically and neuro-logically – is hi-dependency-profiled. He volunteered for "treatment" by Miss Williams in an attempt to avoid transfer to prison.'

Aaliz ignored the clamour of questions that followed, and instead just sat gazing at the image of Burl Standing. The man seemed vaguely familiar, and she racked her brain as to when and where she might have met him in the Demi-Monde. And as Septimus Bole had ensured that the NowLived selected for duplication in the Demi-Monde were *all* 'hi-dependency-profiled', the chances were that she *had* met him.

Aaliz had never been inside a prison hospital before and she decided, very soon after her entry into its sealed environment, that she never wanted to be inside one again. Everything was so confined, which, she acknowledged as she walked along the corridor, was pretty much to be expected.

Not that there was anything else particularly objectionable about the New York Hospital's Drug Dependency Center. They had done their best to disguise the functionality of the building, but inevitably it was decorated in the creams and whites that seemed de rigueur for all such institutions, whether they were in the Real World or in the Demi-Monde. It was also very quiet; the whole atmosphere was hushed and thoughtful. The hospital seemed to be holding its breath, which Aaliz didn't find alto-gether surprising: the smell pervading the place was pretty intense, urine and disinfectant seemingly locked in a battle for supremacy, with urine ahead by a nose.

The orderly accompanying Aaliz stopped in front of a door indistinguishable from the myriad of others lining the corridor. 'This is it, Miss,' he announced. 'Just to remind you: your conver-sation with Standing will be monitored and recorded and should the subject matter of this conversation be deemed, at any time, prejudicial to the rehabilitation or the quiescence of the patient, the conversation will be terminated.'

The orderly placed his hand, palm down, on the wall-mounted scanning pad. Immediately the heavy steel door clicked open.

Taking a deep, calming breath, Aaliz assumed the look of benign understanding she thought most appropriate for her role as saviour and then walked through the open door into the interview room. By agreement with Dr Lord, she was to meet with the patient alone, so when the door closed behind her, she found herself standing in the room with just Burl Standing, five CameraBots and one GuardBot for company.

Burl Standing was lounging on a chair set behind the Impeno-Glaz screen that bifurcated the room. He looked up at Aaliz and smiled. 'Well, bugger me wiv a pineapple, but they didn't tell me that you'd be quite so tasty. Fings is looking up. Nice tits, luv.'

'I didn't realise that you were British, Mr Standing.'

'Burl, call me Burl. And yeah, I'm a Brit, but don't let that put you off.' He smiled a gappy smile. 'So wot do I call you?'

'You can call me Norma.'

'Norma? I like that. You must be the bird wot's come to save me?'

'I've come to help you conquer your addiction to Zip, if that's what you mean, Mr Standing.'

'Burl.'

'Burl.'

'Well, luv, all I can say is that wiv a chassis like yours you can experiment on me any time you fucking well like.'

Aaliz studied Standing carefully. She had expected him to be a dull-witted wreck of a man but instead he seemed almost *too* sharp and alert. There was an intelligent twinkle in his eye that Aaliz found a little disconcerting. This Burl Standing fellow wasn't as stupid as he liked to pretend he was.

Aaliz nodded to the Get-Me-Straighter Meter that sat on the table in front of the Impeno-Glaz screen. 'Shall we begin?'

Standing rapped his knuckles on the armoured screen. 'I think there's something coming between us. Yous gonna have to raise this, luv, iffn you want me to use that box ov tricks ov yours.'

Aaliz nodded towards the GuardBot hovering at her shoulder. 'Before I do that, Burl, you should be aware that I am protected by one of ParaDigm's new GuardBots. It is constantly scanning you for changes in micro-expressions, in pheromonic activity and in skin temperature. Should these changes indicate that you are preparing to assault me, the GuardBot will make a pre-emptive strike, injecting you with a potent but non-lethal sedative.'

'Yeah, yeah, yeah. Shall we get on with it?'

Aaliz blinked towards her Polly, and the Impeno-Glaz screen sighed up into the ceiling. 'You have been prepped, Burl?'

'If you mean those drops they put in me eyes, then yes, I 'ave.'

'Excellent. The drops will dilate the pupils to make you more visually receptive to the modifications I will make to your life force.' Standing gave a careless nod, and Aaliz breathed a silent prayer of thanks to ABBA. With the PINC implant in place, Standing was now amenable to behavioural modification. This was the real secret of the Get-Me-Straighter Meter: the use of advanced and highly illegal implants designed not just to supplement the functioning of the brain but to *alter* it.

'Would you grip the two handles on your side of the Get-Me-Straighter Meter, Burl, and then look into the viewer? There will be a flash of light, but don't be alarmed. It's only to help enhance your psychic concentration.'

Complete nonsense, of course: the light was simply to activate Standing's PINC, but it was rigmarole necessary to satisfy the Polly hacks who would be watching proceedings via the CameraBots.

With a crooked smile for the cameras, Standing did as he was told, and once he was properly settled, Aaliz bent forward to look through the eyepiece on her side of the Get-Me-Straighter Meter. 'Are you ready, Burl?'

'Yus.'

Aaliz pressed a button on the side of the Meter, flashing the hi-intensity light into Standing's eyes and switching on the PINC embedded in his brain. She knew that as they sat there, PINC would be working at enormous speed to alter the messages flickering between synapses, and to moderate the responses of Standing's brain to dopamine stimulation, making it less welcoming to the appetitive motivations caused by Zip. 'If you will concentrate on my voice, Burl.' There was no response – the whole of Burl Standing's attention being directed to the instructions flashing up at subliminal speed before his eyes. Now it was time for Aaliz to perform.

'You have been addicted to Zip, Burl, but from this moment on you will loathe it and you will find that you do not miss inhaling it. From this moment on you will find God entering your life and cleansing you of this perverse appetite. Do you feel God inside you, Burl?'

Prompted by an instruction from PINC, Burl Standing muttered a distant 'Yeah.'

'Then I will count to three, and on the final count you will be free of your addiction. One . . . two . . . three.'

Burl Standing slumped back in his chair, and then drew his hand over his sweat-drenched forehead. 'Jesus . . .'

'How do you feel, Burl?'

'Different . . . better.' He looked up and shook his head, obviously not quite believing what had happened to him. 'That wos really amazing. It wos like someone got inside my 'ead and straightened my brain out. Got rid of all the tangles and the knots that were stopping me thinking proper.'

'That's why it's called the Get-Me-Straighter Meter, Burl, because it gets you thinking straight. You've just let God into your life, and God has rewarded you by lifting the burden of addiction from your soul.'

'Hallelujah.'

# 37

## The Future History Institute: Venice
## The Demi-Monde: Walpurgisnacht, 90th Day of Spring, 1005

JOSEPHINE BAKER VENICE PO BOX 13/26 + + + DEAREST
JOSIE + + + IMPERATIVE REPEAT IMPERATIVE U ENSURE
MR SCRATCH IS NOT TAKEN BY THE BEAST + + + BRING HIM
SAFE TO THE JAD + + + ONLY HE CAN DEFEAT THE POWER
OF DARKNESS + + + B STRONG B COOL B CAREFUL + + +
MAMBO JEZEBEL

**PAR OISEAU**

*Copy of PigeonGram message sent by Doctor Jezebel Ethobaal*
*on 83rd day of Spring, 1005*

Watching Vanka Maykov wolf down a dish of *brodetto di pesce*, Kondratieff found himself wondering just who – or what – Vanka Maykov actually was. He looked normal enough – two arms, two legs and a notable intelligence – but there was no denying that the man was a real puzzlement.

He was undoubtedly a Singularity – one of those special individuals who made a significant impact on Future History – but he was a bloody *odd* Singularity. The computators working in the Institute kept voluminous records of all those in the Demi-Monde who were deemed to be Singularities in order that their actions and proclivities might be understood and then incorporated into HyperOpia. Unfortunately, the file they had on

Vanka Maykov was embarrassingly thin. The information they had on him, prior to his sudden appearance in the Winter of 1000, could be summed up in one word: *absent*. He had materialised out of nowhere.

But there was more to it than simply this dearth of information. After they had input what sparse data they had on the man, HyperOpia had rejected them on the grounds that Vanka Maykov didn't exist. Most odd. And then there was Sister Florence's observation that he had no aura. He was a man with no past, no present and no aura.

Strange . . .

Nikolai Kondratieff had a natural aversion to anything 'strange'. 'Strange' generally meant that the subject under examination simply refused to be decontextualised, and for a machine like the DAEmon, which had – understandably – a somewhat mechanistic and constructuralist outlook on life, this was a problem.

Looking at the man, as he carelessly mopped up the last vestiges of his soup with a piece of bread, Kondratieff had the sinking feeling that Vanka Maykov was the living embodiment of the term 'strange'. Kondratieff worried that 'strange' might be a euphemism for 'irredeemably inDeterminate'. And a free spirit like Vanka Maykov had the ability to overturn all their carefully finessed Temporal Interventions – the tweaks to Future History – that he and de Nostredame had been executing . . . 'executing' being the operative word.

And it wasn't just him who found Vanka Maykov so perplexing. Jezebel Ethobaal had evinced a great deal of interest in the man, especially since Kondratieff had sent her the translation of the Eddic of Loci. The woman was desperate to get Maykov to the JAD so that she and her fellow WhoDooists could examine him more closely. And Kondratieff was fast coming to the conclusion that a holiday in the JAD might be the best thing both for Maykov and for the future of the Demi-Monde. Ethobaal was, after all, the Demi-Monde's greatest exponent of Lilithian lore, so if she thought Vanka Maykov had a vital role to play in the struggle to defeat the Lady IMmanual, who was he to deny her?

The trick would be getting Maykov to the JAD alive.

'I am surprised that you have returned to Venice, Monsieur Maykov,' Kondratieff admitted, 'returned *voluntarily*, that is. You *are* aware that the *lettre de cachet* for your arrest is still in force?'

Maykov shrugged to show his indifference. He was one of those annoying people who could imbue a shrug with a multitude of meanings. He was a Demi-Monde-class shrugger.

Kondratieff tried again. 'It must have been difficult to enter the city.'

Maykov shook his head. 'No. I got across the Canal just after Ella performed her Miracle of the Canal, when the GrandHarms guarding the Rialto Docks had better things to do than protect Venice from ne'er-do-wells like me. They were so blood-drunk that they didn't even see my gondola land in Venice.'

'Mademoiselle Williams did remarkably well in the Medi,' Kondratieff observed casually. 'The destruction of the Awful Tower sent a powerful message around the Demi-Monde. It signalled that the ForthRight is not invincible.'

*That damned shrug again.*

He tried another tack. 'So tell me, what are her plans now?'

'Norma's thinking about returning to the Rookeries, and spreading the word about Normalism there.'

'Striking at the very heart of UnFunDaMentalism, eh? A brave strategy and, I imagine, a very dangerous one. I am surprised that you have left her side at such a crucial time.'

'She doesn't need me. She's got Burlesque Bandstand and Odette Aroca looking after her . . .'

*Now there's a couple whose files are growing thicker by the minute.*

'. . . and anyway, I went to the Medi reluctantly, Docteur. I went to help Norma and by doing that help Ella. I went there to show that violence wasn't the only way of resisting the ForthRight. And now I've accomplished this, it's time for me to try to convince Ella – the Lady IMmanual – that there is an alternative to war and violence.'

'The impression I have is that the Lady IMmanual really doesn't need or want your advice, Monsieur Maykov. In your absence, she has become something of a force here in Venice . . . there are even those calling for her to be awarded the Dogeship. Since she performed the Miracle of the Canal, people are more convinced than ever that she is the Messiah. No, Monsieur Maykov, trying to persuade the Lady IMmanual to change is an exercise in futility.'

'You don't understand, Docteur. I love the woman.'

The problem was that Kondratieff *didn't* understand. He had always had difficulty with the more intense human emotions: they were so very InDeterminate. As best Kondratieff could judge, love caused the rational functions of the mind to become paralysed, and, being a man who had dedicated his life to making the irrational rational, he had given love a very wide berth. Love was a perplexing phenomenon – perplexing and potentially very dangerous.

'I want to speak to Ella,' Maykov persisted, 'to tell her how successful Norma has been with her policy of Normalism, to tell her that, with the ForthRight in retreat, there's no need for her to go on playing the Lady IMmanual.'

'I think you are being a little optimistic regarding the defeat of the ForthRight, Monsieur Maykov – my own belief is that Heydrich still has a few shots left in his locker. Moreover, civil disobedience and passive resistance don't seem to be very popular with the Lady IMmanual, violence does. I understand that she is intent on forging an alliance with NoirVille to fight the ForthRight.'

'Ella is not a person who embraces war and violence. War, it seems, beckons.'

'But the Lady IMmanual is.'

'I have to speak to Ella.'

'And if she won't listen?'

Maykov lapsed into a fretful silence as he pondered this unpalatable possibility.

Kondratieff found it quite sad to see how forlorn the man was, especially as HyperOpia predicted that the only things capable of preventing the Lady IMmanual from following the path leading to Demi-Monde-wide war and destruction were the Messiah . . . and the Lady's assassination. Despite what Ethobaal claimed, Kondratieff's opinion was that any impact Maykov would have on this OutCome would be nugatory.

Kondratieff tried again. 'I repeat: your place is at the side of Mademoiselle Williams.'

'My place is with Ella.' Vanka Maykov looked straight into Kondratieff's eyes. 'I *must* speak with her. And to do that I need your help, Nikolai. It's impossible to get into the Palace without a warrant.'

Kondratieff thought for a moment, his fine brain chewing over the possible OutComes. In a way it was quite refreshing to be faced by a conundrum like Vanka Maykov, which the DAEmon *couldn't* help him with, and to have to rely on his own intellect for once. And what his cogitations and the increasingly urgent advice of Jezebel Ethobaal told him was that it was better to help Vanka Maykov, and therefore know what the man was going to do, than to deny him such assistance and then have him do something *very* unorthodox.

And maybe it would be better to help him see his beloved

Ella. Maybe if he was to see her as she truly was, the scales of love would fall from his eyes.

'Very well, I will appeal to the Doge on your behalf. My belief is that the best time to visit the Lady IMmanual will be tonight, during the Walpurgisnacht celebrations.'

The chamberlain ushered Nikolai Kondratieff into the Receiving Chamber, where he was to attend the Doge. When he saw her, it took all of his self-control to prevent the shock showing on his face. He could see that the woman had aged alarmingly, the travails she had been subjected to of late seemed to have drained her of all her strength and vitality.

'Your message said you had zomething of "great urgency" to discuss mit me, Kondratieff.' She flapped a tired hand to indicate that he should seat himself.

'Indeed, Your Excellency. I have had a visit from the Lady IMmanual's former lover, the Russian Vanka Maykov.'

'But I understand zhat zhere is a *lettre de cachet* for his arrest in force.'

'That is correct, Your Excellency, but Maykov is a very reckless individual who is somewhat indifferent to legal niceties.'

'So vhat does zhis rogue want?'

'To speak with the Lady IMmanual. He is worried she has become besotted with violence. He is of the opinion that she has "changed", and that she has fallen under the influence of unprincipled men.'

The Doge gave an unhappy laugh. 'He might be right zhere. As "unprincipled men" go, zhere are few as unprincipled az zhe Marquis de Sade.'

'Indeed, the man has a somewhat mottled reputation.'

'Mottled? Zhe bastard isn't "mottled", Kondratieff: he's perverted.' The Doge eyed Kondratieff carefully. 'Do you think zhis Maykov can truly influence zhe Lady IMmanual? She really does zeem to have become a proponent of war, unt zhough I have tried to persuade her zhat Venice's power is based on commerce not artillery she zeems not to vish to listen.'

'Well, Maykov is now a Normalist and is, I believe, sincere in his desire to *try* to persuade her that peace is preferable to war. His concern for the girl is quite moving. He loves her.'

'Young love? Very touching. But I am unsure az to vhether his presence vill be a help or a hindrance.'

'Maykov is a determined and resourceful individual who, one way or another, *will* find a way to speak to the Lady IMmanual.'

Doge Catherine-Sophia thought on the matter, obviously weighing her options. Kondratieff knew the last thing she would want was Maykov disrupting the plans she and Sister Florence had made for the Lady's seduction by Casanova. It would be better to have him under her control than to risk him making an unscheduled appearance.

'Zhis Maykov, he has zome reputation as an occultist, has he not? He is a man able to commune mit zhe dead.'

*A strange question.*

'I believe that is the case.'

'Very vell, I vill have zhe chamberlain issue Maykov a varrant to enter zhe palace tonight. He can meet mit zhe Lady IMmanual *after* zhe Walpurgisnacht celebrations.'

# 38

## Rangoon, Venice and Paris
## The Demi-Monde: Walpurgisnacht, 90th Day of Spring, 1005

As ordained by Li, we did on the eighty-eighth day of Spring conduct the Rite of 4Telling, and it is with much disquiet that I record that this reading of the iChing did indicate there to be a great disturbance in the Qi of the Demi-Monde. True HerEticals take comfort in the knowledge that all things in the Kosmos follow a cyclical path, waxing and waning, and that soon will dawn the day when the masculine Yang will yield, once again, to the feminine Yin, and the Demi-Monde will enter the blissful utopia that is MostBien. Until the iChing was consulted during the Spring Rite, it was believed that the rhythm of the Kosmos was moving inexorably towards the Yin, towards the dawning of the Second Age of Femmes, but now it is apparent that there is a new and very disruptive force at work in the Demi-Monde. This force we have identified as the seductive philosophy of Normalism which promotes peace and non-violence between peoples and between genders and thus denies the complementary antagonism of Yin and Yang. Ever the Superior Ruler, the Empress Wu has commanded that steps be taken to remove the obstacle blocking the Path to our achieving that much desired state of MostBien.

*Excerpt from the private diary of Imperial NoN Mao Zedong:*
*88th day of Spring, 1005*

## Rangoon Docks, the Coven

Reverend Deputy Jeanne Dark gazed skyward through her telescope, and had the distinct feeling that the phoney war was over. Today would be the day when the Coven and the ForthRight began their fight to the death.

'What are they?'

The question came from her left, from Colonel-Femme Trung Trac, the officer commanding the Covenite Army's Rangoon defences. She was an able soldier, if a trifle unimaginative.

'Our intelligence reports that they are three of the ForthRight's new Vengeance Weapons, known as the V1. They're dirigibles capable of carrying bombs, designed by a nonFemme called Comrade Engineer Ferdinand von Zeppelin.'

'They're huge!'

Dark took a quick glance at Trung Trac, less than impressed by the tremor of fear inflecting her voice. Sure, the three V1s making up the formation that was so ponderously flying towards the Forbidding Palace were impressively big – they looked like monstrous silver cigars, each being, she guessed, 150 metres long – but they were slow and flew at a very low altitude, and that made them vulnerable, especially as they were full of hydrogen.

'Contain yourself, ColonelFemme. It is incumbent on all commanders to show calm in the face of the unknown.' Dark turned towards the NoN in charge of the rocket battery. 'CommanderNoN Jiao Yu, you will prepare to launch as soon as the V1s cross the Volga. I want all those bastards blown out of the sky.'

Jiao Yu saluted and barked out orders, and coolies started scuttling around, resetting the angle of the launching frames so that the battery's two hundred rockets were aimed at a point five hundred feet above the river. Perhaps 'aimed' was too optimistic a word. The rockets were incredibly arbitrary in what direction they flew after they had been launched, but Dark's hope was that by firing them en masse and at such a slow-moving and very large target, at least *some* of them would find their mark.

With every second that passed the V1s edged closer and closer to Rangoon. Now Dark could see the Valknuts embla-zoned on the lead V1's nose, could see the name of the airship – *Wrath of the ForthRight* – written there and could see the crew manning the nacelle slung beneath the airship as they strug-gled to manoeuvre the craft in the fresh evening breeze.

'Fire!'

Instantly a haze of black and foul-smelling smoke enveloped the 200-metre-long rank of rocket frames. Then came gouts of flame and ear-splitting screams as the rockets hurled them-selves skywards, the smoke trails they laid down behind them twisting and coiling as they went.

They got lucky. The V1s had flown in a suicidally tight forma-tion and as the rockets hammered into the two trailing V1s, the dirigibles exploded in furious fireballs. The *Wrath of the ForthRight* was made of sterner stuff: it staggered under the impact, like a boxer stunned by the fury of a punch but ready to fight back. Then Jeanne Dark saw a fire storm blossom inside the airship. Slowly it began to crumple and then to yaw, grad-ually losing height as it sank, broken, towards the ground.

Or, more accurately, towards the rocket battery.

'Take to the trenches,' Jeanne Dark yelled, and the Covenite soldiers did as they were told. But it did no good: even as she vaulted over the side of the trench, she heard the whoomph of the V1 crashing to earth, felt the air suddenly become oven-hot, felt her clothes and her SAE ignite . . .

## Outside the Doge's Palace, Venice

Semiazaz stood patiently in the shadows of the alleyway opposite the side entrance to the Palace, waiting for his Master's crypto to open the door that would allow him entry. It was a perfect night for murder. The sky was cloudy and the moon obscured, and with the comings and goings of the dozens of steamers bringing guests to the Fleshtival de Walpurgisnacht the streets around the Palace were crowded and confused. No one would give a single man entering the Palace so much as a glance; not even a man as singular as Semiazaz. But it never did to be too confident. He adjusted the wide brim of his hat to ensure his face was well shadowed, then nervously touched the hilt of his sword.

He was right to be nervous. Entering the Palace would be the easy part of his mission, killing the day-hag would be much more difficult. Of course, when he had been questioned by the Master, he had pronounced himself wholly confident of his ability to assassinate the girl, but the nagging doubt remained that she was a more formidable opponent than he cared to admit. She had bested him once and then he had had Baraqel to help him deal with her.

So although honour demanded that he kill her with his blade, he had decided that should matters go awry he would have a second, less chivalrous, means of disposing of her. And that was why he had a holster on his hip holding a beautifully weighted Colt revolver loaded with silver bullets: even the Lilithi, for all their powers, were vulnerable to silver. There would be no mistakes tonight.

Across the street, the door to the servants' entrance eased open, leaking a sliver of light out onto the pavement. For an instant the man opening the door was illuminated and Semiazaz saw the crypto gesture towards him.

It was time.

## The bedchamber of the Lady IMmanual, the Doge's Palace, Venice

Sister Florence made her preparations for the seduction of the Lady IMmanual carefully. She spent almost thirty minutes instructing Sister Bella, who would be attending the Lady IMmanual during Walpurgisnacht, on what she was to do and how she was to do it. She had personally supervised the preparation of the *zelie*, checking that the correct amount of the hallucinogenic plant *ayahuasca* was included in the recipe, and that the apothecary had not forgotten to add the Dizzi, the drug the NoirVillians were so enamoured of and which was reputed to stimulate the libido. She had also seen to it that the incense burners in the Lady IMmanual's chamber were charged with freshly cut horny goat weed, the most powerful aphrodisiac known to the Visual Virgins.

But most importantly of all, she had ensured that Casanova realised the seriousness of the mission he was undertaking, and that the successful seduction of the Lady IMmanual was a matter of Sector security. Even Casanova – dilettante though he was – had grasped the seriousness of what he was about, and the consequences if he were to fail.

The final piece of mood-setting involved the turning of the chamber's gas lamps down low. Now, with only the fire blazing in the grate providing any real illumination, the room had a strange sinuous substance about it, shadows shimmering and swaying around the walls and the ceiling.

Perfect.

Seven o'clock chimed announcing the Lady's imminent arrival, so with a final 'May ABBA be with thee, good Sister Bella,' Sister Florence took her position behind the false panel set in the side wall of the room and pressed her eye to the spyhole hidden in one of the covings. Standing there in the darkness, she mouthed a silent prayer to ABBA, asking HisHer blessing that all would go as planned and that tonight they would come to know if the Lady IMmanual was friend or foe . . . if she was the Messiah or, as Sister Florence was coming increasingly to fear, the Beast.

## Checkya safe house, Paris

Beria might be dead, but Zolotov's mission lived on, and to ensure there were no more mistakes he had taken inordinate care in the planning of the assassination of Aaliz Heydrich. So much so that studying the image reflected in the dressing mirror, Zolotov had difficulty recognising himself. He had abandoned the pearl-pink silk suit he had been wearing and instead adopted a decidedly more workaday outfit comprising a careworn tweed jacket and a pair of frayed corduroy trousers. Over these he'd shrugged an old but still serviceable coat, parked a moth-eaten fur *shapka* on his head, and pulled on a pair of beaten-up boots.

It might have been the elegant and urbane Andrei Zolotov who had walked into the room, but it was the ardent Normalist revolutionary and disorganisationalist Pavel Pavlovich Dazarev who was to leave it.

Easing the door open, Zolotov peeked out, then, satisfied he was unseen by any servants, he slipped through the back door of the safe house and into the black, bleakly cold Spring night. Hunching against the chill, he crunched across the frost-crisped snow – snow in Spring! – covering the courtyard. It was so cold that Zolotov's breath curled around him like steam, his cheeks stiffened in the frost and the wound in his shoulder throbbed. He pulled the ear flaps of his *shapka* down, buried his face deeper in the turned-up collar of his coat and, with hands thrust deep into his pockets, he trudged along the deserted Avenue d'Eylau towards the bar where he was to have his rendezvous with Aaliz Heydrich.

The Bar Papillon was small and seedy and he hated it. But it *was* a popular meeting place for Normalists and that made it perfect for his assignation with the girl. Perfect but smelly. Stepping through the door of the bar, he had to flinch back: the place stank of sweat and stale Solution. He knew the smell well, it was the stench of revolution.

When he had first planned to adopt the alternative persona of Pavel Pavlovich Dazarev, he had known that one of his key tasks would be to get Pavel smelling right. The revolutionaries he'd met as he'd wheedled his way into the confidence of the Normalists didn't wash regularly or use cologne, and so he'd been obliged to ape them . . . ape being a very apposite description. To achieve this, he had hung Pavel's clothes up for a week in the smoke room used to cure meat, in order to endow them with such a malignant odour that any residual fragrance of Andrei Zolotov was obliterated.

But now, edging further into the crowded bar, he realised he needn't have been so fastidious in his preparations. Enduring the olfactory nightmare that was the Bar Papillon surely meant that any sense of smell possessed by the Normalists would have been eradicated long ago.

### Pension des Amis, Paris

Odette had never seen Norma looking so tired, so *used up* – but Odette supposed this was hardly surprising. Everyone wanted something from the girl, forever demanding her blessing and her benediction. Odette had tried to protect Norma, to shield her, but there were just too many supplicants waiting to touch the hem of the wonderful Aaliz Heydrich. They had drained her with their never-ending claims on her genius and her charisma.

Yes, she *was* a genius, Odette had no doubts on that score: the way she had organised the Normalists was proof of that. And she certainly had charisma; every time she walked into a room she illuminated it, exuding an energy and a certainty that was simply awe-inspiring.

And that was the problem: everyone forgot that she was just a girl . . . a very tired girl, who had to be protected, especially when she was intent on doing something dangerous.

'My dearest Norma, I beg you, do not do this foolish thing. Please, allow me and Burlesque and Rivets to escort you.'

The shake Norma gave of her head showed what she thought of that idea. 'Enough, Odette. We've discussed this already. It was agreed by Giuseppe Garibaldi, leader of the Roman Legion of the Peace Corps, that I should go to the rendezvous with Dazarev alone. The man's very skittish.'

Odette sighed. This was the trouble with Yanks, they would never take advice. She edged closer to Norma to try to prevent Burlesque hearing what they were saying. Not that Burlesque would be able to understand the French they were speaking even if he could hear them, but that wouldn't stop him wanting his share of the discussion.

'Norma, we do not know this man Dazarev. He could be a crypto . . . an agent of the ForthRight.'

Norma held up a hand to forestall any further objections from her friend. "No, I don't think so: Garibaldi's given him a great reference. Seems Dazarev's got a crypto buried deep inside the Medi office of the Checkya: he gave the Normalists in Rome a heads up that they were going to be raided and saved ten of them from being strung up by piano wire. Garibaldi thinks he's gold.'

'I hear what you say, Norma, but the guy's come out of nowhere ...'

'Don't worry about me, Odette. Garibaldi will be there at the meeting. He's a reliable man and, as always, Dazarev comes on his personal recommendation.'

But Odette *did* worry about Norma. The problem was that Norma didn't seem to realise how important she had become. This slim, pale girl had changed the Demi-Monde, had changed how people thought, teaching them that violence and war were immoral. And, of course, those in power hated her for it. The last thing they wanted was a change in the status quo and the way these bastards usually dealt with revolutionaries like Norma was by killing them. And that was something Odette was determined would not happen: Norma was too important for her life to be snuffed out by a bullet.

Odette tried again. 'Please, Norma, why not let us escort you to the bar and then you can go in to meet with Dazarev alone?'

'No, you might frighten Dazarev off and that would be a disaster. From what I've heard he's got a plan which will finally topple Heydrich and the ForthRight.' She gave Odette a smile. 'Anyway, I need you to organise our crossing into the Rookeries.'

And that was the other thing that Odette was worried about. Norma's plan to preach about Normalism in the ForthRight seemed to her to be so foolhardy that it bordered on the suicidal.

'I am worried that going there will be very dangerous, Norma. Perhaps it would be better to remain here, in Paris.'

Norma frowned, indicating that she was beginning to lose patience. 'Look, Odette, we've discussed this: my work is done here. The Normalist movement in the Medi is firmly established and Garibaldi is going to make a first-class leader of the Peace

Corps. Now it's important that I take Normalism into the heart-land of UnFunDaMentalism. To defeat Heydrich, we must destroy the ForthRight, and who better to do that than Aaliz Heydrich, preaching on her father's home turf?'

'I do understand, Norma,' persisted Odette, 'but I don't think you realise *how* dangerous it will be for you in the Rookeries. Once there, it will be *impossible* for you to avoid the Checkya. Your face – the face of Aaliz Heydrich, that is – is just too well known there.'

Norma laughed and glanced over at Burlesque. 'If anyone can keep me out of the Checkya's clutches, it's Burlesque Bandstand.'

It was Odette's turn to shake her head, indicating just what she thought of *that* assumption. She loved Burlesque with a passion but even she had to concede that her man went through life evincing all the subtlety of an angry auroch. That was the other reason why she'd insisted on going with him to the Rookeries: she had to be there to make sure he didn't do anything *too* silly. Protecting Norma was one thing, but she also had to protect Burlesque from himself.

With a disconsolate shrug she conceded defeat. 'Very well, Norma, I will do as you ask, but please, I beg you, be careful of this man Dazarev.'

## The Doge's Palace, Venice

After getting the message from Kondratieff that the Doge had granted him amnesty and permission to enter the Palace, Vanka had wasted no time. He'd arrived at the Palace early, and he was early because he was nervous, though he didn't know whether his trepidation was caused by the prospect of meeting with Ella and trying to persuade her to join with Norma in a campaign of non-violence, or by the prospect of her going to the Fleshtival de Walpurgisnacht without him. The thought of other men – and a great many of the women – ogling her . . . and other things . . . was very upsetting.

Vanka hated being in love. Love seemed to stoke up a man's feelings of possessiveness towards his lady, or, in Vanka's case, towards his Lady. Jealousy, he knew, was a silly, juvenile emotion but, try as he might, he couldn't shake it off.

He loved the girl.

'Monsieur Maykov,' came a voice from behind him.

Turning around, he saw he was being addressed by one of the Doge's personal attendants, who, like all of them, was young, tall and had a very well-stocked codpiece.

'You are asked to attend Her Most Reverend Excellency the Doge Catherine-Sophia.'

'What, now? But I'm here to meet the Lady IMmanual.'

'Her Most Reverend Excellency was most insistent, sir. If you would come this way . . . the Doge becomes rather perturbed if she is kept waiting unnecessarily.'


## The bedchamber of the Lady IMmanual, the Doge's Palace, Venice

'That's epimedium you're burning, isn't it?' asked the Lady IMmanual, as she entered the room.

'Yes, my Lady,' answered Sister Bella. 'It's a herb tradition-ally burnt on Walpurgisnacht. It is supposed to drive away harmful humors and to turn the thoughts of lovers to *affaires d'amour*.'

Sister Bella was rather proud that her voice didn't quaver when she'd answered the Lady. The girl scared the wits out of her and it wasn't just her peculiar aura that upset her either: there was something *wrong* about her.

'I've used it myself and I wasn't a great fan of the smell then,' grumbled the Lady, but Sister Bella was pleased to see that she let the herb burn. Probably she was reluctant to interfere with ImPuritan tradition, and the smell of the epimedium wasn't *that* bad. It was a little tart, certainly, but the way it made the senses swim was really quite stimulating.

'There is also a traditional Walpurgisnacht drink, my Lady. This is *zelie* – a herbal drink that makes spirits soar and inhibitions vanish.'

'Sounds like E,' observed the Lady, taking the glass the Sister offered. Sister Bella had no idea what 'E' was but she was pleased to see the Lady sipping the *zelie*, testing it.

'Not bad,' was the Lady's conclusion.

'I added a little port wine, my Lady. I find the sweetness of the wine lessens the bitter flavour of the *zelie*, and makes it a little more palatable.' It also disguised the presence of Dizzi, but Sister Bella left this observation unvoiced.

'Good thinking,' said the Lady, draining the glass. 'And now, Sister Bella, let's decide which gown I'm going to wear to this Walpurgisnacht Fleshtival of yours.'

'I have brought a selection, my Lady. All of them are beautiful, but some are more daring than others.'

'And your preference?'

'This, my Lady.' Sister Bella nodded towards the black gown hanging from the wardrobe door.

The gown was a miracle of craftsmanship, cut to flow from neck to ankle and made from a crystal-speckled lace. It was a cobweb of a dress, and almost reverently the Lady extended a hand and gently stroked its ephemeral fabric, delighting in the way it glided over her fingers. She gave a smile, a nod, and then undid her robe, letting it slide to the ground to stand naked in the middle of the room.

## The bedchamber of the Lady IMmanual, the Doge's Palace, Venice

The lady's robe fluttered to the floor and Sister Florence gave an involuntary gasp. Haloed by the dancing firelight, every curve of the Lady's naked body was emphasised. Without a doubt, she was the most beautiful woman Sister Florence had ever seen, her wonderful form moulded from shadows and the flickering firelight into some chiaroscuran sculpture. More, the light emphasised the beautiful bone structure of her face – all high cheekbones, slanted eyes and full half-open lips – this in turn accentuated by the stark severity of her shaven pate. She was the image of uncompromising, unabashed sexuality, of unashamed carnality.

But there was more to Sister Florence's agitation than the Lady's beauty. There seemed to be something otherworldly about her, so much so that Florence felt almost intoxicated to be in the presence of such loveliness.

It was then that a strange thing happened. The Lady turned towards the place where Florence was hiding, smiled and then raised her arms high in the air above her, stretching, arching, straining up from her toes to her fingertips, displaying her body to its best advantage, advertising her nakedness and her beauty. Florence had the disturbing feeling the Lady was performing for her.

Shocked by the thought that she might have been discovered, Sister Florence jerked back but then, chiding herself that it was impossible for the Lady to know she was hiding there, she resumed her position at the spyhole, watching, mesmerised, as the Lady prepared herself for the Fleshtival. She watched the Lady darken her eyes with mascara, use a deep red lipstick to colour her mouth and then rouge her cheeks. She watched her attach two twists of silver to her ears and a thick steel collar around her neck, and apply black varnish to her nails and her nipples. She watched the Lady transform herself into something . . . pagan.

And while she watched, all of the erotic passions she had been taught to control and contain welled up inside her. Sister Florence found her head swimming with thoughts of strange lusts and denied hungers. She felt . . . uncaged. This fabulous woman – fabulously beautiful, fabulously tall and fabulously erotic – had unlocked the door to the cell where her most secret desires lay captive.

Gazing into those limpid, unfathomable black eyes, Florence found herself enslaved by the Lady's beauty.

## The Doge's private chamber, the Doge's Palace, Venice

The room that Vanka was ushered into was dark: so dark that for a moment it was difficult to see if there was anyone else there. But as his eyes became accustomed to the gloom, he saw the black-robed figure of Doge Catherine-Sophia sitting on a couch near the fireplace.

'Your Excellency, you sent for me?'

'Ah, zhe psychic, Vanka Maykov,' the Doge intoned in a slurred voice. This was one Doge, Vanka decided, who had shipped more Solution than was good for her. 'I have been asked by Kondratieff to allow you to meet mit zhe Lady IMmanual, but first I have a request to make of you.'

Vanka bowed. 'I am your servant, Your Excellency.'

'Gut. Zhat is how it should be.' The Doge paused to refill her glass, and then drained it in one gulp. 'Zhis is a sad night for me, Maykov. It vos on Walpurgisnacht zhat my Current died two years ago.'

'Oh, bad luck,' said Vanka, wondering what this had to do with him.

'I miss Grigori Alexandrovich zo very, very much.' The woman gave a drunken sob and dabbed a handkerchief to her eye.

'Time is a great healer.'

'I understand zhat in zhe ForthRight you vere famous for your occult powers.'

*Infamous*, corrected Vanka silently, as the disturbing realisation as to why he had been brought here dawned on him.

'I vish you to use your metaphysical ability to help me commune mit my dear departed Grisha.'

It was a sign of how distracted Vanka was that it took him a moment to realise that 'Grisha' was the soppy woman's pet name for her former lover, Grigori Alexandrovich Potemkin, a man Vanka knew precious little about. And, having made it a rule never to go into a séance unprepared, his natural reaction was to make his excuses – a bad back, a touch of gout, any excuse would do – and head for the shrubbery. But with it being the Doge making the request, it was difficult to duck out. One word from her and any chance he had of seeing Ella again would vanish faster than the bottle of Solution the woman was chugging.

With a mental shrug of his shoulders, he crossed the room and sat down at a card table. He might be a little out of practice – the last time he had been involved with the occult was back in Dashwood Manor – but he had no difficulty in remembering his old patter.

'To contact those who have passed to the Spirit World we must hold hands, Your Excellency.'

The Doge nodded her understanding, then rose from the couch and tottered unsteadily across the room to join Vanka at the table. He took her hands into his, then gave the woman his trademark smouldering look. This being the Doge, he decided to give her the de luxe edition of the Maykov séance. 'I sense it is not just me who is in tune with the Spirit World, Your Excellency, but you also. The psychic vibrations I feel emanating from you are so very strong: I sense I am in the presence of a fellow adept.' He smiled at her. 'You, Your Excellency, are one of those rare women who have been touched by the Invisible.'

Total bollocks, of course, but the punters loved it.

A gasp from the Doge. 'Do you really think zo? Grisha often used to zay zhat zhere vos zomething of zhe *Zhritsa* about me.'

Vanka suppressed a smile. Potemkin had obviously been a man with a sense of humour. Calling his Current a *Zhritsa* – a spirit woman – was tantamount to telling her that she was away with the fairies. But the Doge fancying herself as a seeress was seriously good news; it would make her so much easier to manipulate. Vanka raised his gaze to look deep into her oh-so-trusting, if rather bleary, eyes. 'Yes, your late Current certainly recognised you for what you are, Your Excellency. I suspect that you are almost powerful enough to . . .' He paused dramatically, pretending to hesitate about how to broach such a delicate suggestion. 'No, that is too serious a magick for one in such a fragile emotional state as you, my Doge. Perhaps at a later séance?'

As Vanka had expected and hoped, the Doge's eyes sparkled with interest. To be told that she was an adept in things spiritual, that she was a powerful seeress, was intriguing enough, but for the dashing Vanka Maykov to hint that she might be especially gifted was *very* exciting. 'Please, Monsieur Maykov . . . Vanka Ivanovich . . . Vanka, I am a voman of zome resilience, unt I would be fascinated to explore zhe Spirit World further.'

'Then I implore you to be open, to be trusting. Without this openness, without this trust . . .' He rolled his head in mock agony, pantomiming that connecting to the Spirit World was a painful experience. 'The Spirit of your dear, departed Current approaches.'

## The Doge's private chamber, the Doge's Palace, Venice

Standing hidden in the secret passage, the only feeling de Sade had watching the pathetic antics of the Doge was one of contempt. This drunken woman communing in such a familiar manner with a wanted criminal was a gross dereliction of her duty as Doge. By his reckoning, she was finished; she was a politician who had reached the end of her useful life. She disgusted him with her maudlin sentimentality and irretrievable weakness. It was high time Venice was rid of her.

Venice needed strong leadership . . . strong, *male* leadership . . . *his* leadership.

And Venice was the prize Bole had offered him in exchange for his help in ridding the Demi-Monde of the Lady IMmanual and that was a service that would – finally – be performed tonight. Oh, he had tried to kill her before . . . tried and failed. Hadn't he been the one who had brought the Lady IMmanual to the Maison d'Illusion when that interfering bitch Sister Florence came between the Lady and Zolotov's blade? Hadn't he been the one who had tried to blow her head off and hit Zolotov by mistake? And hadn't he been the one who had arranged for Armaros to enter the Convent only for her to be defeated by that meddlesome bastard Burlesque Bandstand?

Yes, the Lady had led a charmed life, but tonight there would be no more mistakes. Tonight, with his help, Semiazaz would finish the task he had left undone back in Paris. Tonight the Lady IMmanual would die.

As would two others. De Sade had a little housekeeping to do of his own. Tonight de Sade would become a murderer.

Now *that* was a sobering thought. He had always baulked at murder. Oh, he might revel in the joy of inflicting pain and torment, but he had never actually killed. Indeed, the only time he had tried his hand at murder in the Maison d'Illusion he had been shaking so much that his shot had gone embarrassingly wide.

He had rationalised this weakness of spirit by the thought that intellectuals – and de Sade certainly considered himself an intellectual – never soiled their own hands with butchery, but in the privacy of his own mind he had often wondered whether he had the mettle for murder. Well, tonight he would find out.

## The bedchamber of the Lady IMmanual, the Doge's Palace, Venice

'A final touch, my Lady,' counselled Sister Bella. 'Before you dress, we must apply your perfume.'

The scent Sister Florence had chosen for the Lady was an oriental, the key ingredient of which was vanilla, a potent aphrodisiac, famous for its ability to conjure the sensations of passion. This Sister Bella dabbed to the crooks of the Lady's elbows, the insides of her wrists and to her navel.

Despite herself and despite her training, watching Sister Bella apply the perfume kindled a frisson of lust within Florence's soul. What would it be like, she wondered, to touch that silk-smooth skin, to run her fingertips over those yielding breasts, to kiss those tempting lips . . . ?

She shook her head angrily, trying to dislodge these stupid, ridiculous thoughts.

Perfume applied, the Lady reached for the dress and slipped it over her head, smoothing the delicate lace against her hard, slim body, before turning towards the huge dressing mirror to assess herself.

'Wonderful,' she crooned.

It was indeed wonderful. The dress was breathtaking, the firelight sliding through the material to silhouette the girl's marvellous figure, emphasising its perfection. Even by ImPuritan standards it was a *very* daring dress and if she chose to wear it, not one centimetre of her body would remain concealed.

Sister Florence smiled; perversely, the Lady looked more naked with it on than when she had been truly naked, the lace rolling over her body like noired syrup. It was a wanton, evil dress.

It suited her.

But though the Lady's thoughts had obviously turned towards the erotic, there was still no change in her aura. This girl, Sister Florence began to worry, must be immune to sexual excitements: she could provoke passion but not enjoy it.

## Le Bar Papillon, Paris

Looking about in the smoke-drenched gloom, Zolotov saw Garibaldi sitting in a shadowed booth at the back of the bar. Even if he hadn't known the man, he'd have recognised him by the red shirt he was wearing. So much for secrecy: the fool obviously didn't realise that this sartorial idiosyncrasy of his was known to the Checkya and that it made him incredibly easy to track. But other than his penchant for bright shirts he was an unremarkable wretch. In Zolotov's opinion, the only thing that marked Normalists out from the common weal was their odour . . . and their trusting stupidity, of course.

Zolotov strolled across to the Normalist's table. Garibaldi looked up at him, frowned, and then pantomimed a lack of recognition. 'Are you the friend who has come to meet those who might help him free this land of pestilence?'

Zolotov hated all this cloak-and-dagger rigmarole Normalists delighted in, but he swallowed his contempt and answered, reciting the pass-phrase he had been given with as much cod-seriousness as he could muster. 'Yes, but I need the assistance of the Exhorters of Normality to achieve my lofty goals.'

Garibaldi's smile broadened and he pushed out a hand. Zolotov shook it and then eased himself into a chair.

'Fraternal greetings, Comrade, and I tell you I am honoured to sit at the same table as Pavel Pavlovich Dazarev, nonViolent Fighter for Freedom, and the man who has been so generous in his support of the Normalist movement in Rome.'

'And you, in turn, are generous in your praise, Comrade Garibaldi,' Zolotov replied, doing his best to infuse his words with an appropriate level of revolutionary portentousness. 'It is the duty of all true Normalists to rally round to support your valiant struggle against the agents of oppression.' Zolotov could hardly believe he could utter this mummery that constituted 'Normality-speak' without breaking into a fit of giggles.

But the most amusing thing had been how incredibly easy it had been to insinuate himself into the Normalists' confidence. The Checkya had been watching a Normalist safe house in Rome for several weeks, hoping that one day the ever-elusive Norma Williams might show up, so it had taken hardly any effort on Zolotov's part to organise a sting. In his guise of staunch Normalist, Pavel Pavlovitch Dazarev, he had given Garibaldi a tip-off that there was going to be a raid and then he and the odorous twerp had watched from a bar across the street as thirty Checkya agents descended on the now empty house. After that Garibaldi had thought Dazarev walked on water.

Garibaldi leant over the table, obviously delighted to play the brave conspirator. 'And be under no illusion, Comrade, that your help and munificence has gone unnoticed. Aaliz herself will come tonight to thank you for your support and to hear your plan to rid our land of the tyranny of UnFunDaMentalism.'

This was the bait Zolotov had dangled in front of Garibaldi: the fiction that he had the power to deafeat the ForthRight. And Garibaldi had fallen for his ruse, hook, line, and sinker.

'I trust she will come ready to recognise that my plan is so daring that it will, at a stroke, cause the collapse of the ForthRight.'

'Tell me again . . .'

Garibaldi was silenced by Zolotov placing a finger against his lips. 'Quietly,' he urged. 'The walls have ears.' He looked around pretending to check they weren't being snooped on. 'I have managed to penetrate the mechanisms which allow the Blood Banks to function and now I am able to destroy the access the ForthRight enjoys to the banks.' Bloody nonsense, of course; nobody in the Demi-Monde could alter the way the Blood Banks operated. 'At a stroke, the ForthRight will be brought to its knees. Believe me, Comrade Garibaldi,' he urged, 'by this single act we will announce to the downtrodden masses of the Demi-Monde that political salvation is no longer a distant light on the far horizon. In one night we will humble the ForthRight for ever, and hurl the foul creed of UnFunDaMentalism into the deepest pit of history.'

'But how will this be accomplished?'

'By the sacrifice of many of our lives, my friend,' answered Zolotov, casting his eyes to the floor in a mawkish show of grief. 'To take control of the Blood Banks' nerve centre will need forty brave individuals, and of these, I estimate, not more than a handful will survive.'

Garibaldi preened. Revolutionaries loved it when they were given an opportunity to martyr themselves.

'But *how* will this miracle be accomplished?'

'I beg you, do not press me. If one word of what I am intent on should reach the Checkya, then everything I have dedicated my life to achieving will be lost. More than that, I will not – I dare not – say. I will only divulge the details of my plan to Aaliz Heydrich herself.'


## Pension des Amis, Paris

Packing her meagre belongings into a carpet bag, ready for her departure to the ForthRight, Norma admitted to feeling bone-weary. Suddenly all the efforts of the past few weeks pressed down on her; all the long days and longer nights organising, cajoling, pleading, demanding and ordering had taken their toll. Odette and Burlesque and Vanka had done their best to ease her load, but it had been her will and her energy that had fuelled Normalism, made it the success it was. She had never allowed herself to falter, to show weakness or uncertainty. But now she felt empty, depleted of spirit and so very alone.

Yes, loneliness was the reward for leadership. And maybe that was why she was such an effective leader: she was able to retreat inside herself, to hide her concerns and her worries under a hard, tough carapace, to pretend that she never doubted herself. She could not, *would* not, allow anyone to come too close to her, to touch her emotions. She had to be unfeeling and remorseless. She had to sacrifice herself to bring peace to the Demi-Monde.

It was tough though. The girl inside Norma Williams wanted so desperately to love. But love would have to wait on peace.

Maybe, though, there was a chance of peace. Maybe this mysterious man Dazarev could be the one to finally bring down the ForthRight. Maybe his idea about how the ForthRight's banking system could be sent into meltdown wasn't as wacky as she suspected it might be. Norma knew Ella worked her miracles by doing tricky things in the Blood Banks and that was why she'd agreed to the meeting. If there was even the smallest chance that Dazarev wasn't talking moonshine, she had to see him. And besides, Garibaldi *had* given him a glowing reference. It was just that she was so damned skittish about meeting the Russian on her own. Maybe not bringing Odette along hadn't been such a good idea.

With a fatalistic shrug of her shoulders, Norma wrapped herself into her cloak and slipped out of her room, heading down the stairs to the yard at the back of the lodging house she had been staying in. Stepping into the alleyway beyond, she felt cold, frightened and very alone.

## The bedchamber of the Lady IMmanual, the Doge's Palace, Venice

There was a knock on the door of the Lady IMmanual's room, and when Sister Bella answered she was relieved to find Casanova standing there. He certainly looked the part of a would-be seducer, being handsome, well-made and dressed in the very height of ImPure fashion. She also approved of his choice of codpiece: she had never seen one shaped in the form of a ram's head before.

Without waiting for an invitation, Casanova strode into the room and gave a deep bow to the Lady. 'My Lady IMmanual, it is I, the Count Giacomo Girolamo Casanova de Seingalt,' he began in his awkward English. 'I have been sended by Her Most Reverend Excellency, Doge Catherine-Sophia to escort you to that most erotical of all events, the Fleshtival de Walpurgisnacht.'

'Casanova, eh? So tell me, Monsieur le Comte, why wasn't I told of these arrangements?'

Casanova shrugged. 'I make the most apologises, my Lady,

but the Marquis de Sade is absent from his room so it has been decided that I must take his places at the side of you, who is the most beautiful of all women.'

A spasm of annoyance flickered across the Lady's face. 'Very well. I suppose I should be pleased to have such a dashing gentleman as my escort.' She poured herself another glass of *zelie* and drained it. 'So de Sade has gone AWOL, has he? The worm has finally turned. Now I'll really have to watch my back.' She smiled at Casanova. 'May I offer you a drink?' and without waiting for a reply, the Lady signalled for Sister Bella to provide a glass for her guest and to refill her own.

## The Doge's private chamber, the Doge's Palace, Venice

For two whole minutes Vanka performed his role of medium succumbing to the embrace of a Spirit. He rolled his head and his eyes, he moaned and groaned, and then slumped – miming unconsciousness – across the table. And all the time he was desperately trying to remember something – anything – about this dead bastard Potemkin.

Finally, slowly, ominously, he raised his head and stared deep into the Doge's eyes. 'I am come,' he intoned, lowering his voice an octave, hoping to make it redolent of the sounds of the netherworld. He also imbued it with what was hopefully a passable rendering of Potemkin's Russian accent.

It was obviously a masterful performance. The colour drained from the Doge's Solution-rouged face, her eyes widened in shock, and her hands trembled. 'Grisha? Grisha? Is zhat truly you?'

Immediately Vanka began to twist and jerk in ersatz paroxysms of possession. 'Yeeeees, it is me. I speak to you from the world beyond. I have sent my good friend Vanka Ivanovich to guide you and to care for you.'

The Doge gripped Vanka's hands harder, and then, in an amazing show of strength, pulled them – and him – across the table towards her. Now their faces were only inches apart, their lips almost touching.

*Fucking hell.*

He wrenched his hands out of the Doge's, then wailing and shaking – and, after seeing the predatory look in the woman's eyes, scared shitless – Vanka staggered to his feet and began to sway and totter across the room in the direction of the exit, banging into chairs and knocking ornaments from shelves as he went. Bemused by the Doge's reaction he might have been, but he still had the presence of mind to mutter, 'Catya, Catya'. This was the most common diminutive of the name Catherine, and therefore the one the late Potemkin had probably used when addressing his Current.

His prayers were answered. 'Oh Grisha, my darlink, it iz I, your little Catya.'

Just as Vanka was preparing to make a run for it, the woman struck. She launched herself from her chair, grabbed Vanka into her arms, and began to ravish his mouth with long, wet kisses.

'Grisha,' she moaned, 'I have pined for you. Oh, my darlink, I have been so alone, I have been so frightened, but now you have returned to me.'

*This is fucking ridiculous.*

## The bedchamber of the Lady IMmanual, the Doge's Palace, Venice

Although her aura remained stubbornly unchanging, the Lady IMmanual was obviously much taken with Casanova, and by the way his aura flared, Casanova just as obviously reciprocated her feelings. While Sister Bella made the final touches to the

Lady's make-up, all the man could do was stare at her, smitten by her beauty.

Casanova's reputation as a rake and a roué was confirmed by his aura: the orange mist that surrounded the man was of a shade associated with those who craved constant attention. It was a childish, immature aura but, fortunately for the role he was being asked to play, it also showed that his libido was immensely strong – *fortissimo*-class. Men like him would – according to the ImPure saying – fuck anything with a ticking body clock, and Sister Florence suspected Casanova viewed even this modest stipulation as more of a guideline than a requirement.

'So tell me, Monsieur le Comte,' the Lady asked, 'just what am I to expect of the Fleshtival de Walpurgisnacht?'

'That, my Lady, is entirely in your handies so elegant. Walpurgisnacht is the Night of Lilith, the night when the forces of Light and Dark are in the utmost delicacy of balance, when the duality of the Kosmos it teeters between the Good and the Evil. This is the night when the light will be dimmed in the Demi-Monde and just for a moment – a moment of the greatest shortness to be of the unmeasurability – the power of ABBA will be extinguished and the most confusion will reign. But although this lasts but for the fleetingest of moments, it is dangerous. If this rent in the fabric of the Kosmos is not repaired, then evil – namely the Darkness – will pour into this world. So all of us who are of the greatest virility, use our sexiness and our beauty to distract the Darkness, to stop it entering the Demi-Monde. And the Darkness is easily distracted, my Lady, especially by the presence of beauty.' Casanova gave the Lady a salacious wink. 'And in this regarded, you will be the bestest of all temptations.'

'You are very gallant, sir.'

'Not gallant, my Lady, I merely have the totally truthfulness.'

The Lady IMmanual picked up her glass of *zelie* with a trembling hand though not, Sister Florence suspected, trembling from cold or fear but with excitement: Casanova and the *zelie* had obviously fired her imagination. But not, unfortunately, her aura, which remained steadfastly uniform.

'You are correct in what you say, Monsieur le Comte, but I would go further. I understand that the most effective way a woman might connect with ABBA is through the sexual nirvana offered by orgasm. This is, of course, the cornerstone of ImPuritanism, which teaches that the pursuit of JuiceSense, the ultimate orgasm, is key to achieving Oneness with ABBA. And if a woman, especially one versed in Seidr magic, should reach the blessed state of JuiceSense, then her magical powers will be enhanced manifold and she will be better able to turn back the Darkness.'

Sister Florence frowned. Seidr magic? Was the Lady saying she was a Seidrkona, a practitioner of the dark, shamanistic magic of the Pre-Folk? Florence had read about these strange women who to merge with their spirit guides would seethe, fusing themselves with the Darkness, this being a state most readily achieved during orgasm. But what Sister Florence also knew was that the last Seidrkona had been Marie Laveau and she was reputed to have been the reincarnation of Lilith.

Surely the Lady wasn't suggesting . . . ?

Even while the Sister mulled these troubling thoughts around in her head, the Lady IMmanual gave an idle wave of her hand, shooing Sister Bella from her room. Once she and Casanova were alone, the Lady turned to her guest and spread her arms wide. 'So, Monsieur le Comte, will you help me to achieve JuiceSense?'

## The Doge's private chamber, the Doge's Palace, Venice

Only with a real effort – the Doge was immensely strong – did an increasingly desperate Vanka manage to free his mouth from hers and plead that she stop her onslaught on his body. With the Doge now ripping away at his codpiece and delving around in search of his manhood, his entreaties came out as nothing more than yelps. She had very long and very sharp fingernails.

'Grisha, Grisha, my darlink, I miss you. I yearn for your body,' chanted the mad woman, and then, whilst clasping Vanka prisoner between her substantial thighs, she grabbed the two sides of her bodice and ripped it apart, sending the pretty pearl buttons skittering over the polished wooden floor. Barely contained by her stays, the Doge's plump tits celebrated their liberation by performing a very jolly jig.

The Doge hooked an arm around Vanka's neck and hauled his face into her cleavage. Ever the gentleman, Vanka stabbed kisses onto her breasts and from far away – each of his ears was blocked by a surfeit of breast – he heard guttural murmurs of ecstasy.

*Bloody hell, the woman's an animal.*

The problem was that the animal had an armlock tight around his neck and as her passion grew, so did the constriction of his windpipe. Frantically trying to avoid death by asphyxiation, he wriggled in her arms, gasping for air. He wriggled so hard that he overbalanced, his leather-soled shoes slipping on the pearl buttons. In an instant, he was sent tumbling over, and as he fell his head cracked against the unyielding corner of an oak dining table. With a low moan, he slumped unconscious across the floor.

## The bedchamber of the Lady IMmanual, the Doge's Palace, Venice

The seductive scent of the tendrils of smoke from the incense burners, drifting and coiling around her, made the senses of the Lady IMmanual reel. It was an odd sensation, but a disturbingly enjoyable one: nothing had substance, nothing was real, suddenly all restraint had been removed from her. The walls and the ceiling and the floor flexed and moved, seeming as supple as rubber and as solid as vapour. Reality had became amorphous, bending and twisting. She suddenly felt that she wanted – *needed* – to be wanton . . . to be herself.

She spread her arms and offered herself to Casanova. 'So, Monsieur le Comte, will you help me achieve JuiceSense?'

The sexual tension in the room was so powerful that all Casanova could do was nod, but it was all the encouragement the Lady needed. In a slow, considered manner she drew her hands down along the front of her thighs and caught the ephemeral fabric of the gown between finger and thumb. Then with studied deliberation she drew the dress up over her body, over her head and then tossed it disdainfully aside. Now she stood naked before Casanova.

'Come, use me in any way you desire,' she whispered. 'Do anything you wish with me.' And what she said was true: she wanted to be used, to be violated. The *zelie* and the incense had connived to remove all her restraint and all her self-control. Now she wanted to commit herself, body and soul, to sin.

And as Casanova advanced towards her, she caught a glimpse of herself in her looking glass – and it was a smiling Lilith who gazed back.

## The bedchamber of the Lady IMmanual, the Doge's Palace, Venice

At last! Watching from her hiding place, Sister Florence saw the Lady's aura begin to mutate. Slowly, almost imperceptibly, the unblemished silver corona that surrounded her became suffused with pink – the colour of arousal. Admittedly, the change was so subtle and so gradual that for a moment Sister Florence doubted what she was seeing, but after a moment the pink mist became deeper and more profound.

Hardly daring to breathe and frightened by the thought of what she was about to discover, the Sister pressed her eye closer to the spyhole. Now she would know the truth.

The Lady removed her dress and Sister Florence trembled. The girl, it seemed, had cast a spell over her, now she felt everything the Lady felt. Florence gasped in stunned excitement as a flutter of erotic anticipation rippled over her body. Lost in some sensual, salacious dream, Sister Florence found herself enveloped by a miasma of dark passion, bathed in the hot, aromatic consequences of her lust.

## The Doge's private chamber, the Doge's Palace, Venice

How long he remained unconscious, Vanka couldn't judge, but he opened his eyes to find his head resting on the Doge's lap, her sizeable breasts only centimetres from his mouth. Lying there, a glass of really quite superior Solution was pressed to his lips and as he drank, the sudden, awful realisation of the situation he was in began to dawn on him.

'Your Excellency,' he stammered in a weak, befuddled voice, 'what . . . what happened?'

'My darlink, Grisha, you have come back to me. You have been reincarnated, unt vonce again ve vill be united. '

*Shit!*

Vanka staggered to his feet, his head swimming. He had to get out of there, the woman was obviously stark raving mad, and crazy people, in Vanka's experience, tended to do crazy things. And in the Doge's case that might involve having his head chopped off.

Mouthing incoherent excuses, he plunged towards the door. Every step he took felt like he was wading through thick treacle, but one thought drove him on – to put as much distance between himself and this nutcase as was possible. That, and the need to find Ella.

## The bedchamber of the Lady IMmanual, the Doge's Palace, Venice

Taking the Lady's disrobing as his cue, Casanova stripped off his own clothes and once naked he stood for a moment studying the girl's beauty, his own arousal blatant and proud. Then like some prowling animal, he began to circle her, stretching out a hand, slowly drifting his fingertips over her breasts. And as his fingers moved, delicately touching her, a spasm of anguished excitement flickered through her body, making her writhe and shudder. Now his fingers roved around her nipple, and the Lady felt herself reacting to the man's ministrations, felt her skin tautening, her body rippling with delight.

Casanova's hand moved down, cruising over her flawless flesh, searching out her most sensitive places. Further and further it delved and then . . .

Suddenly her body was aflame, racked by the most profound, the most rapturous pleasure. She stood there, vibrating with lust.

Then Casanova took her by the hand and led her to the couch.

## The bedchamber of the Lady IMmanual, the Doge's Palace, Venice

Abandoning herself to her fantasies, Florence found herself imitating Casanova's blandishments. She gently caressed her fingertips over her own body, tracing them delicately along her welcoming flesh. Now the Lady was inside her head, whispering to her. 'You are very beautiful,' she heard the Lady say, 'but beauty is nothing if you don't use it.' Encouraged by the Lady's entreaties, Florence tracked her fingers over the swell of her full round breast. 'I have dreamt of the moment when I would touch you, Florence,' the Lady purred, and Florence undid the buttons that held her habit together. 'I want to feel your body.' Florence slipped her hand under her habit, her fingertips brushing the hard tip of her breast. 'I want so very much to arouse your soul, to unbind it' – Florence began to toy with the nipple – 'and to have you embrace the carnal.' Florence squeezed her fingers down hard, relishing the pain she provoked. 'You wish to be a wanton woman, don't you, Florence?'

'Yes,' Florence sighed and with a dip of her shoulders allowed her habit to fall to the floor. Now she too stood naked in the shadows.

Somewhere at the back of her mind came a warning for her to run away, that this was fiduciary sex of an intensity she had never imagined, that she was no longer the hunter, but rather the prey. But the soft, seductive voice of the Lady urged her stay and taste forbidden delights. She couldn't run away, she would do anything that was asked of her, anything and more.

The pressure exerted by the fingers on her skin increased, the tips digging hard as they followed the curves of her body. Despite her aversion, her revulsion, of what she was doing, a shudder of arousal echoed through her, the massaging of her body kindling erotic charges. She tilted herself, stretching her arm such that the heel of her hand rested on her mons, and her fingers trailed through her scrub of pubis.

She watched Casanova's fingers tempt and tease the Lady's body and Florence imitated him, butterflying her own fingers and goading an erotic spasm from her own body. Her soul felt like it was being racked by galvanicEnergy: unseen in the darkness, she twisted and bucked, writhed and groaned, at once affronted by her own eager submission and delighted by the reaction it had provoked in her.

## The Doge's private chamber, the Doge's Palace, Venice

As soon as Vanka Maykov had exited the Doge's chamber, de Sade saw his opportunity. The Doge lay sobbing on the couch, her face buried in her hands, emotionally exhausted by the effort involved in communing with her dead Current's spirit. He would never have a better chance. The Doge had to die.

When she was gone and Venice was his, he would remake it in his image. He would make Venetian women suffer for the humiliation and opprobrium they had heaped on him. No longer would men be obliged to conceal their instinctive MALEvolence, no longer would men be obliged to deny their *real* appetites. He would teach men to understand that the erotic – the *real* erotic – was based on the principle of transgression, and any transgressive activity, any breaking of taboos must, by definition, involve the inflicting of pain. He would teach them that pain, not prudence, was the key to pleasure.

More, he would destroy the perverse creed of ImPuritanism. Oh, how he loathed ImPuritanism's hedonistic imperative and its belief that pain, even erotic pain, was anathema to civilised behaviour. He would destroy ImPuritanism and in doing so would bring women to understand what pain truly was. He would make women scream.

Carefully he slipped a catch, pushed open the door hidden in the wooden panelling and oiled his way into the room, tiptoeing across the floor towards the Doge's slumped form. Almost before he realised what he was doing, he had drawn the stiletto from the sheath sewn to the inside of his frock coat and was standing over the woman, blade in hand, poised to strike.

The Doge opened her eyes. 'De Sade . . . at last. It took you long enough to raise zhe fucking courage. Now I can join my dearest Grisha.'

De Sade stabbed the stiletto into the woman's unprotected throat, stilling her scream of protest. He was amazed how easy it was to snuff out a life.

## Le Bar Papillon, Paris

Stepping into the crowded, smoke-drenched bar that Garibaldi had nominated for her rendezvous with Dazarev, Norma felt like turning on her heel and making a run for it. It was a decidedly low-rent sort of place, where the clientele saw every newcomer as a potential victim, and tonight being Walpurgisnacht, the male of the species was in an even more predatory turn of mind than usual.

Fortunately, even as she stood there being evaluated, she heard a friendly voice calling to her. 'Mademoiselle Benoit? Over here!'

It took a moment for Norma to react to her *nom de guerre*. She peered into the gloom and saw Garibaldi beckoning to her, his red shirt unmistakable through the fug of the bar. Crossing the floor, she saw he was sitting with a tall, handsome man with a roguish look in his eye.

*Not your typical Normalist . . .*

When she was seated at the table, Garibaldi made the whispered introductions. 'Mademoiselle Heydrich, may I introduce Monsieur Pavel Dazarev.'

They shook hands and then Dazarev took control of proceedings. 'Forgive me, Mademoiselle, but I do not wish to take a chance on you having been followed. I would suggest we repair to a room I have taken just around the corner. If we leave by the back entrance, I think we might avoid any unwanted attention of the Checkya.'

Before Norma quite knew what was happening, that's exactly what they did. It was when they found themselves in the night-shrouded back yard of the bar that things ran out of control. There was a grunt and Garibaldi pitched forward with a knife in his back.


## Le Bar Papillon, Paris

'I ain't sure this is such a bonne idea, Odette,' moaned Burlesque as they stood in the shadows of a doorway keeping watch on the bar. 'Norma's gonna be très pissed off when she finds out wot yous gorn an' done.'

Odette ignored him. She had never had any intention of letting Norma go to the meeting with Dazarev unescorted. As soon as Norma had left the *pension*, Odette had organised Burlesque and Rivets, made sure that they were armed, that Rivets's muffler was correctly tied around his neck – he'd started coughing, which Odette was a little worried about – and then bustled them off in pursuit of the girl.

She and Burlesque had been standing outside the bar for almost five minutes now, shivering in the cold and stamping their feet to keep warm, while Rivets lurked by one of the windows, keeping a surreptitious eye on what was going down inside and making sure that Norma was safe.

Suddenly the boy began to make frantic signals. 'They've scarpered outta the back,' he shouted, and immediately Odette and Burlesque raced forward, barged through the entrance of the bar, pushed their way through the crowd and exited out of the back door.

The body lying on the cobbles confirmed all of Odette's worst fears. She pulled her Ordnance from its holster. 'Queek, Burlesque, we must find Norma most rapidly.'

Such was Burlesque's anxiety that Odette's sudden proficiency with English hardly seemed to register, all he did was stand stock-still and listen. The sound of heels ricocheting down an alleyway to their left sent them racing in that direction.

## The Doge's private chamber, the Doge's Palace, Venice

'Guards! Guards!' de Sade screamed at the top of his voice, and a few moments later two black-uniformed Signori di Notte rammed their way into the room. 'Raise the alarm,' he shouted. 'Doge Catherine-Sophia has been assassinated by the ForthRight agent Vanka Maykov. He may still be in the Palace. Hunt him down. He is to be shot on sight.'

When the guards had left to raise the hue and cry, de Sade slunk back through the secret door in the panelling.

'Are you ready?' he asked the waiting Semiazaz.

'Of course. We Grigori are always ready.'

Together they scuttled along the dark, humid passageway, moving in the direction of the Lady IMmanual's suite of rooms. There were still two more murders to be performed that night.

## The bedchamber of the Lady IMmanual, the Doge's Palace, Venice

Trembling with excitement, her body racked with lust, Sister Florence watched the Lady IMmanual straddle Casanova as he lay on the couch, settling herself down on him, taking him hungrily inside her body and then rolling her hips in languid circles.

But what Florence saw next drove all erotic thoughts and desires from her mind.

As the Lady IMmanual pleasured herself, she began to seethe, the girl seeming to shimmer, the edges of her body becoming vague like a drop of ink spilt in water. Before her eyes Florence saw the Lady mutate into a different being, a different form: as her arousal was stoked ever higher, so the silvery aura that shimmered around her gradually altered, becoming darker and darker. Sister Florence had never witnessed anything like it, had never even *heard* of anything like it. Certainly, during love-making the nuances of an aura were more readily seen: the colours were more vibrant, the texture of the aura deeper and the halo closest to the body – usually the hardest to see – became visible. But it was a difference of degree, not substance. Not so with the Lady IMmanual. Like a snake sloughing off its skin, she revealed what had been hidden beneath her silver aura.

Hardly daring to breathe, Sister Florence watched the woman being brought to orgasm, the moment when the most intimate details of an aura were revealed. And when the Lady IMmanual screamed out her triumph, Sister Florence saw her *real* aura in all its true, terrifying glory.

It was an aura that showed just how black her soul truly was.

Whilst black might suffuse the aura of Dark Charismatics,

it was a black leavened by the colours of an underlying humanity. But this was not the case with the Lady IMmanual. Her true aura was as black as a moonless night, signalling that she was different, inhuman . . . that she was the Beast.

## The bedchamber of the Lady IMmanual, the Doge's Palace, Venice

Holding his throbbing head, Vanka hobbled along the corridors of the Doge's Palace searching for someone, anyone, who could tell him the way to Ella's rooms. Finally he stumbled on a steward and terrified the man into giving him directions.

He came to the door and knocked. There was no reply but, standing there
, he heard a scream. Frantic with worry, he shouldered the door open. The scene that greeted him left him amazed and emotionally eviscerated. Ella – the girl he loved and who he had believed loved him – was squatting naked over a man. The scream had been one of ecstasy.

Watching Ella pleasure the man, tears blossomed in Vanka's eyes. He felt empty inside, hollowed out. Ella had given him a reason for living. Before Ella he had been a man who favoured the shadows and shunned the spotlight; it had been she who had brought him to life, had persuaded him to engage with humankind. But now that love was broken and his dreams discarded.

He slumped back against the wall, his body bereft of strength, his mind a confusion of anguish and loss. For long seconds he stood paralysed and then, with a slow, mournful shake of his head, he turned on his heel and reeled back along the corridor.

## The bedchamber of the Lady IMmanual, the Doge's Palace, Venice

Florence leant forward, desperate to get a better look at the transformation taking place before her eyes. And it *was* a transformation: the Lady's face had begun to glow, almost to radiate light. But it was her eyes that terrified her the most, the whites becoming almost luminescent, the dark irises reduced to pinpricks, pinpricks that bored into her, searching out her deepest secrets.

Suddenly the door of the Lady's chamber slammed open and Vanka Maykov stood, ashen-faced, in the entrance.

Sister Florence was so shocked by his appearance that she never heard the step behind her. The stiletto pushed through her back and pierced her heart. She died instantly.

## The bedchamber of the Lady IMmanual, the Doge's Palace, Venice

De Sade was getting an appetite for murder. He had felt nothing when he had plunged the knife into Sister Florence's back, but then he had been obliged to kill her. She had begun to look at him rather oddly, so much so that he suspected that his ability to control his aura had started to slip. And then there was the way she had questioned him about why he had deserted the Lady in the Maison d'Illusion and how Zolotov had known that he could find her there.

Yes, he had been careless and he was sure the Visual Virgin had come to realise that he was a double – or was that a *triple*? – agent.

De Sade stepped over the Sister's body, and then waved Semiazaz forward and through the door into the Lady's chambers. This done, he settled himself to watch her destruction through the spyhole the Sister had been using.

## The bedchamber of the Lady IMmanual, the Doge's Palace, Venice

She felt the spirit of Ella Thomas struggling frantically inside her – the girl had loved Vanka Maykov so very, very much – trying to free herself of her power, and for an instant she was fearful that her human side would triumph, that she would run to the man, surrendering herself in his arms. It took all her strength to suppress these Fragile inclinations, to remind herself that she was Lilith, a Goddess, and that love was just a fabricated emotion used by men to subjugate women. She would not . . . could not allow herself to be deflected from her destiny by such stupidity.

But she loved Vanka . . .

With an angry toss of her head she tried to drive these delinquent thoughts from her mind, cursing herself for her lack of resolve and her weakness. She had sworn to forget Maykov and to forget the happiness he had given her. She hauled herself off of Casanova. She knew that the only way to be free of Vanka Maykov was to destroy him. Now her only thought was to have him captured and killed. He had the potential to be a very, very dangerous enemy, so it was better to have him as a very, very dangerous *dead* enemy. That is, if Vanka Maykov *could* be killed.

But Vanka Maykov wasn't the most pressing of her problems.

She recognised the Grigori who entered her room instantly; he was the same swordsman she had fought in the backstreets of Paris. As she looked about her for a weapon, Casanova, gallant fool that he was, moved to defend her.

'Who are you?' he demanded, as he grabbed his sword.

'Death,' answered the Grigori, and then he attacked.

Casanova was a good swordsman – strong, quick, supple – but he wasn't good enough. His rapier thrust if it had been directed towards a Fragile would have been a killing stroke, but Semiazaz's reactions weren't those of a Fragile, they were super-human. In one fluid, hard-to-see motion, he brought his own sword around to block Casanova's attack and if the speed of his parry was amazing, the rapidity with which he turned defence into attack was breathtaking. Semiazaz snaked his blade along Casanova's, and then flicked it up to stab him through his chest. Such was the force of the thrust that the sword was forced hilt-deep, three feet of blade sticking out from the man's back. It was a mark of how strong Semiazaz was that he was able to pull the sword free of the tenacious grip of Casanova's SAE with hardly a grimace.

As Casanova crumpled to the floor, the Grigori turned to look at the Lady. 'So, having dispensed with the Fragile, it is now, day-hag, your turn to die. But die in the knowledge that you have witnessed the first act heralding the dawn of a new age: the Age of the Grigori. Die comforted by the understanding that the world – the Real World – enters a time when strength and determination will hold sway, when weakness and turn-the-other-cheek sentimentality are banished. Thus, I bid you adieu.'

## The bedchamber of the Lady IMmanual, the Doge's Palace, Venice

Without a word, the Lady IMmanual pulled the sword from Casanova's dead hand. It was a beautiful blade, wonderfully balanced and, if the way the gas light flickered on the edge was any indication, viciously sharp. But more importantly it had been gilded with silver which, because of the argyria, made it a potent weapon in a fight with a Grigori. She adopted the *en garde* stance, the tip of her blade hovering unwaveringly towards Semiazaz's chest.

Shaking his head, the Grigori stepped away from the blade. 'You should know, witch, that I must kill you. I am a Grigori and it is our time.' He raised his own blade. 'You are the last of your foul breed and soon you all will be part of a forgotten history.'

From his hiding place an amazed de Sade watched the pair fight. Oh, he had seen them duel before, but what he witnessed now was simply unbelievable – unbelievable because the two protagonists seemed to ignore the laws of nature and of gravity. He wondered for a moment if he was hallucinating.

Their movements were so astonishingly rapid that they defied the eye. In a blur of twinkling steel, Semiazaz was at Ella, stabbing at her in a frenzy of destruction. But the Lady matched him. Her blade parried the attack and then she lunged forward with a thrust that Semiazaz avoided only by luck and a miraculously fast slash of his own sword. The Grigori retreated and then, in a feat of gymnastics that made de Sade gasp, he suddenly leapt over a couch to land more than five metres away on the other side of the room. It wasn't just the length of the jump that was so amazing, but how effortlessly it was performed.

But if Semiazaz's athleticism was breathtaking, the feat performed by the Lady bordered on the incredible. She took just one step and somersaulted the length of the room, landing with balletic precision in a fighting stance in front of the Grigori.

Semiazaz laughed. 'Yes, you were famous for being the best of the bull-leapers, day-hag, but tonight your jumping will serve no purpose.'

For almost three minutes the two of them fought with a deadly, silent concentration, the only sounds to punctuate the contest being the soles of their feet squeaking on the wooden floor and the shrill clash of steel when their swords met. Time seemed to slow, but de Sade could see that the Lady IMmanual was gradually gaining the upper hand as she drove Semiazaz back.

The Grigori must have sensed looming defeat. Suddenly, in a gasping voice he shouted, 'For the Grigori!' and launched one last desperate assault on the Lady. It did no good. With almost contemptuous ease she evaded his attack, and then stabbed him through his sword arm. The effect of the silvered blade was dramatic: he screamed, his face contorted in agony and he let his own blade clatter to the floor, leaving him defenceless in the centre of the room, blood seeping through the fabric of his jacket.

De Sade gawped. He had never seen anyone bleed before. It was an unnatural and disgusting sight. He felt his guts churn and his head swim and for a moment he had to steady himself against a wall.

When he recovered his poise and his place at the peephole, he saw that even wounded, the Grigori wasn't finished. He made a grab for his pistol but the Lady was faster. She ran her blade through his good arm, sending the pistol tumbling out of his hand.

Leaking blood from both of his wounds, all a disabled Semiazaz could do was sink to his knees in shame. 'Who are you?' he gasped.

The Lady IMmanual laughed, and it was a laugh that chilled de Sade's soul. 'I am Lilith come again,' the girl answered in a whisper. 'I am Lilith reborn.'


## Rue Doge Ninon d'Enclos, Paris

Frantic with worry, Odette outpaced Burlesque and Rivets, reaching the corner of the alleyway ahead of them, just in time to see Norma being attacked by a tall, powerful-looking man.

But even as she raised her Ordnance to shoot she felt the cold touch of a muzzle on the back of her neck. 'I would be most obliged, Femme Aroca, if you would lower your pistol.' It was a woman's voice, cultured and refined, but all the more threatening because of it. 'And if you don't, I'll be obliged to blow your fucking head off.'


## Rue Doge Ninon d'Enclos, Paris

'Who the hell are you, and what do you want?' Norma snarled.

'I fear, Mademoiselle Aaliz, that our meeting will be of such a short duration as to make introductions and the normal courtesies redundant, but being a gentleman, I suppose I must make the effort. I am Count Andrei Sergeivich Zolotov. And with regard to what I want . . .'

Norma saw a flash of white teeth in the gloom as the man gave her an evil smile.

'The powers that be believe the Demi-Monde would be a better place if you vacated it, so I have been employed to kill you. But with it being Walpurgisnacht, I see no reason why your demise should not be made as pleasurable as possible. Pleasurable for me, that is: it isn't often one is given the opportunity to fuck the daughter of our beloved Leader.'

He made a grab at Norma's breasts, and got a slap across the face for his trouble.

'Go screw yourself. Try to rape me and I'll put my thumb in your fucking eye.'

'If that is how you wish to conduct yourself, then so be it . . .'

The man attacked and Norma fought back with her nails and her feet, kicking and clawing at him as he came at her, but the Russian was too strong. Ducking to avoid her slashing talons, he smashed a fist into her jaw and, as she buckled, seized her by the wrists, using one hand to pinion her hands behind her back.

'So first the pleasure and then the pain,' said Zolotov, using his free hand to wrench open Norma's cloak. Before she could stop him, he had ripped her blouse away from her body.

'Charming,' he crooned.


## The bedchamber of the Lady IMmanual, the Doge's Palace, Venice

Lilith!

Bole had told him that the Lady IMmanual was a Lilithi but de Sade had refused to believe him; after all, the Lilithi were meant to be an extinct species. Oh, he had recognised that the Lady was different, but he had never been able to bring himself to believe that she might be Lilith reincarnated. Now he realised Lilith was very much alive, that the most fearsome enemy of his kind once again stalked the Demi-Monde. And like every Dark Charismatic he knew that if she were ever to return, she would bring death and destruction in her wake.

Reeling back from the spyhole, de Sade realised that if his people were to survive, then this girl – this *thing* – had to be destroyed. Semiazaz had failed, and it now fell to him to kill her. But even so, he hesitated: the way he had seen the girl fight terrified him. Yet a voice inside him told him that the girl could not be allowed to live.

Almost sleepwalking, de Sade pushed open the panel that separated him from the Lady's chamber and stepped forward. Stooping down, he picked up the pistol that Semiazaz had dropped.

The Lady IMmanual looked up and studied him carelessly. 'Ah, the great deceiver breaks cover. What now, de Sade, have you come to try to destroy me, too?'

De Sade raised the pistol, but somehow with those cold, dark eyes watching him he couldn't find the courage to pull the trigger.

'Kill her . . . kill the day-hag,' urged Semiazaz as he knelt on the floor.

The Lady laughed. 'It *is* difficult to kill when looking into a victim's eyes, isn't it, de Sade? . . . even for a Dark Charismatic like you.'

'You know?' de Sade stammered.

'How could I *not* know? You forget that I created your kind . . . I know you better than any. Oh, you have special talents, de Sade, and your ability to shield your aura is a remarkable one but then so is your passion for pain, and it seems those with souls as distorted as yours are able to suppress their auras. Sadism trumping your residual humanity, perhaps? But your duplicity and conniving was rather . . . obvious. You don't really think I was taken in by that pantomime with Paul Keller in the Maison d'Illusion, now do you? Even Sister Florence had begun to suspect.' She gave de Sade an odd little smile. 'I presume you have disposed of her.'

'Yes.'

'Very sensible.' She took up a glass of Solution and took a long sip. 'But tell me, am I right in assuming you are here at the behest of Septimus Bole?'

'Yes.'

'Bole is nothing if not persistent, but he forgets just how resilient we Lilithi are. And what has he offered for my head?'

'Venice.'

Another laugh. 'A mere bagatelle. Come with me, de Sade, and I will offer you the world to torture and torment.'

'Do not listen,' snarled Semiazaz. 'She is Lilith, the most fearsome enemy of our kind. She has sworn to destroy all of the Grigori and Dark Charismatics.'

The Lady shrugged the accusation aside. 'And so I shall. But I would spare you. I have need of a companion who isn't possessed of a conscience shackled by too many moral scruples. I intend to rule this and other worlds, de Sade, and you have the opportunity to stand by my side when I do. I will make you rich beyond the dreams of avarice, and of course' – here she paused to look down at her nakedness – 'there will be other rewards of a more physical nature. So are you with me, or do you prefer to be swept aside . . . as all the other Dark Charismatics will be?'

'I must destroy you.'

'Then do it!'

De Sade pulled the trigger, the Colt bucked in his hand and the bullet flew true. What happened next astonished him. He had seen illusionists do a 'bullet catch' before, but this he had always ascribed to a feat of theatrical legerdemain, with the magician palming the bullet before it was loaded. Never could he have imagined that he would see the stunt done for real. But that was exactly what the Lady IMmanual did: *she caught the bullet he had fired, out of the air.* Oh, the act was accompanied by a grunt, and the momentum of the bullet as she grabbed it caused her to take a steadying step back, but that didn't distract from the realisation that she had just accomplished the impossible.

Once she had recovered her poise and balance, she turned to smile at de Sade, who stood gawping at her in paralysed shock. 'I see your aim has improved since you tried to blow my head off in the Maison d'Illusion and hit Zolotov instead.'

She tossed the bullet disdainfully aside, sending it rattling across the floor, and then advanced towards him. 'This is your moment of destiny, de Sade: you must choose whether to pledge your life and your soul to me, or die.'

All de Sade could do was stand immobilised by fear. There was a power and a certainty about the girl that brooked no refusal. She truly was Lilith come again.

Finally he found his voice. 'I will be betraying my own kind.'

'Kill her!' screamed a desperate Semiazaz as he tried to stagger to his feet.

The girl ignored the Grigori and and continued to advance toward de Sade. 'But treachery is your forte, de Sade. Your choice is simple: to live as a traitor or to die. Choose.'

De Sade bowed his head.

'Good, then we must move quickly. Your shot will have alerted the guards. You have, I presume, already killed the Doge.'

'Yes . . . and Vanka Maykov is being hunted for her murder.'

'My, you have been a busy boy. We will blame the Sister's murder on Semiazaz here. And your disposing of this Grigori will make you the hero who saved the Lady IMmanual from an assassin sent by a bitter and envious Doge Catherine-Sophia.'

De Sade didn't hesitate. He raised the pistol, took aim and blew a hole in Semiazaz's head.


## Somewhere in the Doge's Palace, Venice

'There!' yelled the Signori di Notte, firing his pistol in Vanka's direction. With bullets whizzing around his head, Vanka's natural instinct for self-preservation kicked in, and he turned to hare back down the corridor in the opposite direction.

Ignoring his grief about Ella, ignoring his confusion as to why these fuckers should be firing at him, Vanka just put his head down and ran – and by his own estimation, given the correct inducement, he reckoned he could show anyone in the Demi-Monde a clean pair of heels. And as inducements went, flying bullets were right up there with the best of them.

The problem was that Vanka didn't have a clue where he was running *to*. He had never been in the Doge's Palace before, and hadn't the remotest idea which way was 'out'. All he could do was run as far and as fast as possible, but he had the awful feeling that tonight far and fast wasn't going to cut it. He could hear police whistles sounding behind him, and a moment later an answering blast came from somewhere ahead. He veered to his right, heading down an almost identical corridor to the one he had just vacated.

And then, just when he seemed to be running out of options, a door to his left opened and he found himself staring at a gun being held by Josephine Baker.

'Whaddya say to a holiday in the JAD, Vanka baby?'


## Rue Doge Ninon d'Enclos, Paris

Norma prepared to die, but then, miraculously, two figures stepped out of the shadows and a pistol cracked. Zolotov buckled and sank to the ground.

'My career seems to be centred on saving the Daemon Norma Williams from death at the hands of some of the Demi-Monde's most repulsive nonFemmes.' A chuckle. 'But, then, according to HerEticalism, *all* nonFemmes are repulsive.'

Although it was dark and her rescuers were masked, Norma was still able to recognise the girl who had spoken. Her laugh was unmistakable. 'Mata Hari? Is that you?'

'I am pleased you remember me,' said the Suffer-O-Gette. 'So much water has passed under the bridge since we last met that I had thought you might have forgotten the one who first befriended you here in the Demi-Monde. Now, Norma, I would be grateful if you would pull yourself and your blouse together, and then follow me to the boat I have moored beside the river.'

'Why? Where are you taking me?'

'To the Coven, of course. The Empress Wu has taken it into her head to examine the leader of the Normalists, and what the Empress Wu wants the Empress Wu generally gets.'

'I'm sorry, I can't—'

It was the last thing Norma remembered, as the second Suffer-O-Gette lashed a blackjack down onto the back of her head.

## Insane Prison, Rangoon

'Prisoner Dashwood, are you awake?' The disembodied voice came from beyond her cell door. But disembodied or not, it was a ridiculous question, thought Trixie; her interrogator's arrival had been presaged by much crashing of steel-shod boots and shouting of orders. She would have had to be deaf not to have been roused by such a furore.

'I'm awake.'

'Prisoner Dashwood, I am Imperial Secretary, NoN Mao Zedong, emissary of Her Divine Majesty the Empress Wu.' The NoN had a peculiar voice, high-pitched and sing-song, and a peculiar bouquet – an unpleasant mélange of flowery perfume and urine. Trixie found both distasteful. 'Know this, you have been imprisoned for all of the Spring Season. So I ask, do you repent the insult you inflicted on Her Divine Majesty the Empress Wu?'

'Insult?'

'You drew a weapon in her presence and attempted to assassinate the emissary of Comrade Leader Reinhard Heydrich.'

'Attempted?'

'SS-Colonel Clement survived.'

*Fuck! How could I have failed to kill the bastard? He'd been standing less than a dozen feet from me when I fired.*

'The only thing I repent is my lousy shooting.'

'Have a care, Prisoner Dashwood, your life hangs by a thread.'

Trixie sat up on her cot and stared towards the slot in her cell door through which Mao was addressing her. From what she'd heard from the gossiping guards, the NoN was one of the

most important people in the whole of the Coven, *too* important to be a death-warrant delivery boy. For the first time since
she had been thrown in prison, Trixie felt a surge of hope.

*This bastard wants something.*

'I have no fear of death. And I would be grateful if you would
address me as "Colonel Dashwood".'

'Then, *Colonel* Dashwood, perhaps you fear the death of your
Preferred Male – the one who goes by the name Wysochi?'

*Fuck the threats. Now's the time to go on the offensive.*

'Imperial Secretary Mao, let's cut to the chase. Wysochi is a
big boy and he can look after himself. So tell me, what do you
want?'

'The Coven has need of a commander for its army.'

'You have Reverend Deputy Dark.'

'The Reverend Deputy was killed today by one of the
Vengeance Weapons employed by the ForthRight.'

'And you want me to replace her?'

'Your reputation as a commander goes before you. You have
a fearsome ability on the battlefield, and you *have* bested the
ForthRight before.'

*By ABBA, things must be really bad if the Covenites have to swallow
their pride and come to me for help.*

'So the Coven is at war with the ForthRight?' After ninety
days in solitary confinement, she had a lot of catching up to
do.

'It is.'

'Have they invaded the Coven?'

'Not yet.'

'When?'

'Soon.'

'Do you have your army mobilised?'

'Yes.'

'And the WFA? Are my soldiers still alive?'

'Yes.'

'And the men are still men?'

'They have been held incommunicado, Colonel Dashwood, and hence it was not felt necessary to castrate them.'

'I wish them freed. They are experienced fighters.'

'That will not be possible. It is against the laws of HerEticalism for Femmes to fight alongside nonFemmes who are still ensnared by their untrammelled sexual inclinations.'

Trixie rolled over on her cot, so that her back was now presented towards Mao.

Silence. *Let the dickless bastard stew.*

'You should be under no illusion, Colonel Dashwood, that if you decline this offer, you and the other members of the WFA will not be executed.'

It was a telling threat. Maybe it was time to give a little.

Without turning around, Trixie answered. 'Okay, then listen to what I say very carefully, Imperial Secretary. I want to see Wysochi so he can tell me, personally, that all my fighters are safe.'

'Agreed.'

I want a full briefing in one hour on the military situation vis-à-vis the ForthRight, and at dawn tomorrow I want the Covenite Army available for my inspection, and their officers ready to receive orders.'

'Agreed.'

In the darkness Trixie struggled to contain a smile. She was going back to war, and this time she would smash the ForthRight.

'And there is one other thing, Imperial NoN Mao: from now on it's *General* Dashwood.'

*Diagram and translation reproduced by kind permission of Snore Igbølinn, Cartographer-General to the Court of Her Most Reverend Excellency, Doge Catherine-Sophia*

# THE EDDIC OF LOCI 6: THE SECRETS OF LILITH

PLATE 6

# Epilogue

## The Real World: 30 October 2018

Septimus Bole was weary. The contrary events in the Demi-Monde had sapped his strength. He had never imagined that Ella Thomas would be so damned durable . . . so damned *lucky*. The girl had survived four assassination attempts, dispatching the formidable Semiazaz in the process, and now it seemed she had turned de Sade, one of Bole's most capable cryptos. And once she had assumed the Dogeship of Venice – an inevitability, in Bole's estimation – she would pose a real and very dangerous threat to Heydrich and the ForthRight's subjugation of the Demi-Monde . . . and, more importantly, to the success of the Final Solution.

The coumn had to be taken, it was, after all, the triggering mechanism for the Great Pyramid and in order to do that the girl had to be neutralised, and quickly. It was an indication of the urgency that Bole had had Billy Thomas, Ella Thomas's twin brother, brought to ParaDigm's research facility just outside Los Angeles. Direct action had failed, so now was the time for something a little more subtle.

He pressed a button to indicate that he was ready to receive his guest, and a moment later the boy was escorted into Bole's office with both Baraqel and Sariel in close attendance. The boy's behaviour was unpredictable and Bole was not in a mood to take any unwarranted risks.

Watching Billy Thomas lope into the room, Bole realised

that this fool epitomised why it was so vital that the Fragile aspect of humanity be eradicated, that the Final Solution be carried through to completion. Although the boy was undoubtedly a Dark Charismatic – albeit a low-grade, γ–Class Singularity – his Grigorian inclinations had been confused and diluted by his Fragile aspect and this confusion was the chief cause for his self-destructive predisposition. Human kindness was deeply subversive, as it instilled doubt and doubt was the godfather of weakness. It was those who acted without doubt – as pure-blood Dark Charismatics did – who would inherit the earth.

Billy Thomas gave Bole an idiot grin and swung himself into the guest chair, but even seated, he radiated a feral energy: his eyes were never still, his crêpe-soled shoes frantically bouncing up and down on the floor and his fingers forever popping. Although he was tall and lanky like his sister, and his skin shade signalled the same Creole contamination, there were differences between the twins. Ella Thomas's eyes sparkled with intelligence, while her brother's twinkled with demonic delight. Billy Thomas was a street warrior, his attitudes and his ambitions blistered and brutalised by the need to survive and flourish in the drab, sad, pointless world he inhabited. He was the apotheosis of violentisation.

'Yo, man, what's happening? Whatcha doin' pulling me off the street without so much as a by-yo-fuckin'-leave? What's the deal, man?' As he mouthed this gibberish, Billy Thomas looked around the room suspiciously, glancing nervously at the two Grigori standing guard behind him, his paranoia teasing at him like lice.

'I am here to offer you a role in a computer simulation.'

Which was why he'd had him brought to Los Angeles: this was where the second – and very secret – Demi-Monde InterFace Unit was housed, well away from the prying eyes of the US military.

It wouldn't do for them to realise that the Demi-Monde wasn't quite the sealed world Bole had portrayed it to be.

Billy Thomas pushed the bright orange fedora he was wearing further back on his head. 'Ah c'mon, man, keep it real.'

'Oh, I am keeping it very real, Mr Thomas, very real indeed. And I am prepared to pay you five million dollars for your services.'

'No kiddin'? Well, lemme tell you, for that amount of money ah'd cap ma mother.'

'Not your mother. I want you to persuade your sister to stop meddling with a particularly important project of mine.'

'What you mean by "persuade"?'

'Your sister is involved with the same virtual-reality simulation – the Demi-Monde – I wish you to participate in, but unfortunately she hasn't been keeping to the script we gave her.'

'That's Ella for yo', man. Always zigging when she should be zagging. That bitch's got issues.'

'Be that as it may, the upshot of her actions is that she's endangering the Demi-Monde, a multi-billion-dollar project of vital importance to this nation's security. She must be made to desist. She must be made to see reason.'

'An' if she don't wanna see no reason?'

'Then she must be eliminated.'

Billy Thomas gave an evil smile and drew back the side of the emerald-green drape jacket that Bole assumed was the uniform of the gutter class, revealing the chromed automatic pistol he had holstered under his armpit.

'No probs, man, ah'm armed and dangerous. And for five million bucks ah'll snap a cap into any cat's cranium, even blood like Ella.'

# Glossary 1

## The Demi-Monde

4Telling:
Predicting the Future. From the declension: 1Telling = Silence; 2Telling = Speaking of the Past; 3Telling = Speaking of the Present; 4Telling = Speaking of the Future.

ABBA:
The chief deity of all religions in the Demi-Monde. God. Referred to as 'Him' in the ForthRight and NoirVille, as 'Her' in the Coven and as 'Him/Her' in the Quartier Chaud.

AC:
After Confinement (see also Confinement).

Aryan:
The racial bedrock of UnFunDaMentalism. The Aryan ideal is to be blond, blue-eyed and fair-skinned, the same physical profile as the Pre-Folk from whom the Aryan people are supposedly descended.

Auralism/Auralist:
A woman (there is no recorded incidence of any males possessing the power of Auralism) who is able to discern and interpret the halo surrounding a Demi-Mondian's body. The most accomplished Auralists are the Visual Virgins of Venice.

Awful Tower, the:
The 350-metre-tall geodetic iron structure built in the heart of the Paris District of the Quartier Chaud to commemorate the signing of the Hub Treaty of 517, which marked the end of the Great War. Always contentious because of its phallic shape, the Tower divided aesthetic opinion, leading to it being generally referred to as the Awful Tower. A corrupted remembrance of the Real World name *Eiffel Tower*.

BC:
Before Confinement (see also Confinement).

BiAlects, the:
The second and probably later of the two MasterWorks of Confusionism, the BiAlects comprise nine books, the teachings enshrined within them relating how the Master grappled with the Five FundaMental Questions of Life and the AfterLife.

Blood Hounder:
A half-human, half-animal creature developed by the SS specifically to track down Daemons.

Blood Standard:
The monetary system adopted on a Demi-Monde-wide basis by which the currencies issued by a Sector are convertible into pre-set quantities of blood.

body clock:
The means by which a Demi-Mondian body records the

passage of time. The ticking that can be heard in the chest of all Demi-Mondians is the sound of a Demi-Mondian's body clock. The NoirVillian sage and scientist Al-Asma'i has determined that the life of every Demi-Mondian is restricted to 2.2 billion ticks of the body clock.

Book of the Profits, the: The holiest book of the nuJus, which comprises 333 epistles written by the Profits.

Boundary Layer, the: The impenetrable, transparent 'wall' which prevents Demi-Mondians leaving the Demi-Monde and entering the Great Beyond. UnFunDaMentalism officially defines the Boundary Layer as 'a Selectively Permeable Magical Membrane'.

Checkya, the: The secret police of the ForthRight, administered by Vice-Leader Lavrentii Beria. A corrupted remembrance of the Real World word *Cheka*.

CIA: The Central Inquisitorial Agency, the Medi's secret police answerable to Tomas de Torquemada. Inquisitors are also known as Quizzies.

CitiZen: The official term for a citizen of the Quartier Chaud.

Clockwork Universe: See Intelligent Design.

Code Noir: The secret society of WhoDoo mambos, dedicated to protecting the Demi-Monde should Lilith ever return.

Confinement, the: The mythical event describing the original sealing of the Demi-Monde behind the Boundary Layer. As a consequence of the Fall of the Pre-Folk from grace with ABBA (see also Lilith), ABBA punished the peoples of the Demi-Monde by confining them behind the impenetrable Boundary Layer in order that they should not corrupt the rest of ABBA's Creation with their Sin. Only when they have repented all their Sins, have come to Rapture and returned to Purity, will ABBA, once again, smile upon them and allow them to be reunited with the rest of the Kosmos.

Confusionism: Confusionism is the religio-philosophical system that held sway in the Coven until it was toppled by HerEticalism in 996 AC. Although it is now something of an anachronism in the Coven, Confusionism (and especially its subform WunZianism) still informs much of Covenite life, thought and moral attitudes.

crypto: Term commonly used to refer to all spies and third-columnists active in the Demi-Monde.

Current: ImPuritans believe marriage to be a repressive and unnatural form of pair bonding, and hence not an acceptable form of union in the Quartier Chaud. Partners who engage in extended sexual or reproductive unions refer to each other as Currents, indicating the non-permanent nature of such unions.

Daemons:
Mischievous and occasionally malignant (when in league with Loki) spirits who manifest themselves in the Demi-Monde. They may be identified by their ability to bleed.

DAEmon, the:
The assemblage of computational engines in the Future History Institute that makes up the Data Analysis and Evaluation machinery used to run the HyperOpia 4Telling program.

Dark Charismatics:
The coterie of men (and only men have been recorded as Dark Charismatics) who exhibit the most extreme and malicious form of MALEvolence. Dark Charismatics, though physically indistinguishable from the host population, are extremely potent and possess a perverted and grossly amoral nature. As such, Dark Charismatics present a morbid threat to the instinctive goodness of Demi-Mondians. The only reliable means of identifying Dark Charismatics is by the examination of their auras by Visual Virgins.

Determinism:
The belief that as all actions of Demi-Mondians are preordained by an omnipotent and omniscient ABBA, they are bereft of free will. A belief in Determinism is central to the Clockwork Universe Conjecture and the concept of Intelligent Design.

Dizzi:
A rare and very potent aphrodisiac, the use of which is much favoured by the ruling class in NoirVille.

Dork:
Derogatory slang for a woman who practises HerEticalism or displays LessBien tendencies.

Dynamics of Sexuality, the:
The means by which the sexual appetites and enthusiasms of individual CitiZens in the Quartier Chaud are measured:

| | |
|---|---|
| *pianissimo*: | very soft |
| *piano*: | soft |
| *mezzo-piano*: | moderately soft |
| *mezzo-forte*: | moderately hard |
| *forte*: | hard |
| *fortissimo*: | very hard |

exCommunication:
Punishment imposed by the CIA on those demonstrating aberrational tendencies or opinions. This generally involves the removal of the miscreant's tongue, thus rendering him or her an 'ex-communicator'.

exCreatures:
The aquatic nanoBites which inhabit the rivers of the Demi-Monde and which are responsible for the consuming of sewage pumped into the rivers, thus rendering it harmless and capable of being washed through the Boundary Layer.

| | |
|---|---|
| *Flagellum Hominum*, the: | The only book to survive the conflagration that followed the Fall, the *Flagellum Hominum* (*Scourge of HumanKind*) is believed to contain all the knowledge and the enchantments of Lilith. Unfortunately as the book is written in the – as yet – undeciphered Pre-Folk A script, the vast majority of what it contains is unintelligible. |
| Fleshtivals: | Masques which celebrate notable events and anniversaries in the Quartier Chaud, and which are associated with the total sexual licence afforded to participants. |
| fiduciary sex: | The sexual activity indulged in by Visual Virgins. As they are unable to enjoy penetrative sex (the loss of their virginity severely impairs their powers as an Auralist), Visual Virgins have perfected the art of provoking orgasms in their 'prey' by the stimulating of their imagination and the generation of sexual fantasies. |
| ForthRight: | The Demi-Mondian state created by the union of the Rookeries and Rodina. A corrupted remembrance of the Real World term *Fourth Reich*. |
| Future History: | The OutComes resulting from the application of preScience and the empiricalisation of 4Telling. |
| Future History Institute: | The organisation established to apply preScience to the prediction of changes and movements in the financial futures markets. |
| galvanicEnergy: | Electricity. Discovered by the ForthRight scientist Michael Faraday. |
| Gang of Three, the: | The group of Medi-based Dark Charismatics (comprising Maximilien Robespierre, Godfrey de Bouillon and Tomas de Torquemada) who led the breakaway of the Medi from Venice, and thus provoked the Great Schism. |
| GrandHarm: | A member of the Quartier Chaud's police force. A corrupted remembrance of the Real World word *gendarme*. |
| Great Beyond, the: | The vast and heavily forested area of the Demi-Monde that lies outside the Boundary Layer. |
| Great Schism, the: | The Unilateral Declaration of Independence (UDI), made by the three city-states constituting the Medi, which signalled their break from Venice. |
| Hel: | The Demi-Mondian term for the underworld. A remembrance of the Norse word *Hel*. |
| HerEticalism: | The official religion of the Coven. HerEticalism is a religion based on female supremacy and the subjugation of men. The HerEtical belief is that Demi-Monde-wide peace and prosperity – an idyllic outcome given the HerEtical tag 'MostBien' – will only be realised when men accept a subordinate position within society. Such is the extremist attitude of MostBiens that they are lampooned throughout the Demi-Monde as 'LessBiens'. |

| | |
|---|---|
| HimPerialism: | The official religion of NoirVille, based on an unwavering belief in male supremacy and the subjugation of women (or, as they are known in NoirVille, woeMen). |
| Holistic Feminism: | This is a term coined by Carolina Otero in her book *Let's All Be Pulled Together* to describe a nuSociety where men and women function in perfectly compatible and mutually supportive unison. In a nuSociety governed by Holistic Feminism not only do Women equal Men, and Men equal Women, but neither is intent upon dominating or subjugating the other. |
| Hub, the: | The grass and swampland area situated between the urban area of the Demi-Monde and Terror Incognita. |
| HyperOpia: | The Future History program employed by the Future History Institute. |
| iChing: | The Covenite method of divination and 4Telling. |
| ImPuritanism: | The official religion of the Quartier Chaud, ImPuritanism is a staunchly hedonistic philosophy based on the belief that the pursuit of pleasure is the primary duty of HumanKind and that communion with ABBA can only be achieved during orgasm. The ultimate aim of all those practising ImPuritanism is the securing of JuiceSense: the experiencing of the extreme pleasure that comes from an unbridled sexual orgasm. To achieve JuiceSense requires that men and women are spiritually equal and that man's proclivity towards MALEvolence is controlled and muted. |
| InDeterminism: | The contention that ABBA has (by the use of Daemons and Dark Charismatics) made certain aspects of the Demi-Monde unpredictable. |
| Intelligent Design: | First proposed by the Covenite thinker Pierre-Simon Laplace, the acceptance that the Demi-Monde (and hence Demi-Mondians themselves) was designed and created by an omnipotent, omniscient and omnipresent deity – ABBA or, as Laplace calls it, the Intelligence – has given rise to the widely held belief that all actions by Demi-Mondians are preordained, that the Kosmos is Deterministic in nature (and in Nature), and that Demi-Mondians are consequentially denied free will. The success of preScience in discovering an underlying pattern to the history of the Demi-Monde (the so-called Clockwork Universe Conjecture) has done much to promote the success of Intelligent Design among the thinking classes. |
| jad: | The swing music that came out of the JAD. A corrupted remembrance of the Real World word *jazz*. |
| JAD: | The nuJu Autonomous District, the area of NoirVille |

settled by the nuJus and granted independence by His HimPerial Majesty Shaka Zulu, in exchange for the supply of *Aqua Benedicta*.

JuiceSense: The ultimate orgasm. A corrupted remembrance of the Real World word *jouissance*.

Li: The precise and unbending protocol that determines all HerEtical conduct within the palaces of the Empress Wu.

'Liberté, Egalité, Fornication': Slogan of ImPuritanism and of the Quartier Chaud.

Lilith: The semi-mythical Shade witch – an adept in the esoteric knowledge of Seidr magick – who corrupted the Demi-Monde and brought down the Pre-Folk. The Dark Temptress who initiated the Fall.

Living&More: The dietary and life-style mantra of UnFunDaMentalism designed to detoxify the body. A corrupted remembrance of the Real World word *Lebensreform*.

Living, the: The fundamental element of life, usually portrayed as two snakes or dragons spiralling around one another.

MALEvolence: The theory developed by the Quartier Chaudian thinker Mary Wollstonecraft which postulates that war is caused by men but suffered by women. In her Theory of MALEvolence, Wollstonecraft identified that men, by their natural and undeniable inclination to obey orders (no matter how nonsensical or barbaric such orders are), are susceptible to disproportionate influence from their more unbalanced superiors, and hence are inevitably and inexorably drawn towards violence as a solution to disputes. The muting of MALEvolence is the ambition which led to the creation of ImPuritanism. Consideration of MALEvolence was also instrumental in prompting Michel de Nostredame to identify the malignant Dark Charismatics lurking within the Quartier Chaudian population. A corrupted remembrance of the Real World word *malevolence*.

Man²naM: The practice of NoirVillian men who exchange bodily essences in order to enhance their Manliness.

Mannez: Symbol of ImPuritans.

Mantle, the: The impenetrable crust of the Demi-Monde, situated below the topsoil.

Mantle-ite: The indestructible material used by the Pre-Folk to construct sewers, water pipes, Blood Banks and the Mantle.

Medi, the: The area of the Quartier Chaud which has made a unilateral declaration of independence and broken away from the hegemony of Venice and the Doge. The Medi comprises the Districts of Paris, Rome and Barcelona.

MostBien:
: The more extreme HerEtical belief that a state of MostBien – or the achieving by women of political, religious, economic, intellectual and sexual supremacy in the Demi-Monde – will only be secured when the male of the species has been removed from the breeding cycle.

nanoBites:
: The submicroscopic creatures which inhabit the soil layer of the Demi-Monde. They consume everything (except Mantle-ite) and convert it into soil.

NoN:
: The official term in the Coven for a eunuch. A corruption/contraction of the phrase *he ain't got none*.

nonNix:
: The ForthRight term for an individual who has – because of racial, social, political or sexual deviancy – relinquished all rights and protection enjoyed as a citizen of the ForthRight.

Normalism:
: The philosophy of nonViolence, civil disobedience and passive resistance developed by Aaliz Heydrich.

nuJuism:
: The religion of the nuJu diaspora, this is an unrelentingly pessimistic religion that teaches that suffering and hardship are life-affirming, and are endured to prepare the followers for the coming of the Messiah who will lead them through Tribulation to the Promised Land.

Par Oiseau:
: The pan-Demi-Monde communication network, established by Guglielmo Marconi, linking all city-states by the use of pigeons trained to home on specified Par Oiseau Boxes (PO Boxes). Weight considerations make PigeonGrams necessarily brief.

PigeonGram:
: See Par Oiseau.

Pre-Folk:
: The semi-mythical race of godlings who ruled over the Demi-Monde before the Confinement, and who were brought low by the sexual connivings of the Seidr-witch Lilith. The demise of the Pre-Folk is known in Demi-Mondian mythology as 'the Fall'. UnFunDaMentalism teaches that the Pre-Folk were the purest expression of the Aryan race. Also known as the Vanir.

preScience:
: A Venetian school of philosophy dedicated to the study of (and the making of) prophecies and 4Tellings, especially in the areas of economics and finance. The greatest of all preScientists are Professeur Michel de Nostredame and Docteur Nikolai Dmitriyevich Kondratieff of the Future History Institute, Venice. A corrupted remembrance of the Real World word *prescience*.

Qi:
: A Confusionist concept, Qi is the energy flow which surrounds and permeates all living things. It is the unseen and unseeable *élan vital* of the Living, which in turn energises the soul which resides in all things constituted by the Living.

| | |
|---|---|
| Quizzies: | Slang name for Inquisitors. |
| RaTionalism: | An avowedly and uncompromisingly atheistic creed developed by the renegade Rodina thinker and ardent royalist Karl Marx. RaTionalism rejects all supernatural interpretations with respect to events in the Demi-Monde. |
| RightNixes: | The youth wing of the ForthRight. |
| Seidr: | The ancient magick of the Vanir and of Lilith. |
| Shades: | The slang term for NoirVillians. |
| Solidified Astral Ether (SAE): | The substance which makes up the soft tissue of all Demi-Mondians. |
| Solution: | A cocktail of vodka and soda with one or more shots of blood. Usually available in 5 per cent, 10 per cent and 20 per cent strengths of blood. |
| SS: | Soldiers of Spiritualism, the military wing of the Ordo Templi Aryanis. |
| steamers: | Steam-powered vehicles popular in the Demi-Monde. |
| SubMISSiveness: | HimPerialism contends that as punishment for Lilith's connivance in the Fall of Man, ABBA decreed that henceforward woeMen would be required to conduct themselves according to the precepts of subMISSiveness, that is, they must be at all times Mute, Invisible, Subservient and Sexually Modest. Only in this way may woeMen earn the forgiveness of ABBA. |
| Suffer-O-Gettism: | A contraction of Make-Men-Suffer-O-Gettism, the militant/terrorist wing of the HerEtical movement. Suffer-O-Gettism is dedicated to the use of violence and intimidation to achieve female supremacy, the subjugation of men and the ushering in of MostBien. The leader of the Suffer-O-Gette movement is Jeanne Dark. |
| Terror Incognita: | The area extending in a radius of four miles around Mare Incognitum, and bounded by the Wheel River, constituting an unexplored region of the Demi-Monde. No explorer venturing into Terror Incognita has ever returned. A corrupted remembrance of the Real World term *Terra Incognita*. |
| ThawsDay: | The 60th day of Spring, when the nanoBites wake from their Winter hibernation. After ThawsDay, only the most desperate or the most stupid of Demi-Mondians venture into the Hub. |
| UDI: | see Great Schism, the. |
| UnderMentionables: | A catch-all term for those considered by UnFunDa-Mentalism to be racially inferior and hence subhuman (including, *inter alia*, nuJus, Poles, Shades, HerEticals, Suffer-O-Gettes, HimPerialists, RaTionalists, those of a sexually deviant disposition and those deemed to be genet- |

THE DEMI-MONDE SPRING | 520

ically flawed). A corrupted remembrance of the Real World word *Untermensch.*

UnFunDaMentalism: The official religion of the ForthRight, UnFunDa-Mentalism is a religion based on the philosophy of Living&More, or life reform, which espouses clean living, vegetarianism, and homeopathy and an abstention from alcohol, blood, tobacco and recreational sex. Heavily suffused with the occult and a belief in the existence of a Spirit World. Aleister Crowley is head of the Church of UnFunDaMentalism.

UnFunnies: The slang name for UnFunDaMentalists.

UnScrewed-Liberation Movement, the: A female-only protest organisation formed by Jeanne Deroin and Aliénor d'Aquitaine in response to the policies of the Medi Senate, acting under the influence of the Gang of Three, to impose UnFunDaMentalism as the religion of the Medi.

Valknut: The emblem of the ForthRight, comprising three interlocking triangles.

Visual Virgins: A Venetian order of Sisters established by Doge Oldoini as the Sacred and All-Seeing Convent of Visual Virgins. This Convent is dedicated to the selection and training of girls adept in Auralism (only virgin females have the power of Auralism) in order that they might be used to screen men living in the Quartier Chaud, and hence identify Dark Charismatics masquerading as CitiZens.

WhoDoo: The cult religion of NoirVille, based on a distorted remembrance of Seidr magick.

Whorealist: Derogatory slang term for an Auralist or Visual Virgin.

woeMen: The NoirVillian term for women.

Ying: The Confusionist concept that teaches that when the Messiah has brought Rapture to the peoples of the Demi-Monde, Yin will fuse with Yang to create Ying, the ultimate transcendental Peace.

zadnik: Demi-Mondian slang for a male homosexual and, more generally, for a NoirVillian male. The word is derived from the Russian *zad*, meaning arse.

# Glossary 2

## The Real World

ABBA:  ABBA (Archival, Behavioural, Biological Acquisition) is a Quanputer-based system developed and operated by ParaDigm CyberResearch Limited. By utilising an Invent-TenN® Gravitational Condenser incorporating an Etirovac Field Suppressor®, ABBA is the only computer to achieve a full SupaUnPositioned/DisEntangled CyberAmbiance. As a consequence, ABBA is capable of prodigiously rapid analysis (a fully tethered 30 yottaQuFlops) to give the bioNeural-kinetic engineers at ParaDigm access to almost unlimited processing power.

BaQTraQ:  Ever since its inception, ABBA has been a treasure trove for genealogists, containing, as it does, digitised records of all government, parish, court and tax information back to the year 1700. But since the introduction of the PollyScan in 2018, whereby documents can be scanned into ABBA simply by laying a Polly on top of a pile of documents, the ABBA-platformed BaQTraQ program has been gathering pace and has now reached a level where the role of the historian in our society is being reassessed. BaQTraQ encourages everybody in the country to scan *everything* into ABBA: holiday snaps and postcards; letters from husbands, wives, uncles and aunts; bills and invoices; old cine films; school-report cards . . . anything and everything.

bioSignatures:  The means by which a digital identity can be verified. BioSignatures include, *inter alia*: fingerprints, retinal scans, DNA and pheromonic analysis.

biPsych:  Those who have a simultaneous existence in both the Real World (as a NowLived) and in the Demi-Monde (as a Dupe).

eyeMail:  An ABBA-platformed means of transmitting person-to-person messages, the privacy and integrity of the message being assured by ParaDigm's RetinQek Verification Program.

eyeSpy:  Hover-capable and independently programmable SurveillanceBot.

| | |
|---|---|
| eyeVid: | An ABBA-platformed means of transmitting person-to-person digital moving-image messages. |
| Flexi-Plexi: | Digital wallpaper. When connected to a Polly a wall covered with Flexi-Plexi is able to display any digital image to a size and shape determined by the viewer. |
| Fun/Funs: | Street/marketing name for the Fun-Loving Fundamentalists, the Christian youth movement established and headed by Norma Williams. |
| Get-Me-Straighter Meter: | Aka GMS Meter. A device used by Norma Williams to eradicate addictive behaviour. |
| INDOCTRANS: | Indoctrination and Training Command: the department of the US military responsible for the operation of the Demi-Monde. |
| moteBots: | Nano-sized, independently viable and dynamically flexible surveillance cameras. The use of moteBots was declared illegal by the League of Nations' Universal Charter of Human Rights and Privacy of 2015. |
| PINC: | A Personal Implanted nanoComputer; developed by ParaDigm Technologies as a means of radically reducing training times and to find a more efficient method of inculcating students and trainees with specific knowledge sets. PINC is a nano-sized Memory Supplement which is biologically compatible with the human brain. Once in contact with the brain, PINC fuses with its organic tissue and is able to graft information – painlessly and seamlessly – into a person's memory bank. |
| PanOptika: | The ABBA-platformed program which links all surveillance apparatus (whether private or state) and all databases (whether private or state) to develop a full 360-degree cyber-portrait of individual citizens. |
| Polly: | Street name for a polyFunctional Digital Device which encompasses, in one dockable device, an individual's complete computational, communication, security, biomonitoring and entertainment requirements. |
| PollyMorph: | An ABBA-based program which enables digital modifications applied to one part of a moving-image digital stream to be automatically replicated through the digital stream. Analogous to PaintShop for videos. |
| Shielders: | Anti-SurveillanceBots. |
| Socialistic Surveillance: | The belief that to be both successful and acceptable, surveillance must be indiscriminate and totally arbitrary, and that it is utterly fair and equal in its scope. It is the rather naïve understanding that 'everyone is equal before a surveillance camera'. |

TIS: The Total Immersion Shroud used to encase the bodies of Real World visitors to the Demi-Monde in order to preserve muscular viability.

Young Believers: The name of the Christian youth movement established and run by the American evangelists Jim and Marsha Kenton, and subsequently subsumed into the Fun/Funs.

Step further inside the Demi-Monde...

Sign up for The Seasons newsletter
to get exclusive outtake material from
The Demi-Monde Spring and be the
first to hear Demi-Monde news.

☛ Go to www.thedemimonde.co.uk

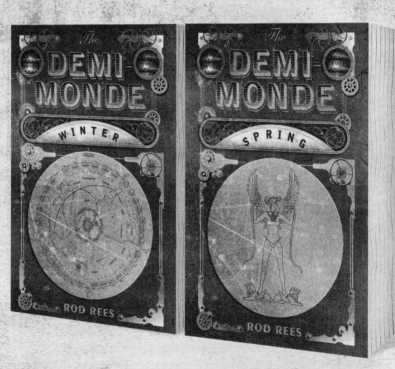

The Demi-Monde Winter is now available in paperback and eBook

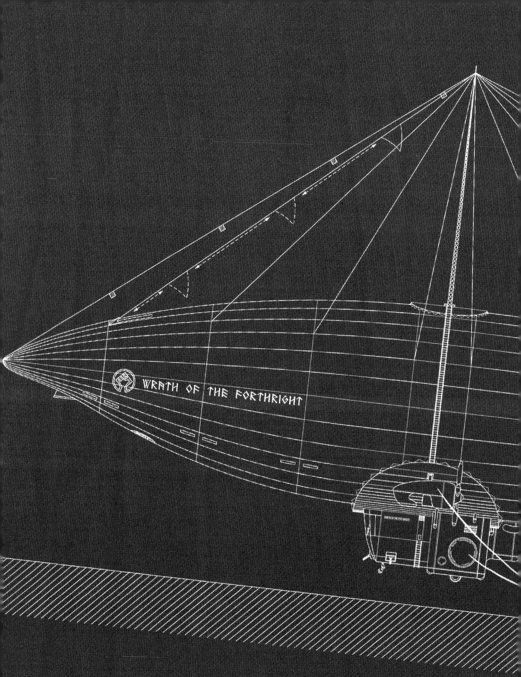

WRATH OF THE FORTHRIGHT

MODEL:            VENGEANCE WEAPON VERSION 1: ZEPPELIN FLIGHT-

LIENT:            SS-ORDO TEMPLI ARYANIS MATERIEL AND MUNITION

ONTRACTOR:        DIRIGIBLE DESIGN DEVELOPMENTS (BERLIN) LIMITE

ESIGNER:          COMRADE ENGINEER FERDINAND VON ZEPPELIN

TE:               17TH DAY OF WINTER 190

# The Social Context of Birth

Edited by

## Caroline Squire

*Senior Lecturer, Faculty of Health and Human Sciences,
Thames Valley University*

~v Rov~ ınty Hospital, G

Radcliffe Medical Press

**Radcliffe Medical Press Ltd**
18 Marcham Road
Abingdon
Oxon OX14 1AA
United Kingdom

**www.radcliffe-oxford.com**
The Radcliffe Medical Press electronic catalogue and online ordering facility.
Direct sales to anywhere in the world.

---

British Library Cataloguing in Publication Data

A catalogue record for this book is available from the British Library.

ISBN 1 85775 554 5

Typeset by Aarontype Ltd, Easton, Bristol
Printed and bound by TJ International Ltd, Padstow, Cornwall